SOIL
FERTILITY

C. E. MILLAR

Professor Emeritus of Soil Science
Michigan State College

JOHN WILEY & SONS, INC., NEW YORK

CHAPMAN & HALL, LTD., LONDON

Library of Congress Catalog Card Number: 55-7565

PRINTED IN THE UNITED STATES OF AMERICA

This book is affectionately dedicated to my wife,
Lucile Kays Millar, our daughter, Margaret Millar Welles,
and my mother, Fannie Knowles Millar

Preface

This book is concerned primarily with the interrelationships of soils and growing plants. In preparing the material I have endeavored to keep the plant and its growth requirements constantly in mind. At times it may seem that I have strayed too far into the realm of soil chemistry, or soil physics, or possibly soil microbiology, but some knowledge of the subject matter in each of these fields is essential for an understanding of soil characteristics and the reactions occurring in soils which influence plant growth. Likewise some familiarity with plant physiology is needed to understand the reactions of plants to the dynamic conditions in the soil surrounding their roots. Environmental conditions to which the aerial portions of plants are submitted influence the functioning of the root system as well as of the leaves and stems, and accordingly it is essential that the environment of both the roots and tops of plants be reasonably satisfactory if so-called "normal growth" is to take place. With this point in view, air temperatures and light are discussed.

The volume has been prepared as a textbook for students taking a course in soil fertility and as a reference book for students in soil-management courses. An effort has been made to avoid too much "applied" material, which would be included in courses dealing specifically with soil-management practices. Rather it has been the object to deal with fundamental principles that can be applied to crop-production problems when local conditions are taken into consideration. However, I have tried never to lose sight of the practical problems of soil management and crop growth. An appreciable amount of data has been compiled which it is hoped will be useful as reference material.

Considerable attention has been given to results of field experiments, as they are the "proving ground" of soil-management practices. Some space has been devoted to a consideration of the older field experiments with the thought that advanced students should have some familiarity with the pioneer work which has paved the way for the modern field trial with its statistical background. Furthermore, the results of some of these earlier studies are well worth careful examination. Some consideration has also been given to various theories regarding soil productivity, as they are thought-provoking and should not be discarded until proved unsound.

I take pleasure in expressing appreciation to the following men, whose reviews of various portions of the manuscript have been most helpful: D. I. Arnon, F. C. Bauer, N. C. Brady, R. L. Cook, J. F. Davis, J. E. Gieseking, L. Jacobson, K. Lawton, J. E. McMurtrey, Jr., W. P. Martin, A. R. Midgley, M. F. Miller, F. W. Parker, W. H. Pierre, J. D. Romaine, H. T. Rogers, M. B. Russell, L. M. Turk, and E. T. York, Jr. Valuable suggestions have also been received from numerous other soil scientists.

C. E. MILLAR

East Lansing, Michigan
January 1955

Contents

Contents

1

The Development of Agriculture

Agriculture always has and always will play an important role in man's activities. As was true with all arts and sciences the beginnings of agriculture were most elemental and development was slow. When man developed an inquisitive interest in his surroundings doubtless plant growth was one of the first phenomena to engage his attention. How to increase the production of plants which furnished food for him and his animals was of vital concern to him. Observation and the results of accidental soil and plant treatments were virtually his only tools for advancement in food production. From these, "rule-of-thumb" procedures were gradually developed, and they formed the basis of early agricultural writings. It is well for any advanced student in agriculture to know something of the early history of this great industry and the steps by which we have accumulated our present fund of knowledge. It is also well for mature students to spend a little time looking through some of the early books on farming. Brief discussions of some of the most outstanding points in agricultural history are presented.

Discussion Topics

Ancient agriculture.
Roman agriculture.
Farming after the fall of Rome.
Beginning of scientific agriculture.
Early chemistry and its application to plants.

ANCIENT AGRICULTURE

There are grounds for believing that prehistoric man gave some attention to the cultivation of crops 10,000 or 12,000 years ago, or possibly earlier. Improvement in methods of growing food crops was doubtless very slow until about the time of Abraham, some 2000 B.C. Recent investigations of ancient cave dwellings in Palestine indicate that plowing was practiced between 2500 and 3000 B.C., and ancient

1

drawings depict Egyptian plowing scenes in the fourteenth or fifteenth centuries B.C. In a cave at Gezer a small slab of limestone was found which had evidently served as a slate for a Hebrew child in Solomon's time (1000 B.C.). The boy who signed his name as Abijah was apparently trying to memorize the sequence of the months by writing down the farm work to be done beginning with the middle of September, which was the start of the Hebrew year. The inscription points out that olive harvest lasted two months, followed by two months of grain planting and two months of late planting, then grain harvest began about the middle of March followed by a month for flax cutting, one for barley harvest, and one for wheat. Then came two months for vine tending, and the year ended with a month of "summer fruit."

The earliest authenticated writings discussing farming practices are those of the Greeks, more than fifty of whom gave some attention to agriculture in their manuscripts. Among the most noted to pay considerable attention to farming was the poet Hesiod, who set down some rules for crop production before 776 B.C. Also the historian Xenophon (430–355 B.C.) mentions plowing under green plants as a means of soil enrichment. A Carthaginian named Mago was a voluminous writer on agriculture, compiling some 28 books on the subject. These were translated into Greek and condensed into 20 volumes by Cassius Dionysius. When Carthage was conquered in 146 B.C. Mago's books were carried back to Rome and were translated into Latin by order of the Roman Senate. These books appear to have been read extensively by Roman writers. Democritus (about 460–360 B.C.) exerted an outstanding influence on the development of chemistry. He believed all matter to be made up of very small indivisible atoms, which were different in shape, size, and weight, although all were made of the same basic material. Variations in space between the atoms accounted for differences in the density of substances, and the properties of substances were determined by the shape and size of the atoms composing it. Also, he stated that the atoms were in constant motion.

ROMAN AGRICULTURE

Agriculture was held in high esteem by the early Romans, and farm work was the only manual labor deemed honorable for free men. Farming methods were very primitive, and gradually the land passed more and more into the large estates of influential men to be worked under the "precarium" system or by slaves. Many thousands of slaves were impressed as a result of the conquest of one country after another as the empire expanded. Slave labor reduced to still lower levels the methods used in handling livestock and growing crops.

A number of Romans wrote extensively about farming. Several of the most noted will be mentioned.

Cato (234–149 B.C.) was the earliest Roman agricultural writer, and he drew much information from the Greek literature. He considered good plowing more important than manuring but urged careful conservation of manure. Cato advocated a self-sustaining farm with a maximum of sales and a minimum of purchases. Directions were given for the care of livestock and cultivation of the soil.

Varro (116–27 B.C.) was a traveler, soldier, farmer, statesman, and scholar. His treatises on agriculture may be divided into three parts: one dealt with the culture of fruits, grains, and legumes; one discussed the raising of large animals; and one considered the care of small animals, poultry, and bees. He also prepared a volume on the selection and operation of a farm to serve as a guide for his wife after his death.

The 13 short books of Columella (first century A.D.) are more readable than those of Cato and Varro. His first 12 books cover every phase of agriculture. A discussion of the selection of land and the arrangement of buildings is followed by a consideration of tillage, soil improvement, and the production of various field crops. The propagation and care of fruit trees and of vines are discussed, and then follow directions for selecting, breeding, and the general care of farm animals, both large and small. Methods of treating diseases are included. After giving directions for the management of poultry, bees, and fish ponds, Columella outlines the duties of an overseer and his wife and gives recipes for wine making and the preserving of fruits and vegetables. The tenth book is in verse. The thirteenth book is an elaboration of the discussion of the care of trees and wines.

Among the practices advocated in these Roman books may be listed the following: (1) thorough tillage, (2) green manuring, (3) crop rotation, (4) use of lime, (5) application of manure, and (6) growth of legumes for soil improvement. There is some reason to believe that many of the desirable practices listed were discussed by writers to a greater extent than they were actually utilized by most farmers.

FARMING AFTER THE FALL OF ROME

With the overrunning of Italy by the barbarians, around 410, a long period without progress set in. Following the actual deposing of the Roman emperor by the barbarian Odoacer in A.D. 476, agriculture as well as other forms of civilization lost ground for many years. In fact what knowledge had accumulated would have been lost had it not been preserved by the monks.

During the Middle Ages the system of land ownership was not conducive to progress. The fields were divided into a number of small strips, often an acre or less in size. Each tenant worked several such strips, which were scattered over the field or farm. All the strips in a given field were planted to the same crop. Pasture land, which was usually too rough for cultivation, was shared by the tenants. A 3-year system of cropping was followed, namely, a winter grain, a spring crop of oats, barley, peas, beans, or a crop mixture, and a year of fallow. Just before the Crusades there was some awakening of thought, and the Crusades (approximately 1096 to 1212) themselves brought about some exchange of ideas.

About 1240 Petrus Crescentius collected and condensed the early Roman writings into one volume, and in 1563 Palissy published a book on agriculture. Thus the stage was set for a revival of interest in agricultural improvement.

BEGINNING OF SCIENTIFIC AGRICULTURE

By 1669 there was some use of fertilizing materials. Sir Kenelur Digley wrote of doubling the yield of crops through application of saltpeter. Also the early colonists found North American Indians using fish and the South American Indians using guano to increase crop growth. It is probable also that the use of ashes, lime, manure, and similar materials was revived. Substantial progress, however, waited on the development of some scientific background.

As knowledge of the physical sciences, primarily chemistry, developed an attempt was made to apply it to the problems of plant growth. In fact the early history of chemistry is intimately associated with studies of plant nutrition and composition. Thus, in the period 1630–1750, when any one of the five "elements," fire, water, air, earth, and nitre, was considered the active ingredient involved in vegetable matter and its alterations, an attempt was made to find the "principle of vegetation." It was during this period that Van Helmont (1577–1644) conducted his classic experiment with a willow tree. A 5-pound willow tree was planted in 200 pounds of soil in an earthen container. It received nothing but rainwater for a 5-year period, by which time it had reached a weight of 169 pounds, 3 ounces. The annual weight of fallen leaves was not taken. Oven-dry weights of the soil showed a loss of only 2 ounces. No dust could accumulate in the container because it was covered with a sheet of perforated galvanized iron. The experiment was exceedingly well planned, and Van Helmont was justified in his conclusion that water was the "principle" or sole nutrient of plant growth. Boyle repeated the experiment in 1661 using a type of squash, but he went a step farther and distilled the plant tissue. The products of distillation, earth, salt, spirit, and oil, were considered to be produced from water. Francis Bacon in 1627 subscribed to the theory that water is the "principal nourishment" of plants. However, he believed that each plant extracted a "particular juyce" from the soil and accordingly a soil might become depleted for a particular plant.

Glauber about 1656 found that saltpeter could be extracted from cattle manure and that this salt when applied to soil greatly increased plant growth. From these facts he concluded that the cattle obtained the saltpeter from their food (plants), which in turn took it from the soil. Accordingly saltpeter must be the growth substance or "principle" of growth. Glauber maintained that the fertilizing value of bones, feathers, hair, horn, and manure was due to the saltpeter. Glauber's idea was supported by the work of Mayow, who found the nitre content of the soil to be high in the spring, when plants were starting growth, but low later in the season, after plants had made a luxuriant growth.

John Woodward published the results of a most interesting experiment in 1699. Spearmint was grown in: (1) rainwater, (2) water from the Thames River, (3) effluent from the Hyde Park conduit, (4) effluent from the conduit plus garden mould. Because the amount of growth increased with the sediment in the water, and in all cases the mint had an abundance of water, water could not be the "principle" of growth. He ascribed growth to absorption of a "certain peculiar terrestrial matter." The decrease in crop yield after successive cropping for several years was explained by Woodward as due to the removal of this "material" from the soil by the crops. The fertility could be restored by fallow, during which the rain brought down a new supply of the required "material," or by manuring with animal or plant substance.

No discussion of this period, however brief, would be complete without mention of Jethro Tull (1731), an Oxford man who considered soil the growth substance of plants. His theory included these points: (1) All plants live on the same food, namely, fine soil particles. (2) Pressure caused by the swelling of roots forced the minute soil particles through the "lacteal mouths of the roots" and hence to enter the circulatory system. (3) Cultivation of the soil increased its fineness and thus the feeding opportunity of plants. Also fineness enabled the soil to absorb the nutritious vapors condensed from the air more effectively. (4) A rotation of crops is a convenience but not a necessity. (5) Any soil will nourish any plant if temperature and moisture supply are in proper adjustment. (6) Applications of manure were effective because they brought about a fine, crumbly soil condition. Tull also advocated planting certain crops in rows so that the soil could be cultivated between them, and he invented a drill to make such planting possible.

Another noteworthy achievement of this period was the development of the Norfolk rotation by Lord Townhend of Norfolk County, England. This 4-year cropping system, established between 1730 and 1738, consisted of a small grain (wheat), an intertilled crop (turnips), another small grain (barley), and clover or beans. Manure was also applied. During the following 100 years the gradual adoption of this new cropping system served to increase wheat yields in England from around 8 bushels per acre to about 20 bushels.

EARLY CHEMISTRY AND ITS APPLICATION TO PLANTS

Growth Problems (1750–1800). During this period agriculture received much attention. Many books were written, there was considerable experimentation, scientific societies were formed to promote agricultural advancement, and real progress was made in the science of chemistry and its application to agricultural problems. Some of the most noteworthy achievements will be mentioned.

The Edinburgh Society for the improvement of arts and manufactures persuaded Francis Home to try the application of chemistry to the solution of agricultural problems, primarily the problem of plant nutrition. He employed two methods, pot cultures and plant analysis, which were to be of great service in coming years. He established that plant growth depends on several factors in place of one and listed them as air, water, earth, salts of different kinds, oil, and fire in a fixed state. His thinking was still dominated by that of the preceding period, and necessarily so until more advance was made in chemistry. The proposal of Wallerius (1761) that humus is the source of plant food was accepted by many workers. The belief developed that lime and other mineral salts increased plant growth because they made the nutritive substance in soil usable by plants. As soluble salts were not found in rainwater, and only in small amounts in soils, they must be produced by plants.

A study of the effects of growing plants on air composition between 1770 and 1780 afforded much valuable information, but the significance of it in growth processes was not fully appreciated until later. For example, Priestley (1775), knowing that breathing of animals, fire, etc., made the air impure, found that living mint plants restored its freshness. Ingen-Housz (1779) showed that the purification process went on in the light only, and that in darkness plants had the same effect on air as did animals. Jean Senebier of Geneva went further and showed that plants extract something from the air which he designated as "fixed air." He explained the growth of Van Helmont's willow tree on the basis of the absorption of this fixed air.

Period of Rapid Scientific Development (1800-1880). During this period much progress was made in the knowledge of chemistry, and the information was applied to the study of soils and plant growth. Although oxygen was discovered in 1774 by both Priestley and Scheele the significant part played by this element in respiration was not understood for many years.

Theodore de Saussure (1804) introduced the quantitative method of experimentation which made possible the work of many noted men in the following years. He grew plants in known mixtures of CO_2 and air and measured changes in the composition of the mixture, thereby showing the absorption of oxygen and evolution of CO_2 in respiration and the reverse process in photosynthesis. Air, not soil, was thus shown to be the source of carbon in plants. Other contributions of de Saussure were: (1) Only a small part of the weight of plants comes from the soil but this part is nonetheless essential. (2) Nitrogen is taken from the soil, not the air. (3) The root exerts some selective action in the intake of mineral matter. (4) Water can be taken in by roots without the dissolved salts, thus resulting in a concentration of the soil solution. (5) The ash of plants is variable in composition, being affected by soil composition and the age of the plant. (6) A plant grown in water from seed contains no more ash than did the seed. Thus the old theory that plants produced salts is incorrect.

Unfortunately de Saussure's discoveries were not accepted by other scientists to any great extent, and the two most prominent books of the period, one by Davy and the other by Thaer, gave little attention to these new and important facts. Both writers believed that plants obtained their carbon and other nutrients largely from soil humus.

To Boussingault we owe the idea of field experiments. In about 1834 he laid out a series of trials on his farm in Alsace in which he weighed and analyzed the materials applied to the soil and the crops produced. The discussion of his data is most interesting. Georges Ville of France was also a strong advocate of field experiments. He insisted that fertilizers were more profitable than animal manures and that their use constituted the only scientific method of maintaining soil fertility. Ville relied on the results of field trials to determine the proper fertilizer for a given crop. His treatments consisted of a complete or "normal" fertilizer and of this fertilizer minus single ingredients such

as nitrogen and phosphorus.   Figure 1 shows the results of a trial with
wheat.

A report to the British Association in 1840 by Liebig served to
attract wide attention to agricultural investigations.   Through ridicule
and sarcasm he brought the various theories of plant nutrition into
critical review.   His main contentions were: (1) To consider humus
as the source of carbon for plants is ridiculous.   (2) The real function

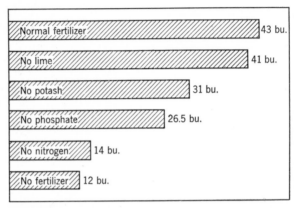

Fig. 1.   Results of field tests with wheat by Ville in France between 1860 and
1875.   As a result of this trial Ville decided that the needs of this particular soil
were, in descending order, nitrogen, phosphorus, potassium, and lime.   Prepared
from data in *On Artificial Manures, Their Chemical Selection and Scientific
Application to Agriculture,* translated by W. Crookes, London, 1879.   After
Russell, *Soil Conditions and Plant Growth,* 1950.   Longmans, Green & Co.,
London.

of humus is to decompose and yield CO_2 for two purposes: (*a*) to help
dissolve some of the mineral compounds, and (*b*) to supply additional
carbon to young plants through their roots while the leaves are too
small to absorb a sufficient quantity.   (3) Plants obtain their carbon
from the air.   (4) Nitrogen is taken from the air or soil as ammonia.
(5) Hydrogen and oxygen are obtained from water.   (6) Alkalies are
needed to neutralize acids produced in plants.   (7) Certain minerals
are essential, including phosphates for seed formation and potassium
silicates for the growth of grasses and cereals.   (8) The presence of
a substance in a plant is evidence that it is needed because, although
plants might absorb anything soluble in the soil, they excrete what is
not needed.   (9) When a sufficient number of plant analyses have
been made tables can be prepared showing what should be added to
the soil for any crop.   Acting on this last conclusion Liebig made up
a mineral fertilizer and placed it on the market.   However, it proved

a failure because the minerals were rendered insoluble through fusion in the preparation of the mixture.

The statement in Liebig's book,[1] "by the deficiency or absence of one necessary constituent, all the others being present, the soil is rendered barren for all those crops to the life of which that one constituent is indispensable," gave rise later to the law of the minimum. Another statement to the effect that, if a soil contains sufficient minerals, the plants will obtain all the nitrogen needed from the air as ammonia, gave rise to much controversy and experimentation. In 1843 Lawes established the Rothamsted field experiments, some of which are still in operation with only minor changes. These are discussed in another section of this book. By 1855 Liebig's theory, that an ash analysis of a crop gives dependable information as to the amounts of the different nutrient elements needed, had been disproved. Furthermore it had been shown that under field conditions leguminous crops require little nitrogen fertilizer whereas non-legumes require large amounts. These results cast doubt on Liebig's theory that plants obtain nitrogen by absorption of ammonia from the air. The explanation of the unusual behavior of legumes was not found for many years. Nodules had been observed on the roots of legumes in early studies, and in 1858 Lachmann found living organisms in the nodules but did not connect this fact with the nitrogen problem. It was 1885 before Berthelot showed that certain microorganisms could assimilate nitrogen from the air. The following year Hellriegel and Wilfarth presented a paper proving that legumes grew well in sterilized sand when inoculated with soil extract, but that the same extract did not always serve for all legumes. The relationship between microorganisms and nitrogen fixation was then established, but it was not until 1892 that the specific organism, *Bacillus radicicola,* was isolated by Beijerinck.

In the latter part of this period much progress was made in the field of bacteriology and its application to soil processes. The production of nitrites and their conversion to nitrates was shown to be the result of bacterial action. Also, the decomposition of organic matter was proved to be a biological and not a chemical process.

It may be seen that, with the exception of nitrogen fixation, many of the basic principles of plant nutrition recognized today were established between 1800 and 1880. In the following chapters will be presented some clarification and elaboration of the early ideas and certain new concepts of plant-growth factors and the role of soil as a plant-growth medium.

[1] *Chemistry in Its Application to Agriculture and Physiology.* 1840.

REFERENCES

Browne, C. A. *A Source Book of Agricultural Chemistry.* Chronica Botanica, Vol. 8. Chronica Botanica Co., Waltham, Mass., 1944.

Cato and Varro *Roman Farm Management.* Translated by a Virginia farmer. The Macmillan Co., New York, 1913.

Cato the Censor on Farming. Translated by Ernest Brehaut. Columbia University Press, New York, 1933.

Columella, L. Junius Moderatus *Of Husbandry* in Twelve Books and his *Book cerning Trees.* Translated into English. A. Millar. London, 1945.

Dauberry, C. *Lectures on Roman Husbandry.* J. H. and Jas. Parker, Oxford, 1857.

Liebig, J. *Chemistry in Its Relation to Agriculture and Physiology.* John Wiley & Sons, New York, 1849.

Reed, H. S. *A Short History of the Plant Sciences.* Chronica Botanica Co., Waltham, Mass., 1942.

Russell, E. J., revised by Russell, E. W. *Soil Conditions and Plant Growth,* eighth edition. Longmans, Green & Co., London, 1950.

Weir, W. W. *Soil Science.* J. B. Lippincott Co., Philadelphia, 1936.

2

Essentials for Plant Growth

All higher plants have the same basic requirements for growth, though in widely varying amounts or degrees. They are light, heat, water, air, and certain nutrient elements. The soil must supply the needed moisture and nutrients, with the exception of carbon dioxide. Also, the soil is intimately concerned with the control of temperature both in the root zone and around the aerial portions of plants. In productivity studies soil moisture and air must be considered integral parts of the soil even though the composition and quantities of them are constantly changing. In the six sections of this chapter will be discussed briefly the requirements of plants for satisfactory growth and, in addition, some concepts involved in the terms "productivity" and "fertility" as applied to soils.

Discussion Topics

Soil fertility vs. productivity.
Temperature and growth.
Light requirement of plants.
Water and the growth of plants.
The plant and the atmosphere.
Nutrient requirement of plants.

SOIL FERTILITY VS. PRODUCTIVITY

There is no generally accepted concept of the term "fertility" as applied to soils. Some scientists consider that a fertile soil must supply, in reasonable amounts and in suitable balance, all the nutrients which a plant takes from the mineral and organic soil fractions and also be located in a climatic zone which provides moisture, light, and heat sufficient for the needs of the plant under consideration. Also, toxic materials must not be present in sufficient quantities to limit growth appreciably, and soil structural conditions must be reasonably satisfactory. Naturally the textural make-up of a soil has much to do with its capacity to supply adequate moisture under a given climatic condition.

11

It is generally agreed that a soil such as described is both productive and fertile. But are all the conditions described necessary for a soil to be considered fertile? Some scientists maintain that the above-described soil would be fertile even if located in a region of low rainfall because all that is needed to make it productive is the application of water. In other words, ability to supply adequately the nutrients normally taken from the soil by plants, associated with freedom from toxic materials, is taken as sufficient basis for designating a soil as fertile but not productive. In this concept environmental conditions such as temperature, light, precipitation, and drainage are ignored. The idea of *potential* capacity to produce crops is involved. Although this is a limited interpretation of the term it is one held by many American scientists. In conversation with farmers there is a tendency to use the words "productive" and "fertile" synonymously, and in the discussions in this book the writer may frequently take the same liberty.

TEMPERATURE AND GROWTH

Of the factors that influence seed germination and plant growth temperature is one of the most critical. No plant or plant part is free from the influence of temperature at any time. It is obvious that temperatures which are satisfactory for the growth of one plant or plant part may be entirely unfavorable for the growth of another plant or development of another part of the plant. Unfortunately it is not practical for man to modify either soil or air temperatures to an appreciable extent or over more than relatively small areas. Fortunately relatively small changes in temperature for a short period may be sufficient to avoid frost damage to crops of high value. A knowledge of temperature relationships is helpful in selecting sites for fruit crops and early vegetables, in the choice of crops for certain fields on farms with rolling topography, in deciding on locations for some crops in which quality is a special consideration, and at times in reaching decisions concerning the practicability of installing irrigation and drainage systems. In a discussion of temperature, both soil and air temperatures must be considered. In the following paragraphs attention is called to some of the pertinent facts concerning temperature and plant growth.

Source of Heat. Solar energy supplies the heat requisite for the growth of vegetation but only a fraction, perhaps 25 per cent, of the sun's energy directed toward the earth ordinarily reaches the soil surface. The earth quickly reradiates much of the heat it receives but largely in longer wavelengths, which are more effective in heating the atmosphere than is direct solar radiation. Figure 2 shows the theoretical radiation, the maximum probable radiation, and the radiation normally received by the earth's surface at East Lansing, Michigan.

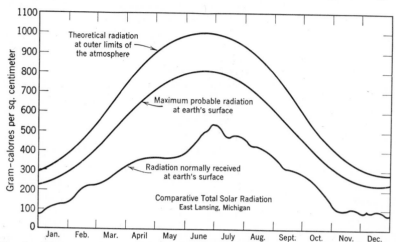

Fig. 2. The atmosphere materially reduces the amount of radiation that reaches the earth, as is shown by the space between the two upper curves. Furthermore the radiant energy that reaches the earth at a given location may be much further reduced by cloudiness and air impurities as is indicated by the space between the two lower curves. From *Michigan Agr. Exp. Sta. Tech. Bull. 222.* Data from cooperative hydrologic project of Soil Conservation Service and Michigan Exp. Sta.

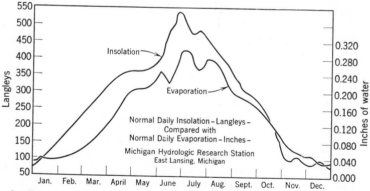

Fig. 3. Evaporation from a free water surface correlates closely with insolation. From *Michigan Quart. Bull.* 35: 186, 1952. Data from cooperative hydrologic project of Soil Conservation Service and Michigan Exp. Sta.

Because the pyrheliometer was on the roof of a low shed the amount of radiation recorded was much greater than that received by the surface of a soil supporting a crop or one covered with crop residues. The relation of radiation to evaporation is shown by Fig. 3.

Soil Temperature and Living Organisms. Studies have shown that soil temperatures to a depth of several inches usually change appreciably during a 24-hour period in the growing season. The extent of the change decreases with depth and is generally of little significance at 10 to 12 inches. It is evident, however, that the portion of a plant's root system which is in the surface few inches of soil is submitted to quite wide temperature variations during a clear summer day. It is also true that the roots or parts of the roots occupying different depths of the 8 inches of surface soil must function under decidedly different temperatures during the heat of the day and the colder part of the night in many climates.

Studies of soil temperatures at different depths show that the portions of the root systems of plants that occupy the lower soil areas must also function under quite different temperature conditions than do the roots in the surface soil. Also species which are grown over a wide range of climatic conditions, as is alfalfa, must adapt themselves to quite different temperature relationships. These temperature differences must exert an appreciable influence on the availability of nutrients and on the intake of both nutrients and water by plants. These effects are discussed in the following sections of this chapter.

Effect of Soil Temperature on Absorption of Nutrients by Plants.[1] Because energy is required for the intake of nutrients, the process is governed in part by metabolic activities within the plant and not merely by the permeability of the protoplasmic membrane of root cells. The rate of translocation and utilization of nutrients also influences the absorption process. It is difficult, therefore, to determine the effect of temperature on the specific process of nutrient absorption by a plant, because temperature also influences the other activities mentioned. Hoagland and Broyer [2] attacked the problem by studying the accumulation of nitrate, potassium, and halide in the cell sap of excised barley roots at different temperatures. Their results, expressed in terms of the concentration of the substance in the sap divided by the concentration in the solution containing the roots (known as the "accumulation ratio"), showed a marked increase in nutrient accumulation with rise in temperature. Also the rate of increase in accumulation was not the same for each nutrient, and the accumulation ratios were shown to vary with the concentration of the nutrients in the external solution. Furthermore, the effect of temperature on nutrient absorption is less noticeable in concentrated than in dilute solutions, according to Wan-

[1] See "Soil Physical Conditions and Plant Growth," p. 345, for a discussion of this topic by Hagan. *Agronomy*, Vol. II. Academic Press, New York, 1952.
[2] *Plant Physiol.*, 11: 471, 1936.

ner,[3] because of the lower energy requirement for absorption from a concentrated solution. Although the influence of temperature on metabolic activity in the roots, mobility of nutrient ions, fluidity of protoplasm, and surface exchange phenomena cannot be ignored in considering the relation of temperature to nutrient absorption, it appears well established that the process is appreciably affected directly or indirectly by temperature.

Many plants make an unsatisfactory growth in cold soils, and also there is much variation in the growth rates of different plants in such soils. To what extent these phenomena are due to the effect of temperature on nutrient absorption is not known. It has been shown, however, that apple and peach trees [4] can absorb nitrates at quite low temperatures and tomatoes [5] absorb nitrate equally well at temperatures of 55°, 70°, and 95° F. Little work has been reported on the intake of nutrients other than nitrate at low temperatures. Although nitrate appears to be absorbed by the roots of some plants at relatively low temperatures, the assimilation of the nitrogen and especially its transport to other parts of the plant are quite a different matter. Different species, and in fact different varieties, have been shown to vary considerably in this respect.

Water Absorption and Soil Temperature.[6]   The absorption of water by plant roots is retarded both by low and by high temperatures. The reduction in intake at low temperatures varies considerably with different plants and is greater for plants normally grown in warm soils than in those accustomed to lower soil temperatures. For example, Kramer found the transpiration of collards in a soil at 34.2° F. to be 63 per cent of that of plants in a soil at 77° F., while the transpiration of cotton was only 7.4 per cent as great in the colder as in the warmer soil. Also, Brown [7] noted wilting of Bermuda grass at a temperature of 50° F. although Kentucky and Canadian bluegrasses, which are adapted to growth in cold climates, absorbed ample water to maintain turgor.

The extent to which reduced water absorption is responsible for the inferior growth of some plants in cold soils is largely a matter of conjecture.

Although an increase in temperature results in an increased absorption of water up to a given point, further temperature increase brings

[3] *Ber. schweiz. Botan. Ges.,* 58: 383, 1948.
[4] *Proc. Amer. Soc. Hort. Sci.,* 42: 69, 1943.
[5] *Bot. Gaz.,* 95: 35, 1933.
[6] This topic is ably discussed by Kramer in *Plant and Soil Water Relationships,* p. 227, and by Hagan in "Soil Physical Conditions and Plant Growth," p. 350.
[7] *Missouri Agr. Exp. Sta. Res. Bull.* 299, 1939.

about a decrease in the process.   For example, Haas [8] reported a decrease in transpiration of grapefruit cuttings when root temperatures
exceeded 80.6° F. and of lemon cuttings above 87.8° F.   This reduced
intake of water by plant roots at higher temperatures is possibly caused
by injury to some fine roots and by rapid maturing of others with a
consequent reduction in absorbing surface, according to Hagan.

Soil Temperature and Root Growth.   There is an inseparable
interdependence between activity in the roots and in the aerial portion
of plants.   Food must be supplied to roots if they are to grow and
carry on their normal functions of absorption.   In consequence, root
activity will be greatly restricted, regardless of favorable soil temperatures, if photosynthesis is distinctly limited or if translocation in the
plant is markedly retarded.   Also, accelerated respiration may result in
an insufficient supply of carbohydrates for the roots.   Likewise an unfavorable soil temperature may result in a limitation of the activities in
the aerial plant parts because of restricted absorption of water or nutrients by the roots and their translocation.

Root growth is greatly affected by soil temperature, and the effect
varies in different plants.   Growth, however, in both roots and tops of
plants is a complicated process, and the response to temperature cannot
be expressed as a simple mathematical relationship unless it be through
a narrow range near the optimum temperature.   In general, root growth
increases with rise in temperature from a minimum through an optimum
and then decreases with further temperature increase.   This response
is illustrated for tomato roots by Fig. 4.   Apparently when a maximum
is reached a further temperature increase results in a rapid decrease in
root growth.

Studies of grasses by Stuckey [9] show a rapid development of new
roots in several species in the spring and again in the fall, with a limited growth in the summer.   Likewise elongation of old roots is limited
during the hot season.   The most favorable temperature range for root
development in most species tested lies between 59° and 68° F.   For
some species, such as Bermuda grass, which are adapted to warmer
climates, temperatures around 90° F. are most favorable.

Studies of temperature effects on root growth of many crop plants
have given variable results because of both the differences in methods
used and the many factors aside from soil temperature that influence
root development.   From the excellent review of available data on the

[8] *California Citrograph,* 21: 467, 1936.
[9] *Amer. J. Botany,* 28: 486, 1941.

subject presented by Hagan,[10] the optimum temperature for root growth of different plants is shown to vary from 95.0° F. for oranges to 60.8° F. for wheat.

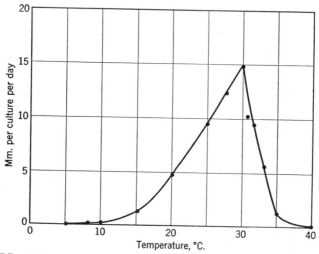

Fig. 4. Effect of temperature on the growth of excised tomato root tips in nutrient solution. After White. *Plant Physiol.,* 12: 183, 1937. Used with permission.

Effects of Soil Temperature on Growth of the Aerial Portion of Plants. Unfortunately, data on this topic are limited. As pointed out in a preceding section, there is an inseparable relationship between the activities of the roots and the tops of plants, and a long-continued satisfactory growth of neither part could be anticipated if the other portion were maintained in a suboptimal environment.

Soil Temperature and Activity of Microorganisms. A study of the effect of soil temperature on microbial activity in the soil is complicated because of the great number of microscopic life forms involved and because in given temperature ranges the rapid development of one or more forms may limit or obscure the activities of others. It can be stated that the majority of the microscopic organisms which normally inhabit the soil grow best in a temperature range between 50.0° F. and 104.0° F.

The important process of organic-matter decomposition goes on over a wide range of temperature because of the vast number of microbial forms which participate in it. In general, the rate increases with rise in

[10] "Soil Physical Conditions and Plant Growth," p. 379, *Agronomy,* Vol. II. Academic Press, New York, 1952.

temperature up to about 80.6° F. during the early stages. As the process continues, temperatures between 44.6° F. and 98.6° F. appear to affect it very little, according to the results of Waksman and Gerretsen.[11]

Ammonia production proceeds rapidly at temperatures between 68.0° F. and 104.0° F. if other conditions are favorable, but nitrate formation is less active at 68.0° F. than it is at 77.0° F. Also, the process appears to decrease somewhat above 95.0° F. The temperature range for optimum ammonification and nitrification coincides closely with that for optimum growth of many commonly grown crops.

It is also fortunate that Rhizobia are active in approximately the same temperature ranges that are favorable for the growth of the host plants. Freezing of the soil does not appear to be harmful to nodule bacteria although they are not active at such low temperatures. Temperatures frequently attained at the immediate surface of soils during the summer in most highly developed agricultural areas are detrimental to these bacteria, but seldom do soil temperatures below an inch or two get sufficiently high to destroy or greatly limit the activities of Rhizobia.

The activities of many organisms causing diseases in crops are also greatly influenced by soil temperatures. A number of diseases are known to be prevalent at low soil temperatures but not to cause appreciable damage at moderate to high temperatures. On the other hand, damage from some diseases occurs only when soil temperatures are comparatively high.

In general it is considered that temperatures which are reasonably favorable to the development of the disease organisms but are either too high or too low for the best growth of the host plant lead to greater prevalence of diseases. In other words, temperature exerts its influence on plant diseases through its effect on both the pathogen and the host plant. In his summary of the effect of temperature on plant diseases Hagan calls attention to the bibliographies on the subject presented by Dickson [12] for field crops and by Walker [13] for vegetables.

Relation of Air Temperature to Plant Life. Air temperatures and hence the temperature of the aerial portions of plants are subject to more frequent and greater fluctuations than are soil and root temperature, although there is of necessity a close correlation between average soil and air temperatures.

Of the three factors, latitude, altitude, and bodies of water, influencing air temperatures, the effect of water is the most interesting. Water bodies change temperature with relative slowness because of the high

[11] *Ecology*, 12: 33, 1931.
[12] *Diseases of Field Crops.* McGraw-Hill Book Co., New York, 1947.
[13] *Diseases of Vegetable Crops.* Edwards Brothers, Ann Arbor, Mich., 1930.

specific heat of water, the ease with which heat is distributed through the water by mixing, and the reduction in radiant energy received and reradiation due to the high humidity of the atmosphere. The effect of a body of water therefore is to reduce temperature changes over nearby land areas. Temperature changes of air over areas of land far removed from large bodies of water are extreme. For example a low of $-93.6°$ F. has been recorded in the interior of Siberia and a high of $134°$ F. in Death Valley, California.

The cardinal temperatures for plant growth, that is, the maximum, minimum, and optimum, extend over a range which is modified by several factors, some of the most influential of which are: (1) time of exposure; (2) plant species; (3) the part of the plant concerned; (4) stage of development; (5) physiological condition; and (6) humidity.

Low Temperatures and Plant Life. It is generally considered that growth in higher plants takes place very slowly if at all below $32°$ F. The seeds of certain plants tolerant of low temperatures, such as wheat, oats, rye, and certain vegetables, will germinate at temperatures slightly above freezing, and slow growth will be made. Also, certain arctic algae live and reproduce at temperatures which are never appreciably above $32°$ F. On the whole, however, growth of most plants is very slow below $40°$ F.

The difference in resistance of plant tissues to damage by low temperature has not been adequately explained. Differences in moisture content alone cannot account for the susceptibility to injury of various plant parts by low temperatures. Undoubtedly the state of the water in the protoplasm is a pertinent factor in determining the response.

Effects of High Temperatures. Temperature increases above the minimum result in rapid increases in growth until the optimum temperature is reached. The increase in growth with rise in temperature is not a simple relationship. Increases in temperature above the optimum range result in quite rapid decreases in growth rate until the maximum temperature is reached. Although certain single-celled organisms survive in hot springs with a temperature near boiling, most higher plants are greatly damaged or killed by shade temperatures ranging from $110°$ F. to $130°$ F. Many growth processes are retarded at temperatures appreciably below the maximum. Naturally the temperature for best growth or, in fact, for undamaged development to take place varies considerably for different plants.

The stems of plants are more often damaged by high temperatures than are the roots or leaves. The high temperature of the immediate soil surface frequently results in a scorch of the tender stems giving rise to "stem girdle." Likewise a soil temperature of $113°$ F. or slightly above may be injurious to seedlings of certain conifers, while other species may withstand temperatures up to 158° F. The disorder known as "sunscold" arises from the heating of the bark on branches and trunks of woody plants exposed to the sun during the dormant period. Wrapping or whitewashing the trunks of newly set trees is often resorted to as a protection from this type of heat damage. Likewise fruits of different kinds are frequently injured by direct sun heat under certain conditions. It appears to be the rapid change in temperature rather than the high temperature that produces "sunscold" and similar disorders.

LIGHT REQUIREMENT OF PLANTS

The sun is the primary source of all energy used in life processes on the earth. This energy is made available to animals and to plants not containing chlorophyll through the ability of chlorophyll to absorb radiant energy and store it as chemical energy in the form of simple sugars. Furthermore, light exerts an influence on germination of seeds, the growth characteristics of plants, the differentiation of plant organs and tissues, blossoming, and various physiological processes in plants. A few of the more important effects of light on plant growth will be discussed briefly.

Divisions of Radiant Energy.[14] The very short light waves and especially ultraviolet waves may cause a dwarfed growth by inactivating growth hormones which cause stem elongation. This phenomenon is frequently observed at high altitudes although light intensity and short growing season may contribute to dwarfness under such conditions. Formation of anthocyanins is also stimulated by these very short wavelengths.

Very long wavelengths, infrared, to which the eye is not sensitive seem to stimulate stem elongation. These are the so-called heat waves which animals feel.

Energy waves of medium length, 750 to 400 millimicrons,[15] constitute what we know as light. Light makes up approximately 50 per cent of the total radiant energy received from the sun. Although all the wavelengths in light are used in photosynthesis, those lying in the violet-blue and orange-red color bands are absorbed to the greatest extent. Those producing yellow and green are used to a small extent only.

[14] Much of the information contained in this and several of the following sections was obtained from *Plants and Environment* by R. F. Daubenmire. John Wiley & Sons, New York, 1947.

[15] A millimicron (mμ) equals 0.000001 mm. or 10 angstroms.

Light Intensity. Adequate light intensity is requisite for the optimum growth of all green plants. However, the intensity of light required by different species varies greatly. The shading effect of trees on the vegetation growing under them and on the activity of the leaves on the lower branches is a common phenomenon. The failure of grass under dense-growing and low-branched trees is a constant source of irritation in lawn maintenance. One of the main reasons for pruning fruit trees and staking and trellising vines and vegetables is to obtain more light on the leaves. Experiments in the spacing of rows of corn and alternate planting of sets of rows of corn and soybeans are based on the need for additional light.

Although adequate light is essential for satisfactory growth, exposure to very high light intensity is harmful to some plants. This result comes about through several activities such as some reduction in photosynthesis, increased transpiration, and a retarding of cell division. Some plants, such as ginseng and ferns, grow best in partial shade. A higher quality of product is also produced by some crops in reduced light, and hence coffee and cigar-wrapper tobacco are grown in partial shade.

Photosynthesis. As previously mentioned all the wavelengths of light are used to some extent in the process of photosynthesis although some have little value. Full sunlight is not required for maximum photosynthesis to take place in any single leaf. For example, in an apple leaf only 25 to 33 per cent of full sunlight is required for maximum photosynthetic activity. However, few leaves on a plant receive full sunlight, hence a plant may need to stand in direct sunlight for maximum photosynthesis to be obtained.

In addition to furnishing the energy by means of which carbon dioxide and water are combined into glucose, light performs other indirect functions in the process of photosynthesis. The carbon dioxide of the air must pass through the stomata in order to reach the moist parenchyma cells and be absorbed, and hence the extent to which the stomata are open has a determining effect on the amount of carbon dioxide available for combination with water. Unless moisture is a limiting factor the stomata open in response to light and close in the dark. Light then is a major factor in the supply of carbon dioxide to the food-manufacturing cells of the plant.

There is also some relationship between soil fertility and the light requirement of plants, because plants growing in fertile soils have a higher chlorophyll content in their leaves and hence have a greater photosynthetic power with a given amount of light. There are, however, very definite limits to this relationship.

Photoperiodism. Many plants are sensitive to the length of day or length of time they are exposed to light in each 24-hour period. Photoperiodism is the term used to designate the response of plants to this light-time relationship. Some species are not affected by this factor, but the large majority are. Several plant characteristics influenced by

Fig. 5. Both length of day and temperature have a marked influence on the growth characteristics of many plants, as is illustrated by the specimens of Christmas Pink variety of stock shown above. Conditions of growth from left to right were: [1]short day, cool temperature (55° F.);[2]long day, cool temperature;[3]short day, medium temperature (65° F.);[4]long day, medium temperature;[5]short day, warm temperature (75° F.);[6]long day, warm temperature. Courtesy of R. H. Roberts.

length of day are: (1) length of internode, (2) flower production, (3) length of life cycle, (4) degree of branching, (5) dormancy, (6) susceptibility to parasites, and (7) chemical composition. If plants requiring long days are subjected to short, daily light periods the internodes may be shortened sufficiently to give the plant a rosetted form. Furthermore, flower-bud initiation may not occur, or if formed they may drop off. On the other hand short-day plants submitted to long light periods may grow abnormally large and fail to produce flowers. Light and temperature both exert a marked influence on the growth habits of plants, as is shown in Fig. 5. Photoperiodism plays a large part in the natural distribution of many crops. Attempts to move varieties and species from north to south and vice versa are usually unsuccessful.

In reality it is not the length of day that affects the production of flowers in plants so much as it is the length of the dark periods to which they are exposed. For example short-day plants need relatively long dark periods in order to induce flower-bud differentiation. On the other hand long-day plants will not produce flowers if they are submitted to relatively long dark periods. In fact short-day plants may blossom when exposed to more hours of light than long-day plants provided the light period is broken by a relatively long dark period. Furthermore, the effect of the long dark period may be nullified if broken by a very short period of light.

Artificial Light. Studies of the effect of artificial light on plant growth were begun in 1861 and have continued until the present time. The use of artificial light to supplement sunlight and thus shorten the time for maturity is a common procedure in plant-breeding work. Also, in agronomic studies artificial light is frequently used in greenhouses to obtain more rapid growth of plants, especially during the winter months.

Studies with light of high intensity have shown that weight of tissue produced and carbohydrates increase with length of day until the rate of growth is retarded by injury to the foliage. A 17- to 19-hour day appears to be optimum for many plants, including cabbage and several of the common grains and forage crops. A longer day frequently results in injury, although increased growth may result from more hours of light during the earlier part of the growing period. There is evidence that plants need a rest period of several hours during the 24-hour day, or else that they have become adjusted to a shorter day during the latter part of the growing period, a condition which would not appear to pertain to small grains. It is generally recognized that there is much difference in the response of different plant species to light.

WATER AND THE GROWTH OF PLANTS [16]

Water is contained in all living tissue, and plants absorb more of it than of any other soil constituent. A large part of the moisture taken in by plant roots is transpired, although some is retained in the various tissues as water and some is broken up to supply the hydrogen and possibly a part of the oxygen contained in carbohydrates.

[16] The discussions of Kramer in *Plant and Soil Water Relationships* have furnished much material for this section. McGraw-Hill Book Co., New York.

Crop production is limited more often by an inadequate moisture supply than by any other factor. The capacity to retain available moisture is a soil characteristic given much consideration in evaluating land for agricultural use. Some soil-plant-water relationships will be discussed briefly.

Water Content of Plants. Water is the largest single constituent of plants making up, on an average, 75 per cent or more of green plant tissue. In fact, herbaceous plants contain a considerably higher moisture content when growing rapidly. For example, Miller [17] states that the tip of a young cornstalk or the basal portion of the leaves may contain 92 to 93 per cent of water and the leaves of cabbage and tomato 86 and 84 per cent respectively. On the other hand, woody plants are lower in moisture content and the percentage of water present varies with the season, quantity of water in the soil, and other factors.

Water and Growth Processes. An ample supply of water is necessary to maintain turgor in plant cells, and when they cease to be turgid vital processes for the growth and activity of the plant are affected. It is turgor pressure which supplies the energy needed for elongation of cells, and when a water deficit exists cell enlargement and division are reduced. Sometimes active tissue may withdraw moisture from older parts of the plant so that they may shrink while the growing tips are elongating.

A water deficit also results in a decrease in photosynthesis. Although stomatal openings are rapidly restricted with an increase in water deficiency, there are ample data to warrant the conclusion that a decrease in photosynthesis is more closely associated with water deficiency than it is with the closing of the stomata. There is little doubt that dehydration of the protoplasm is an active factor in the reduction of photosynthesis when a water deficit exists.

Water Movement and Moisture Supply for Plants. The processes by which plant roots are able to contact and absorb the tons of water required to produce an average acre yield of commonly grown crops have been the subject of much speculation. Evidently the root system cannot be in contact with this much water at one time. In fact, the soil to the average depth of root penetration does not contain so much water at a given time. Rain or irrigation water must therefore be carried within reach of the roots at intervals during the growing season.

With the establishment of the fact that capillary moisture moves with relative slowness in soils, and the inability of this phenomenon to supply

[17] *Plant Physiology.* McGraw-Hill Book Co., New York, 1938.

an appreciable part of the moisture requirement of plants, has come the realization that moisture must be secured through root extension. This fact is especially true for rapidly growing annuals. The extent and rate of development of the root systems of crops, therefore, becomes of much significance. Studies of the root systems of plants have shown them to be much more extensive under favorable conditions than was believed by early scientists, and the rate of extension of the root system of many plants is unbelievably rapid. For example, Dittmer [18] reported the average daily increase in length of the root system of a 4-month old rye plant to be 3.1 miles, and if the length of the root hairs produced each 24 hours were added the total would be 58 miles. The total length of the root system, excluding root hairs, was 387 miles. During the most active period of growth the rate of increase was considered to be higher.

The quantity of moisture made available to a plant by root extension will vary with the species and with soil characteristics. This point is illustrated by the work of Corey and Blake,[19] who found 8-week old sweetcorn roots to reach a depth of only 14 inches in a Sassafras loam soil while those of tomato plants of the same age had penetrated 36 inches. On the other hand, in 12 weeks tomato roots had only reached a depth of 11 inches in Penn silt loam because of the unfavorable nature of the underlying soil horizon.

Soil Moisture and Nutrient Availability. In a fertile soil a decrease in soil moisture below the field capacity results in an increased concentration of readily soluble nutrients such as nitrate and chloride ions. The effect on the availability of nutrients exerted by a decrease in soil moisture content to or below the wilting coefficient is pertinent to plant growth, but the problem has not been investigated to any great extent.

A number of studies indicate that the roots of many plants will not penetrate soil with a moisture content much below the wilting point. However, there is some variation in the ability of roots of different plants to continue to develop in soil after the moisture content has been reduced to a low level. Under field conditions, however, it is a common occurrence for the crop roots in the surface soil to be submitted to a moisture content at or considerably below the wilting coefficient while the lower portions of the root system are in contact with soil containing available moisture. Work by Breazeale [20] and Breazeale and McGeorge [21] shows that under such conditions moisture absorbed from the

[18] *Amer. J. Botany,* 24: 417, 1927.
[19] *Soil Sci. Soc. Amer. Proc.,* 17: 314, 1953.
[20] *Arizona Agr. Exp. Sta. Tech. Bull.* 29, 1930.
[21] *Soil Sci.,* 68: 371, 1949.

lower soil depths may be given off by the roots in the drier surface soil.
There is also some evidence that this exuded moisture may lead to the
absorption of potassium from the drier soil and possibly of nitrates, but
there is a question as to the intake of phosphorus.

Several investigators have reported symptoms of boron deficiency
in crops during dry seasons on soils which produce plants free from
such symptoms during wet seasons.

Volk,[22] in 1934, and several workers more recently, found little fixation of potassium in an unavailable form by acid soils kept moist, but
wetting and drying resulted in rapid fixation of the nutrient. Calcareous
soils, however, fix potassium when moist, and the process is stepped up
as the moisture content is decreased. These results offer a plausible
explanation for the low potassium content observed in plants grown in
soil of low moisture content.

Phosphorus fixation is also accelerated by a reduction in soil moisture
content, and according to Neller and Comar [23] the extent of the fixation
coincides with the clay content of the soil. A survey of available literature led Richards and Wadleigh [24] to the conclusion that plants grown
at low soil-moisture contents are relatively high in nitrogen, low in potassium, and sometimes low and at other times high in phosphorus,
calcium, and magnesium. The insufficient moisture supply resulted in
decreased growth of the plants studied, and under these conditions the
intake of potassium was decreased to a greater extent than potassium
utilization by the plant. On the other hand utilization of nitrogen was
limited more than was the intake. Soil conditions and the absorption of
other ions appeared to have much effect on the relative intake and utilization of the other nutrients studied.

Detrimental Effects of Excess Water. An excess of moisture in
the soil is detrimental to the growth of a large majority of commonly
grown crops. On the other hand, a few crops and a number of wild
species thrive when submerged, and others grow well in a saturated soil.
The poor growth of many plants in a wet soil is usually ascribed to
three factors, namely, (1) the development of toxic substances, (2)
insufficient oxygen for respiration, and (3) the lack of nitrate formation. One of the detrimental effects of an overabundance of soil moisture is a limited root development and a correspondingly large top
growth in proportion to the roots. This situation leads to excessive
crop damage in the event of drought. Plants growing in excessively

[22] *Soil Sci.,* 37: 267, 1934.
[23] *Soil Sci.,* 64: 379, 1947.
[24] "Soil Physical Conditions and Plant Growth," p. 203, *Agronomy,* Vol. II.
Academic Press, New York, 1952.

wet soil are also inclined to be abnormally succulent, are more susceptible to disease, and are less productive than if moisture conditions are normal.

Irrigation. The supplying of water by irrigation is a determining factor in the productivity of large acreages in the United States. This practice is not confined to arid or semiarid regions but is of growing importance in virtually every state of the Union. The possibilities of profitable, supplemental irrigation in humid areas are being more fully realized each year.

THE PLANT AND THE ATMOSPHERE [25]

Respiration is a process common to all living cells, and in consequence a source of oxygen to support the oxidation is essential, but many anaerobes need no atmospheric oxygen. The aerial portions of plants depend on the atmosphere for their supply of this element and the roots of higher plants on the soil air. On the other hand, some elementary plants normally utilize the oxygen from highly oxidized compounds such as nitrates and sulfates, and others are capable of reducing these compounds when the supply of oxygen in the soil air is very low. Carbon dioxide is another component of the atmosphere used by green plants for photosynthesis, and certain bacteria and possibly some algae can utilize nitrogen from the soil air if insufficiently supplied with combined nitrogen. No higher plant is known which can make use of elemental nitrogen without the cooperation of microorganisms. The gaseous mixture within the soil exists under such decidedly different conditions from that above the ground that the composition and movements of the two vary greatly, and hence they should be considered separately.

The Atmosphere. The most variable constituent of the atmosphere is water vapor, and changes in the amount present have more influence on plant processes than observed variations in other atmospheric components.

Quantities of the other principal air components, namely oxygen, nitrogen, and carbon dioxide, do not vary greatly except locally when gases from heating and industrial plants pollute the atmosphere. Damage to crops and decorative plants by fumes from smelters and chemical works has been the basis of many lawsuits.

Air normally contains about 0.03 per cent by volume of carbon dioxide and 20.96 per cent of oxygen. Plants in general thrive with these

[25] A detailed discussion of soil aeration and plant growth is given by Russell in "Soil Physical Conditions and Plant Growth," p. 253, *Agronomy,* Vol. II. Academic Press, New York, 1952.

percentages of the two gases, and attempts to accelerate growth by increasing the concentration of carbon dioxide have not proved practical. The effect of an increased sulfur content of the atmosphere on plant growth is discussed in Chapter 11.

The Soil Air. The sum of the carbon dioxide and oxygen contents of the soil air usually approximates the sum of the percentages of these two gases in the atmosphere. The per cent of each gas present, however, varies appreciably. For example, the carbon dioxide content of soil air varies from 10 to 1,000 times that of the atmosphere, and the oxygen content is usually slightly lower than that of the air above the soil and may be reduced to only 10 or 12 per cent.

Various methods have been proposed for determining whether a soil is sufficiently well aerated. Of these, determination of oxidation-reduction potentials [26] has been widely used, but the conclusion has been reached that these measurements do not correlate well with plant response.[27] Also, tests for ferrous iron [28] have given valuable information concerning poor soil aeration but, because other soil conditions influence the quantity of ferrous iron present, the test is not infallible. Measurements of the partial pressure of oxygen in the soil air should be especially helpful, but for some reason they do not correlate as well with plant response as do measurements under field conditions of the diffusion rates of oxygen.[29]

Plant Root Processes and Aeration. An adequate supply of oxygen is needed for normal rates of respiration in the underground parts of plants, but the actual partial pressure of oxygen in the soil air that is essential for different plant species varies within wide limits. Apparently the oxygen needs of aquatic plants are far less than those of plants adapted to growth on well-drained soils. Also, a greater concentration of oxygen is needed at higher temperatures because of accelerated respiration and also possibly because of the decreased solubility of the gas in water.

Growth is another process which is affected by oxygen supply, and again plants differ in their response to different oxygen levels. The rate of renewal of the oxygen supply is also a contributing factor to the partial pressure of oxygen required.

Although experiments [30] have shown that extremes in the concentration of oxygen in the air of the root zone may have a marked influence

[26] *Rep. Amer. Soil Survey Assoc.*, 16: 85, 1935.
[27] *New York Agr. Exp. Sta. Bull.* 625: 1, 1935.
[28] *Soil Sci. Soc. Amer. Proc.*, 10: 263, 1945.
[29] *Soil Sci. Soc. Amer. Proc.*, 14: 61, 1949.
[30] *Proc. Amer. Soc. Hort. Sci.*, 37: 19, 1940; also, 42: 53, 1943, and 36: 1, 1939.

on root growth, the effect of high concentrations of carbon dioxide are probably of more significance. For example, Leonard and Pinchard [31] found that growth of cotton roots in nutrient solution was not affected by 10 per cent of carbon dioxide when oxygen percentages ranged from 10 to 21. However, even with 21 per cent of oxygen, root growth was reduced about one-half by the presence of 30 per cent carbon dioxide and ceased with 60 per cent. In considering experiments dealing with the effects of different partial pressures of oxygen and carbon dioxide on root activities it should not be forgotten that the relative concentrations of these gases at the root-soil interface are doubtless of much more significance than those in the air in the larger pore spaces. Also, most studies of this nature have been made with solution or sand cultures where highly artificial conditions prevail, and it is doubtful that the extremely high or low concentrations which caused plant response are frequently encountered in normal soils under field conditions. However, poor drainage or very compact, slowly permeable soil horizons may result occasionally in these extreme percentages of oxygen and carbon dioxide.

Effect of Aeration on Water Absorption. About a century and a half ago it was demonstrated that poor aeration results in a decreased absorption of water by plant roots. Aeration studies have indicated also that the reduction in water intake accompanying poor aeration results more from high partial pressures of carbon dioxide than from a decreased oxygen supply. Furthermore, the decreased water absorption has been ascribed to the toxic effects of products of anaerobic respiration and to decreased permeability of root cells caused by carbon dioxide. Russell [32] expresses the opinion that the depressed water intake shown experimentally to occur with high concentrations of carbon dioxide are of "minor significance" under field conditions except where large quantities of easily decayed organic matter occur in water-logged soils within the root zone.

Nutrient Intake and Aeration. Arnon and Hoagland [33] found that tomato plants growing in unaerated culture solutions absorbed smaller quantities of all nutrients than plants in aerated solutions. The limiting influence on nutrient absorption of a low oxygen supply or of a high carbon dioxide content in the growth medium has been demonstrated by several investigators, and it is established that different plant species vary in their response to given concentrations of the two gases.

[31] *Plant Physiol.,* 21: 18, 1946.
[32] "Soil Physical Conditions and Plant Growth," p. 277, *Agronomy,* Vol. II. Academic Press, New York, 1952.
[33] *Soil Sci.,* 50: 463, 1940.

Figure 6 shows the influence of oxygen supply on the absorption of K, NO_3, and Br. Bower, Browning, and Norton [34] studied the growth and nutrient intake of corn on three Iowa soil types as affected by method of seedbed preparation. Methods of tillage which did not result in as complete stirring of the soil as did plowing gave lower yields and decreased intakes of nitrogen and potassium. The investigators ascribe

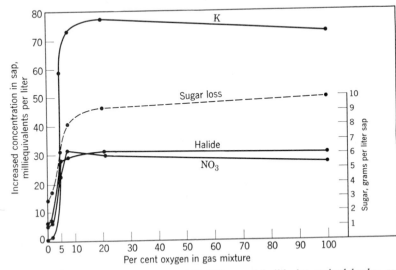

Fig. 6. Relation of accumulation of K, NO_3, and halide by excised barley root systems to the oxygen tension in the gas stream which was passed through the nutrient solution. The plants were grown from March 29 to April 24 in a complete culture solution. The root systems were then placed in 4-liter bottles containing 3 liters of solution, which contained 0.005M KBr, 0.005M KNO3, and 0.002M Ca(NO_3). From an article by Hoagland and Boyer in *Plant Physiol.,* 11: 485, 1936. Used with permission.

these results to differences in soil aeration, especially as the season was abnormally wet.

A study by Lawton [35] under controlled conditions in the greenhouse showed decreased growth of corn and reduced nutrient intake as a result of high soil-moisture content and also of soil compaction. On the other hand, forced aeration increased the absorption of nutrients. Also, soil characteristics influenced the effect of the treatments on the intake of the different nutrients. For example, the order of the reduction of nutrient absorption by high moisture content was K > P > N > Ca > Mg for Clarion soil, but on Clyde soil it was K > Ca > Mg > N > P.

[34] *Soil Sci. Soc. Amer. Proc.,* 9: 141, 1944.
[35] *Soil Sci. Soc. Amer. Proc.,* 10: 263, 1945.

Likewise, forced aeration increased nutrient intake in the following order on Clarion soil: K > N > P > Ca > Mg; and K > N > Ca > Mg > P on Clyde soil.

The above-mentioned and numerous other experiments have established the depressing effect of poor aeration on nutrient absorption by several plants. This fact raises the question as to what extent, if any, limited nutrient intake is responsible for the poor growth of crops under field conditions when reduced aeration is suspected because of poor drainage, unusually heavy rainfall, soil compaction from use of heavy farm implements, or a poor structural condition of the soil due to other causes. In general, substantiating data are not available to prove that aeration has been reduced to a detrimental level or that absorption by roots has been appreciably reduced.

NUTRIENT REQUIREMENT OF PLANTS

The exact nutrient requirement of plants is not known. Some scientists are of the opinion that any element found in a plant plays some role in the growth process although we may not know what it is. Certain it is that, with more careful studies, better equipment, and purer reagents, several elements have been added to the list of those that were originally considered essential. There is no question as to the necessity of having present in available form the following: carbon, hydrogen, oxygen, nitrogen, phosphorus, potassium, calcium, sulfur, iron, manganese, magnesium, copper, zinc, and boron. Evidence is accumulating which indicates that molybdenum belongs in the essential list, and for cereals and other plants high in silicon content this element is considered necessary. Also, plants inhabiting saline soils are thought to require sodium and chlorine. There is evidence that beryllium, strontium, and several other elements are needed by fungi. There appears to be some variation in the nutrient requirement of different kinds of plants. One effect that an insufficient supply of one or more nutrients may have on a plant or part of a plant is shown in Fig. 7.

Classification of Elements Found in Plants. Plant nutrient elements are sometimes classified on other bases than essentiality. For example, they may be grouped on their behavior during burning, carbon, hydrogen, oxygen, and nitrogen being lost and the other elements remaining in the ash, and again the functions of the nutrients may offer grounds for grouping as follows: those concerned with energy exchange, as hydrogen and oxygen; those that offer opportunity for storage of energy, as carbon, nitrogen, sulfur, and phosphorus; elements concerned with translocation of nutrients, as potassium, calcium, and magnesium;

and elements having to do with oxidation and reduction, including manganese, iron, and copper.

Many more elements are frequently found in plants, among which may be listed: arsenic, barium, aluminum, bromine, cobalt, fluorine, iodine, lithium, nickel, selenium, titanium, and strontium.

Fig. 7. The left side of this tree has received an insufficient supply of nutrients and hence has dropped its leaves prematurely. Although moisture taken up by any part of the root system is distributed through the entire plant the nutrients absorbed by a root are delivered to the aerial portions above its point of attachment only.

It is customary to divide the essential nutrient elements into two groups on the basis of the quantity occurring in plants. Those which are present in very small quantities are classed as micronutrients, and the list usually includes copper, zinc, boron, and manganese. The other essential elements that are obtained from the soil by plants are termed macronutrients. The supply of micronutrients in soils and their functions in plant growth are discussed in Chapter 12. Likewise, nitrogen, phosphorus, potassium, sulfur, and calcium and magnesium are discussed in separate chapters.

REFERENCES

Baver, L. D. *Soil Physics*. John Wiley & Sons, New York, 1948.

Bear, F. E. *Soils and Fertilizers* (fourth edition). John Wiley & Sons, New York, 1953.

Bonner, J., and Galston, A. W. *Principles of Plant Physiology*. W. H. Freeman & Co., San Francisco, 1952.

Bouyoucos, G. J. An investigation of soil temperature and some of the most important factors influencing it. *Mich. Agr. Exp. Sta. Tech. Bull.* 17, 1913.

Conway, V. M. Aeration and plant growth in wet soils. *Bot. Rev.,* 6: 179, 1940.

Curtis, O. F., and Clark, D. G. *Introduction to Plant Physiology*. McGraw-Hill Book Co., New York, 1950.

Daubenmire, R. F. *Plants and Environment*. John Wiley & Sons, New York, 1947.

Duggar, B. M. *Biological Effects of Radiation*. McGraw-Hill Book Co., New York, 1936.

Gardner, V. R. *Basic Horticulture*. The Macmillan Co., New York, 1942.

Kramer, P. J. *Plant and Soil Water Relationships*. McGraw-Hill Book Co., New York, 1949.

Kramer, P. J., and Coile, T. S. An estimation of the volume of water made available by root extension. *Plant Physiol.,* 15: 743, 1940.

Keen, B. A. The limited role of capillarity in supplying water to plant roots. *Proc. and Papers First Int. Cong. Soil Sci.,* Vol. 1, Com. 1: 504, 1927.

Lyon, T. L., and Buckman, H. O. *The Nature and Properties of Soils*. The Macmillan Co., New York, 1922; also fourth edition, 1943.

Meyer, B. S., and Anderson, D. B. *Plant Physiology*. D. Van Nostrand Co., New York, 1939; second edition, 1952.

Miller, E. C. *Plant Physiology*. McGraw-Hill Book Co., New York, 1938.

Parker, M. W., and Barthwick, H. A. Day length and crop yield. Bur. of Plant Ind., Agr. Res. Ad., *U.S.D.A. Misc. Pub.* 507, 1942.

Peterson, J. B. Relations of soil air to roots as factors in plant growth. *Soil Sci.,* 70: 175, 1950.

Roe, H. B. *Moisture Requirements in Agriculture*. McGraw-Hill Book Co., New York, 1950.

Russell, E. J., revised by Russell, E. W. *Soil Conditions and Plant Growth*. Longmans, Green & Co., London, 1950.

Russell, E. J., and Appleyard, A. The atmosphere of the soil, its composition, and the causes of variation. *J. Agr. Sci.,* 7: 1, 1915.

Shaw, B. T. "Soil Physical Conditions and Plant Growth." Vol. II of *Agronomy,* prepared under the auspices of the American Society of Agronomy. Academic Press, New York, 1952.

Veihmeyer, F. J., and Hendrickson, A. H. Some plant and soil-moisture relations. *Amer. Soil Survey Assoc. Bull.* 15: 76, 1934.

Vernalization and Photoperiodism (a symposium), 1948. Chronica Botanica Co., Waltham, Mass.

Wollny, E. Untersuchungen über den Einflus des Pflanzendecke und der Beschattung auf die physikalischen Eigenschaften des Bodens. *Forsch. Gebiete Agr.-Phys.,* 6: 197, 1883.

3

The Soil Solution and Nutrient Absorption by Plants

Early investigators looked upon the soil solution as the source from which plants absorb their mineral nutrients. It was assumed and is still held by some scientists that nutrients must be in solution in the soil water before they can be taken up by plants. The supply of nutrients in the soil solution was supposed to be renewed through the decay of organic matter, from applied manures and fertilizer salts, and by solution from the mineral soil particles.

A few early scientists, as Liebig, and virtually all workers of the present generation have looked upon the colloidal fraction of the soil as the main source of supply of nutrients for the soil solution. Also, some investigators consider soil colloids as a direct source of supply of nutrients for plants. Furthermore, the process by which nutrients enter plant roots has puzzled, and still does, all students of plant nutrition. The soil solution and intake of plant nutrients will be considered under three headings.

Discussion Topics

The soil solution.
The nutrient intake of plants.
Factors affecting nutrient absorption.

THE SOIL SOLUTION

Definition of Soil Solution. The soil moisture with the solids and gases dissolved in it is commonly considered to be the soil solution. Occasionally reference is made to the "inner" and "outer" soil solution. The inner solution refers to the moisture in intimate contact with the soil particles, particularly the finer ones, in which the concentration and composition of the solutes are more or less in equilibrium with the solid phase of the soil. By the outer solution is meant the liquid in the

34

larger capillary spaces which is considered to be much more dilute than is that in close contact with the particles. At times the term "soil solution" is used in referring to the liquid obtained from the soil by some of the displacement or dilution methods.

Composition of the Solution. The soil solution is not homogeneous. Not only is the portion of the solution that is held closely by the finer particles more concentrated than that in the larger pore spaces, but there is much variation in the proportion of the various ions held in solution in different locations in the soil. This comes about through the heterogeneity of the mineral portion of the soil. For example, moisture in contact with fragments of limestone or other minerals high in calcium content contains much calcium in proportion to other cations. On the other hand, soil moisture films surrounding orthoclase particles are relatively richer in potassium ions than the soil solution as a whole. Another factor which affects the make-up of the soil solution is the activities of microorganisms, particularly their production of nitrates.

Furthermore the composition and concentration of the soil solution is constantly changing. Rain dilutes it, and evaporation and plant transpiration concentrate it. Also, the proportions of the various ions change with dilution and concentration. It is evident from this short discussion that as a plant root moves through the soil it is constantly coming in contact with solutions of different concentrations and compositions and must adjust itself to this changing environment if the nutrient needs of the plant are to be supplied.

Changes in Soil Solution.[1] In general, the nitrate and chloride ions, which form few insoluble salts, decrease rapidly in concentration as the soil solution is diluted, and vice versa. Contrariwise, the concentration of the phosphate ion is very low and does not vary so much with dilution. Among the cations, potassium and sodium vary less than does calcium with changes in dilution, and the quantity of calcium present is usually much greater than the quantity of other cations.

The nitrate content of the soil solution is more variable than is that of other common constituents. In the early spring, in humid climates with distinct seasonal temperature changes, the concentration of nitrates is low. The quantity increases rather rapidly with warmer weather but is decreased again as rapid plant growth supplemented by leaching reduces the supply. In the fall the concentration again increases. Calcium is the cation occurring in largest quantity in most soil solutions, except those of soils very high in salt content. Magnesium ranks second in amount, with potassium third and occurring in small quantities only.

[1] A brief but quite complete discussion of this topic is given in *Soil Conditions and Plant Growth,* p. 438, eighth edition, 1950.

The quantities of sodium are very small except in the solutions of some saline soils.

Data concerning the composition of the soil solution are based on analyses of the solution obtained by displacement or dilution methods as described in Chapter 13. There is always a question as to how accurately the solution obtained by these methods represents the total solution as it exists in the soil. Anderson et al.[2] have shown that the extracted or displaced solution bears little relation to the total composition of the soil.

Nature of Solution in Saline Soils. Until recent years few studies had been made of the properties of the solution in saline soils. The work of Magistad and Reitemeier[3] on the solutions of seventeen soils representing a wide range of salinity conditions supplies valuable information on the subject. The solutions from the soils "at moisture contents within normal field range" were obtained by means of the pressure-membrane method of Richards.[4] The concentration of the soil solution at 15 atmospheres of the soils studied varied from 2,370 p.p.m. to 339,000 p.p.m.

The results showed that good growth of the crop on the fields sampled took place when the concentration of the soil solution, at moisture contents such that the moisture was held with a tension of 15 atmospheres (about the wilting point), was less than 10,000 p.p.m. or not more than 4.0 atmospheres' osmotic pressure. Plant growth at higher concentrations was reduced, and at pressures above 9 to 10 atmospheres growth was poor. It has long been known that the osmotic pressure of the cell sap of plants is influenced by the concentration of the solution, either soil or artificial, in which they grow; also that plants may be damaged by a too high concentration of salts in the growth medium or by the toxicity of certain ions even in dilute soil solutions. Although plants vary in their tolerance to salt concentration in the growth medium it has been shown that for a number of commonly grown crops the decrease in growth bears a linear relationship to the increase in concentration above the critical point. If the plant is salt-sensitive the regression line is very steep, but it slopes slightly for salt-tolerant crops. Livingston[5] reports that concentrations in a good growth medium in excess of about 2.5 atmospheres generally reduce absorption of water. There is reason

[2] *U.S.D.A. Tech. Bull.* 813.

[3] *Soil Sci.,* 55: 351, 1943.

[4] *Soil Sci.,* 51: 377, 1941.

[5] B. E. Livingston, Mineral requirements of plants as indicated by means of solution cultures. Liebig and after Liebig. *Pub. Amer. Assoc. Adv. Sci.,* 16: 83, 1942.

for believing that high salt concentrations are somewhat more detrimental in regions of higher than in those of lower temperatures.

A study of the composition of the soil solutions showed that the nitrate ion made up a high proportion of the anions in the productive soils. In solutions with higher concentrations, however, either the sulfate or chloride ion or both were present in relatively large amounts. Also, calcium was the dominant cation in most of the productive soils. In this respect the solutions were similar to those from humid-area soils. As solution concentration increased the quantities of sodium ion approached or exceeded the quantities of calcium ion. Likewise there was much more magnesium in the concentrated solutions than in the more dilute ones. In only one soil was there an appreciable concentration of potassium ion although the denser solutions usually contained several times the quantities found in the less concentrated ones.

The tolerance of plants to the toxicity of certain ions considered especially objectionable in irrigation water and saline soils is quite variable. For example, for sensitive crops more than 1.0 p.p.m. of boron in irrigation water is objectionable, but for tolerant crops 3.0 p.p.m. are permissible.[6] Of the cations sodium is the most objectionable although some studies indicate that its ill effects are due more to its detrimental influences on soil structure and to the increase in osmotic pressure of the soil solution than to any toxic effect.

Adequacy of the Soil Solution as a Growth Medium. Because the quantity of nutrients in the soil solution at a given time is insufficient to grow a crop to maturity there must be some means of renewing the supply. Likewise each of the required nutrients must be supplied in sufficient quantity to meet plant needs. Cameron [7] held to the theory that virtually all soils contain fragments of most of the common rocks and minerals, and because the soil moisture is in contact with them for long periods all essential mineral elements are dissolved in appreciable quantities. He also considered that because of removal of water from the soil by evaporation and transpiration the movement of solutes into the upper soil horizons by capillarity was greater than the loss by leaching. In consequence the soil solution was an adequate and inexhaustible source of mineral nutrients for crop production. Cameron was aware of adsorption phenomena in the soil and that nutrients were supplied to the soil solution from this source. Great stress was laid on the presence of toxic organic compounds in unproductive soils, and the view was held that the chief value of fertilizers and other soil amendments lay in their capacity to counteract the harmful effects of such toxins.

[6] *U.S.D.A. Cir.* 784, 1948.
[7] *The Soil Solution.* Chemical Publishing Co., Easton, Pa., 1911.

Gradually data have accumulated to disprove Cameron's theories and to show that the supply of available nutrients in the soil must be replenished by additions of soil amendments if high crop yields are to be maintained. It is of course true that there is much difference in the durability of soils, and some of them may be cropped many years before additions of fertilizing materials need to be made, whereas others require fertilization a short time after being placed in cultivation.

THE NUTRIENT INTAKE OF PLANTS

Process of Nutrient Absorption. The process by which nutrients gain entrance into plant roots has puzzled plant physiologists for many years. Early scientists assumed that the nutrients in solution were imbibed with the water that plants absorbed from the soil, in other words, that plants drank the soil solution much as animals drink. This opinion persisted for years even though the work of de Saussure in the early part of the nineteenth century indicated that plants absorb proportionately more water than salts from the soil solution. Gradually data accumulated showing that plants exert a selective action in the absorption of nutrients, and finally such convincing evidence has been presented, including that of Hoagland and his associates, that no doubt remains concerning the entrance of nutrients into roots independently of the intake of water. It is true that transpiration results in the rapid movement of water in the xylem, and this process hastens the translocation of nutrients and so reduces the concentration in the cell sap. The movement upward of nutrients which have entered the xylem appears to depend largely on the speed of the transpiration stream. Radioactive phosphorus has been detected in the top of a rapidly growing tomato plant 6 feet high within 40 minutes after its addition to the nutrient solution.[8] Accordingly transpiration may influence indirectly the intake of nutrients.

Many experiments indicate that factors affecting metabolic activities of the plant influence nutrient intake. For example, Arnon and Hoagland [9] showed that tomato plants growing in aerated solutions absorbed larger quantities of all nutrients than those growing in unaerated solutions. On the other hand rice will absorb an adequate supply of nutrients under seeming anaerobic conditions by the utilization of oxygen transported from the tops to the roots. Plants evidently vary in the extent to which environmental factors affect their intake of nutrients.

[8] *Amer. J. Botany,* 27: 791, 1940.
[9] *Soil Sci.,* 50: 463, 1940.

Variations in temperature also influence nutrient intake. The quantity of a given ion absorbed is also influenced by the concentration of other ions present. On the other hand the pH of the soil or nutrient solution appears to have less influence or nutrient intake aside from the effect on the solubility of certain ions. Some of the factors that affect the absorption of nutrients will be discussed later.

The extent to which plants may exert a selective action on the absorption of nutrients is illustrated by Hoagland's [10] studies with *Nitella*. He found the concentration of potassium, calcium, and phosphate in the cell sap to be 2,000, 13, and 870 times, respectively, the concentration of these ions in the pond water in which the *Nitella* was growing. Abundant data showing that various nutrient ions are accumulated in the cells of plant roots in a much higher concentration than they occur in the soil solution have discredited an earlier theory that nutrients enter roots by the simple process of diffusion.

It is not within the province of this book to discuss in detail the several theories advanced to explain the process or processes by which nutrients pass from the soil to the conducting tissue of the plant root. It should be mentioned, however, that in the opinion of some workers a difference exists between the processes of absorption of cations and of anions. According to Burstrom [11] cation absorption proceeds in two steps: First, a reversible adsorption on the surface of the colloidal root surface. This is considered to be somewhat similar to a Donnan equilibrium. The second step is the accumulation of the cation in the vacuole through excretion from the cytoplasm. On the other hand, anion absorption is not reversible and takes place against the diffusion gradient and the negative charge of the cell and hence the adsorption potential. The energy for the process is supposed to be derived from a portion of the respiration designated by different workers as "anion respiration" or "salt respiration." Needless to say, all workers are not in agreement with these theories.

Kramer [12] summarizes the present ideas of nutrient absorption substantially as follows: There is not sufficient evidence to consider anion and cation intake as the result of separate processes. Two steps are involved in ion absorption: First, some type of exchange process involving cations and anions (largely H^+ and OH^- or HCO_3^-) on the

[10] *Lectures on the Inorganic Nutrition of Plants*, p. 49. Chronica Botanica Co., Waltham, Mass., 1944.

[11] H. Burstrom, The mechanism of ion absorption, *Mineral Nutrition of Plants*. University of Wisconsin Press, Madison, 1951.

[12] P. J. Kramer, *Plant and Soil Water Relationships*. McGraw-Hill Book Co., New York, 1949.

root surfaces and the ions in the soil solution or on the soil colloids. Second, the movement into the cell vacuoles of the ions adsorbed on the cell surfaces. This process requires energy and appears to be closely associated with respiration, but the details of the process are not established. The nutrients are moved into the stele and then into the xylem vessels. It has been suggested that, because of the decreasing aeration from the outer cortex cells to those near the stele, there is a decrease in ability to accumulate and hold solutes. Accordingly, because of the difference in concentration the nutrients are moved by diffusion to the xylem. Protoplasmic streaming may assist in the process. There are many difficulties which beset the determination of the exact processes by which nutrients penetrate roots. Perhaps when this procedure is definitely understood the information may be helpful in solving some problems of soil productivity.

FACTORS AFFECTING NUTRIENT ABSORPTION

Kind of Plant. The variation in the capacity of different plants to absorb nutrients from soils has long been recognized and made use of by farmers. It has been customary to classify those crops that make good yields on fertile soils only as "delicate feeders." On the other hand crops that can produce fair yields on relatively infertile soils are frequently referred to as "coarse" or "rough" feeders. Various explanations of this difference in the ability of crops to obtain nutrients have been advanced. Difference in extent of root system or in the abundance of fibrous roots has been suggested. Also tolerance of soil conditions giving rise to a low pH value has seemed a possible explanation in some cases, as has a low calcium requirement. Truog suggested that the ability of certain legumes to use phosphorus from a relatively insoluble source such as rock phosphate was due to the utilization of calcium, which was made soluble when the phosphate was acted upon by carbon dioxide and water.

That there is a genetic difference in the power of plants to absorb nutrients was shown by Collander [13] in a study of twenty species grown in solution cultures. The maximum quantities of sodium and manganese absorbed were some 60 times the minimum amounts. Little sodium was taken up by wheat, corn, and sunflower although large quantities were absorbed by halophytes. Likewise there was considerable difference in the intake of magnesium. On the other hand differences in the quantities of potassium, rubidium, and cesium absorbed were not

[13] *Plant Physiol.,* 16: 691, 1941.

great. Miller [14] also cites the example of *astragalus bisulcatus* (two-grooved milk vetch), which accumulated 1,250 p.p.m. of selenium from a soil containing only 2.1 p.p.m., in contrast to *A. Missouriensis* (Missouri milk vetch), which took up only 3.1 p.p.m. of the element. Similarly Mehlich and Reed [15] list the following crops in decreasing order of calcium requirement compared to their content of potassium and magnesium: turnip, cotton, alfalfa, red clover, soybeans, alsike, oats, and timothy.

By studying the composition of four crops grown on two soils with varying additions of calcium, potassium, magnesium, and sodium, Marshall [16] gave a qualitative ranking of the crops, based on the quantity of the different nutrients they contained, as follows: Magnesium content; sweet clover > redtop > bluegrass > Korean lespedeza. Calcium content; sweet clover > Korean lespedeza > redtop > bluegrass. Manganese content; redtop > bluegrass > Korean lespedeza = sweet clover.

Within plants the content of nutrients in the seed or fruit is more characteristic of the plant than is the nutrient content of the root, which is influenced more by the concentration in the soil. The composition of the leaves and stems is intermediate between that of the roots and the fruit. No entirely satisfactory explanation for the difference in intake of nutrients by plants has been advanced.

Effect of Other Nutrients Present. It has long been recognized that the intake of a given ion by plants may vary considerably with the concentration and nature of other ions present. For example, Beeson et al.,[17] working with tomato plants growing in sand cultures, found that the calcium content of the leaves increased when the potassium content decreased. Russell points out that in general the following effects may be anticipated when the concentration of various ions is increased in the soil: "increasing the calcium in the soil depresses the magnesium in the leaves more than the potassium; increasing the magnesium depresses the calcium more than the potassium; and increasing the potassium may depress the calcium more than the magnesium, or may decrease them about equally."[18] The effects of varying the concentration of calcium, magnesium, and potassium in the soil on the relative quantities of these elements in bluegrass and sweet clover, as

[14] *Plant Physiology.* McGraw-Hill Book Co., 1938.

[15] *Soil Sci.,* 66: 289, 1948.

[16] *Missouri Agr. Exp. Sta. Res. Bull.* 385, 1944.

[17] *Plant Physiol.,* 19: 258, 1944.

[18] *Soil Conditions and Plant Growth,* eighth edition. Longmans, Green & Co., London, 1950. Used with permission.

TABLE 1.   EFFECT OF A GIVEN INCREASE OF A CATION IN THE SOIL ON PLANT
COMPOSITION *

Milliequivalents of Cation per 100 Grams of Dry Plant Tissue

	Bluegrass				Sweet Clover			
Added to Soil	Ca	Mg	K	Total	Ca	Mg	K	Total
Basal	35	42	54	131	102	62	47	211
+Ca	41	37	53	131	124	57	45	226
+Mg	30	63	50	143	100	97	42	239
+K	23	24	95	142	72	38	102	212

* From *Soil Conditions and Plant Growth*, by E. J. Russell, revised by E. W. Russell. Longmans, Green & Co., London, 1950. Used with permission. The results are the mean of the crops on two soils and at two levels of calcium supply. Prepared by Russell from data in *Missouri Agr. Exp. Sta. Res. Bull.* 385, 1944.

found by Marshall, are shown in Table 1. In considering these data Russell points out that the potassium content of a plant is not so easily changed as is the magnesium content, and, in turn, the magnesium content is not so readily altered as is the calcium content by variations in the concentrations of other cations in the root zone. Mehlich and Reed [19] point out that an unequal distribution of the various cations in the growth medium of the plant will affect markedly the influence of a given ion on the intake of others.

It has frequently been demonstrated that increasing the concentration of a given cation in the medium in which a plant is growing generally increases the quantity of that ion in the plant. Also a corresponding decrease in the quantity of 1 or more of the other cations in the plant has been noted. Such studies have led several investigators to suggest that the equivalent cation content (particularly calcium, magnesium, and potassium) of a given plant is approximately a constant. Some data bearing on this point, obtained by several workers, are shown in Table 2.

These data show that the variation in total milliequivalents of cations in a given crop is considerable for a constant. Probably a number of factors, including the supply of certain anions, influence the total accumulation of cations in a given plant.

Internal and External Salt Concentration. Although the total concentration of salts in the root is generally greater than that outside of it, and an ion may be readily absorbed when the root contains much more of it than the soil solution, there is some relationship between

[19] *Soil Sci.*, 66: 289, 1938.

TABLE 2. RANGE IN TOTAL CATION CONTENT OF SEVERAL CROPS GROWN
WITH DIFFERENT TREATMENTS AND/OR ON DIFFERENT SOILS

Milliequivalents per 100 Grams of Plant Tissue

	Total of Ca, Mg, K	Investigator
Alsike	123–140	Lucas et al.
Alfalfa	117–163	Lucas et al.
Red clover	118–145	Lucas et al.
Italian rye grass	186–208 *	Van Italli
Cotton	60–138	Mehlich and Reed
Alfalfa †	157–198	Bear and Prince
Tobacco leaves	359–443	Anderson et al.
Soybeans	130–153	Mehlich and Reed
Oats	114–149 *	Mehlich and Reed
Turnips	216–264 *	Mehlich and Reed

* Includes Na also.   † First crop from 20 soils.

concentrations of nutrients inside and outside of the root and nutrient absorption. Intake of nutrients is usually more rapid when the concentration within the root is low, and also nutrient absorption is accelerated when the plant is growing rapidly and thus using the nutrients.

Experiments have shown that increasing the concentration of an ion in the soil solution up to a certain point will increase the intake of that ion. Higher concentration, however, will result in no greater absorption of the ion by the plant. Just what concentration of each nutrient ion is best for plant growth is not known. Unquestionably the optimum concentration of the different nutrients will vary for different species and possibly varieties. There is evidence also that a given plant may grow equally well within a range of concentration of the required nutrients provided a balance is maintained between the quantities of the different nutrients.

Aeration and Respiration. Although plants vary in their requirement of oxygen in the root zone, it is well recognized that for most crops an adequate air supply is necessary for rapid absorption of nutrients. Experiments have shown that, with an abnormal increase in carbon dioxide content of the growth medium, a rapid decrease in nutrient intake results. This result may be due not only to a decrease in oxygen supply but also to the effects of the carbon dioxide itself on the metabolic activity of the cells and their ability to absorb nutrient ions. No salt accumulation has been found to occur in the cells when oxygen is lacking.

Furthermore, nutrient intake appears to be closely associated with respiration. Any factor that decreases the rate of respiration of growing plant roots reduces their nutrient absorption. Apparently the intake of ions is closely associated with various other growth processes of the plant. For example, a decrease in the movement of carbohydrates to the roots may depress the intake of nutrients.

Availability of Adsorbed Nutrients. Not long after the adsorption of nutrient ions by the soil was demonstrated by Way in 1850 it was suggested by Liebig [20] that these ions were in some way utilized by plants. Further studies have substantiated the idea, and a measurement of the quantity of certain cations held by the soil complex is now considered an index of the availability of those nutrients to crops. There is, however, some disagreement concerning the process by which adsorbed ions are rendered available for absorption by roots.

The Solution Theory. Many investigators believe that the adsorbed ions are first displaced from the colloidal material and exist as solutes in the soil solution before being taken into the plant. The release of the ions is supposed to result from the interaction of carbon dioxide, given off by plant cells or by soil organisms, with water with the production of H^+ and HCO_3^-. The H^+ replaces the adsorbed cation which is then available for absorption by the roots. On the other hand, some workers think there is a more direct interaction between the root and the adsorbed ions.

The Contact-Exchange Theory. Jenny [21] and his associates have postulated a direct ionic exchange between the root cell and the colloidal matter of the soil. If the root and the soil colloid are in very intimate contact, the ion swarms of the root and of the colloid will intermingle. In other words, the oscillation volumes of some of the cations on the soil colloid would overlap those of some of the hydrogen ions of the root cell. Under such a condition there could be a direct exchange of root hydrogen for soil colloid cation. This process would not involve the soil water nor the intermediate reactions of carbon dioxide. It is further assumed that ions may move from plant cell to plant cell by this same process through overlapping oscillation volumes. It is also possible for the ion swarm of closely associated colloids to overlap, and hence ions may move from one particle to another and ultimately into the plant root.

Jenny supports his theory by citing the greater uptake of sodium by barley roots from a sodium-clay suspension than from a solution of sodium chloride or sodium bicarbonate having equal concentrations

[20] *Natural Laws of Husbandry,* London, 1863. Also, *Soil Conditions and Plant Growth,* p. 441, 1950.

[21] *Mineral Nutrition of Plants,* p. 10. University of Wisconsin Press, Madison, 1951.

of cations. It should be mentioned, however, that the intake of potassium from a solution of potassium chloride was greater than from a potassium-clay suspension. Another phenomenon showing the interaction of roots and clays is the giving off of a large quantity of potassium by barley roots when placed in a suspension of either hydrogen, calcium-hydrogen, sodium, or ammonium clay. On the other hand, the roots gave up no potassium when washed with a large volume of distilled water. It was further shown that barley roots accumulated more potassium and zinc from a suspension of montmorillonite clay than from one containing kaolinite. This fact is significant because the kaolinite releases more of the two ions to carbonated water, pure water, and hydrochloric acid than does the montmorillonite.

Supporters of the contact-exchange theory do not maintain that plants obtain all or even a large share of their cations by this process, and they freely admit the operation of the carbon dioxide-solution procedure. They do insist, however, that contact exchange can and very probably does take place. Such direct passage of the nutrient ions from the colloid to the root precludes the loss of such ions in drainage water which might occur if the nutrients entered the soil solution. It has been suggested that, instead of placing too much stress on either the soil solution or the adsorbed ions as sources of plant nutrients, we should think in terms of the "root environment" as a whole.

Variations in the Availability of Adsorbed Ions. All ions adsorbed on the colloidal soil fraction are not equally available. As is well known, some are more easily replaced than others. Also, all the ions of the same nature may not be equally accessible to plants, as some are held quite closely to the colloidal surface whereas others move in the outer portions of the ionic swarm. Furthermore, the availability of ions which have entered the crystal and are held between the layers of the crystal is not definitely known. The relative abundance of the different ions also influences their availability. An ion which satisfies a considerable part of the total exchange capacity of the colloid, as calcium frequently does in soils of humid areas, would be readily available. On the other hand, an ion which satisfied only a small part of the exchange capacity would be comparatively difficultly available. This fact suggests the idea that possibly there is a certain distribution or partition of ions satisfying the exchange capacity which is quite favorable to plant growth. Bear [22] has suggested that a satisfactory distribution of ions on the colloidal complex of a soil with a high exchange capacity would be 60 per cent of the capacity satisfied by calcium, 10

[22] F. E. Bear, *Soils and Fertilizers.* John Wiley & Sons, New York, 1953.

per cent by potassium, 10 per cent by magnesium, and 20 per cent by hydrogen. Although this arrangement may be satisfactory for some crops a different assortment of ions would probably be better for others, as all plants do not require essential elements in the same proportion. In some soils of arid or semiarid regions the large proportion of sodium and often of calcium on the colloidal complex results in a starvation of the plants for less abundant ions. The other ions on the complex also influence the availability of a given ion. For example, it has been shown that more potassium was available from the complex when the other ion present was largely calcium or magnesium than when it was largely hydrogen. However, an increase in potassium decreased the availability of Ca and Mg. On the other hand, Albrecht and Schroeder [23] have shown that the presence of a significant concentration of hydrogen facilitates the uptake of calcium, magnesium, and some other cations except potassium by the plant.

Renewal of Adsorped Nutrients. Additions of fertilizers and lime, as well as of manures, green manures, and plant residues, which yield soluble salts upon decay, serve as sources of ions for replenishing the supply on soil colloids. In addition, the ions made soluble through the natural processes of weathering of the soil minerals are readily adsorbed by the colloids. Further, it has been shown that unsaturated clay minerals can extract considerable quantities of cations from mineral particles of the size of silt. There appears to be much variation in the extent to which various minerals yield cations to unsaturated clays. How effective clays, which are only partially unsaturated, are in extracting cations from minerals has not been demonstrated.

Effect of Degree of Saturation of Clays on Nutrient Absorption by Plants. That the degree of base saturation of the soil colloids has an influence on nutrient absorption was indicated by the work of Stohmann.[24] He found the yield of corn plants increased with the degree of base saturation of organic colloids. Several studies have shown that calcium is more available to plants as the degree of saturation of the complex with this ion increases. Work by Chu and Turk,[25] using montmorillonitic clay, kaolinitic clay, and a sandy loam soil containing illitic clay, mixed with quartz sand and saturated to different degrees with calcium, magnesium, and potassium, has given significant data. Yields of oats and rye bore an almost linear relationship to base saturation of the montmorillonitic clay, but yield increases on the kaolinitic clay with saturations above 40 per cent were negligible. Yields

---

[23] *Soil Sci.,* 53: 313, 1942.
[24] *Landw. Vers. Sta.,* 6: 424, 1864.
[25] *Michigan Agr. Exp. Sta. Tech. Bull.* 214, 1949.

of tomatoes on the illite-containing soil were not increased by saturation above 75 per cent and of oats above 50 per cent. The determining effect of degree of base saturation is shown by the fact that, in general, plant growth was more closely related to this factor than to the total supply of exchangeable bases. Figure 8 shows some of these relationships in rye.

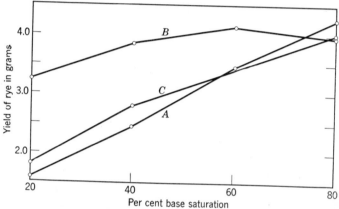

Fig. 8. Type of clay mineral and percentage base saturation are important factors in availability of nutrients as indicated by the growth of plants. Curve *A* shows that the yield of rye increases with per cent of base saturation in a bentonite-sand mixture. On the other hand, in a kaolinite-sand mixture yield increases were small above 20 per cent saturation (curve *B*). Cation-exchange capacity of the mixture was 2.0 m.e. per 100 grams for each. That the degree of base saturation is important, as well as the supply of bases, is shown by curve *C*. The rye was grown in bentonite-sand mixtures having exchange capacities of 2, 4, and 8 m.e., the percentages of saturation being 80, 40, and 20 respectively. All the mixtures contained the same quantity of bases (1.6 m.e. per 100 grams). Prepared from data in *Michigan Agr. Exp. Sta. Tech. Bull.* 214, 1949.

Further evidence of the influence the kind of clay mineral has on nutrient intake of plants is afforded by the fact that with montmorillonite calcium intake was greatly increased when calcium saturation was raised from 30 to 40 per cent but increased little with higher percentages of saturation. For kaolinite, however, the calcium content of plants did not increase appreciably with per cent saturation above 30. Likewise, with an increase in per cent potassium saturation of the kaolinite from 5 to 10, there was a large increase in potassium content of rye with little further increase for higher per cents of saturation. With montmorillonite, however, potassium content of rye increased with each increase in per cent saturation of the element. Furthermore, the calcium and magnesium contents of plants grown on kaolinitic media were higher than those grown on montmorillonitic material, that is, with total base saturations below 60 per cent. In contrast, potassium contents of plants were higher in those grown on the montmorillonite-sand mixtures.

Data available at present show that degree of base saturation is an important factor in nutrient absorption by plants and that the type of clay mineral present also exerts much influence on the total and individual nutrient intake.

REFERENCES

Albrecht, W. A., Graham, E. R., and Shepard, H. R. Surface relationships of roots and colloidal clay in plant nutrition. *Amer. J. Botany,* 29: 210, 1942.

Albrecht, W. A., and Schroeder, R. A. Plant nutrition and the hydrogen ion: I. Plant nutrients used most effectively in the presence of a significant concentration of hydrogen ions. *Soil Sci.,* 53: 313, 1942.

Anderson, M. S., Keyes, M. G., and Crower, G. W. Soluble material of soils in relation to their classification and general fertility. *U.S.D.A. Tech. Bull.* 813, 1942.

Cameron, F. K. *The Soil Solution.* Chemical Publishing Co., Easton, Pa., 1911.

Chu, T. S., and Turk, L. M. Growth and nutrition of plants as affected by degree of base saturation of different types of clay minerals. *Mich. Agr. Exp. Sta. Tech. Bull.* 214, 1949.

Collander, R. Selective absorption of cations by higher plants. *Plant Physiol.,* 16: 691, 1941.

Curtis, O. F., and Clark, D. G. *Introduction to Plant Physiology.* McGraw-Hill Book Co., New York, 1950.

Graham, E. R. Calcium transfer from mineral to plant through colloidal clay. *Soil Sci.,* 51: 65, 1941.

Graham, E. R. Primary minerals of the silt fraction as contributors to the exchangeable base level of acid soils. *Soil Sci.,* 49: 277, 1940.

Hoagland, D. R. *Lectures on the Inorganic Nutrition of Plants.* Chronica Botanica Co., Waltham, Mass., 1944.

Hoagland, D. R., and Arnon, D. I. Physiological aspects of availability of nutrients for plant growth. *Soil Sci.,* 51: 431, 1941.

Jenny, H. Contact phenomena between adsorbents and their significance in plant nutrition, *Mineral Nutrition of Plants,* p. 10. Univ. of Wisc. Press, Madison, 1951.

Kramer, P. J. *Plant and Soil Water Relationships.* McGraw-Hill Book Co., New York, 1949.

Livingston, B. E. Mineral requirements of plants as indicated by means of solution cultures. Liebig and after Liebig. *Pub. Amer. Assoc. Adv. Sci.,* 16: 83, 1942.

Lucas, R. E., and Scarseth, G. D. Potassium, calcium, and magnesium balance and reciprocal relationship in plants. *J. Amer. Soc. Agron.,* 39: 887, 1947.

Lucas, R. E., Scarseth, G. D., and Sieling, D. H. Soil fertility level as it influences plant nutrient composition and consumption. *Indiana Agr. Exp. Sta. Bull.* 468, 1942.

Magistad, O. C., and Reitemeier, R. F. Soil solution concentrations at the wilting point and their correlation with plant growth. *Soil Sci.,* 55: 351, 1943.

Magistad, O. C., Ayers, A. D., Wadleigh, C. H., and Gauch, H. G. The effect of salt concentration, kind of salt, and climate on plant growth in sand cultures. *Plant Physiol.,* 18:151, 1943.

Marshall, C. E. The exchangeable bases of two Missouri soils in relation to composition of four pasture species. *Missouri Agr. Exp. Sta. Res. Bull.* 385, 1944.

Mehlich, A., and Reed, J. F. The influence of degree of saturation, potassium level, and calcium additions on removal of calcium, magnesium, and potassium. *Soil Sci. Soc. Amer. Proc.,* 10: 87, 1945.

Mehlich, A., and Reed, J. F. Effect of cation-exchange properties of soil on the cation content of plants. *Soil Sci.,* 66: 289, 1948.

Miller, E. C. *Plant Physiology.* McGraw-Hill Book Co., New York, 1938.

Richards, L. A. A pressure-membrane extraction apparatus for soil solution. *Soil Sci.,* 51: 377, 1941.

Stohmann, F. Versuche mit absorbisten Nahrstoffen. *Landw. Vers. Sta.,* 6: 424, 1864.

Van Itallie, T. B. Cation equilibrium in plants in relation to the soil. *Soil Sci.,* 46: 175, 1938.

4

Colloids and Soil Productivity

The colloidal constituents of the soil are the seat of most of the chemical and physical reactions taking place in the soil. Also the activities of the soil microorganisms are concerned primarily with the organic fraction which is considered to be colloidal.

Without the colloidal material in soils plants would make very little growth in humid climates unless fertilizers were applied in adequate amounts and at opportune times. Only relatively small quantities of nutrients can exist in the soil solution, for if not taken up by plant roots they are carried away by percolating water. It is essential, therefore, that the soil have the capacity to hold in reserve considerable quantities of nutrient elements and to release them as the supply in the soil solution becomes depleted. In fact the quantity of nutrients in the soil solution at a given time is not so important in productivity as is the ability of the soil to renew the supply. In most instances it is the colloidal fraction that performs this essential function in meeting plant requirements.

Other contributions to the productivity of soils are made by colloidal material. Moisture relationships are influenced and structural conditions are modified. These effects may be beneficial or detrimental, but in general they are useful in plant growth. The colloidal fraction of the soil will be discussed under the following headings.

Discussion Topics

The colloidal content of soils.
Constituents of soil colloids.
The clay minerals.
Processes of ion adsorption and exchange.
Ion fixation and soil productivity.

THE COLLOIDAL CONTENT OF SOILS

The inorganic colloids in soils result from mineral decomposition. They may be either the direct products of mineral decay such as the hydrated oxides of iron, aluminum, and silicon, or they may be minerals synthesized from the decay products. It does not follow, however, that climates which are conducive to rapid decomposition of rocks and minerals necessarily give rise to soils high in colloidal content. Many soils are developed in material composed very largely of minerals which resist weathering, and hence only a small quantity of colloidal material is produced. On the other hand other soils develop in sediments which are already high in colloidal content. Furthermore, soils containing much colloidal material may develop in climates which are not especially favorable for mineral decomposition because the parent material contained a high percentage of readily weathered rocks and minerals.

The content of organic colloids in soils is also highly variable. Factors which affect accumulation of humus in soils, such as moisture conditions both climatic and soil, temperature, vegetative cover, and supply of mineral nutrients, determine primarily the quantity of organic

TABLE 3. THE COLLOID CONTENT OF THE SURFACE HORIZON OF SEVERAL SOILS *

Soil and Location	Colloid Content, per cent	Soil and Location	Colloid Content, per cent
Miami silt loam, Indiana	15.8 †	Ruston fine sandy loam, Georgia	7.3 ‡
Chester sandy loam, Maryland	14.2 †	Bladen loam, North Carolina	11.4 ‡
Cecil sandy loam, Georgia	10.2 †	Hillsdale sandy loam, Michigan	15.7 §
Amarillo silty clay loam, Texas	23.9 ‡	Yolo loam, California	48.5 §
Nipe clay, Cuba	50.2 ‡	Marion silt loam, Minnesota	45.4 §
Davidson clay loam, North Carolina	25.9 ‡	Brookston clay loam, Michigan	33.4 §
Orangeburg fine sandy loam, North Carolina	3.0 ‡	Sandy loam, Rhode Island	17.7 §
Pima clay, Arizona	59.2 ‡		
Pierre clay, South Dakota	57.4 ‡		

* From *Fundamentals of Soil Science*, by C. E. Millar and L. M. Turk. John Wiley & Sons, New York, 1951. Used by permission.
† Determined by the water-adsorption method.
‡ Determined by the pipette method.
§ Determined by the heat-of-wetting method.

colloids in a given soil. The colloidal content of a number of representative soil types is given in Table 3.

CONSTITUENTS OF SOIL COLLOIDS

Organic Colloids. Because animal and plant tissues are primarily colloidal in nature *all* the organic material in the soil may be looked upon as a part of the soil colloids. It is customary, however, to consider only that part of the organic matter which exists in the state designated as humus as a part of the colloidal system in soils. As is pointed out in Chapter 6, this substance is considered to be a combination of protein, derived largely from the bodies of microorganisms, and lignin.

Inorganic Colloids. The mineral colloids consist of the oxides of iron, aluminum, and silicon in various stages of hydration and a group of crystalline compounds known as clay minerals. The proportion of the colloidal fraction made up of hydrated oxides is extremely variable, ranging from a very small part to virtually all of it, and in fact to a high percentage of the entire soil in some tropical soils. Likewise the quantity of clay minerals is very small in some soils and makes up a large share of the colloids in other soils. The hydrated oxides appear to represent residues of quite complete decomposition of soil minerals. On the other hand the clay minerals are usually considered to be synthesized in the process of soil development and represent some of the products of the constructive phases of soil formation. Since the clay minerals are the most active part of the inorganic colloidal fraction in supplying nutrients to plants and in modifying the physical condition of the soil, more detailed consideration will be given to them.

THE CLAY MINERALS [1]

Structure of Clay Minerals. Until about 1930 the mineral colloids of the soil were thought to be amorphous gels with variable composition. One argument advanced against the idea of a crystalline structure was the fact that no large crystals had been isolated. Through use of X-rays, however, the crystalline nature of the material was established, and extensive study has been carried on of the clay minerals and their effect on soil properties which influence productivity.

Clay Minerals and the Physical Properties of Soils. The clay minerals have been shown to exist as very small and thin plate-like crystals. Their size and shape result in the exposure of an extremely large amount of surface for a given weight of colloid. The minerals also are very adhesive and have the property of swelling when damp-

---

[1] A comprehensive discussion of the clay minerals is presented by Gieseking in *Advances in Agron.,* 1: 159, 1949.

ened and of shrinking upon loss of water. This latter characteristic varies with different minerals. And, furthermore, the properties of the minerals are influenced considerably by the quantity and nature of the cations adsorbed on them. Because of the high activity of the clay minerals a comparatively small quantity of them will influence greatly the physical characteristics of a soil.

Granulation in soils is due to the colloidal fraction and in most soils largely to the clay minerals. Granulation results in better aeration, greater intake of rain, and freer movement of soil moisture. Furthermore, the large surface area of colloids, as well as the soil granulation induced by them, greatly increases the water-retaining power of soils. Wind and water erosion are also reduced through the binding of soil particles together by colloids. The different clay minerals vary in their adhesive properties, with the montmorillonite type having much more binding power than the kaolinite type. Stability is a highly desirable property in soil granules, and there is some evidence to show that organic colloids are effective in imparting this quality to granules, possibly by forming a coating on the surface. It is well recognized that a granular soil provides a good seedbed, which results in rapid seed germination and emergence of young plants. Also increased water-retaining capacity of a soil, with good aeration, promotes plant growth and increases productivity.

The effects of colloids on soil properties are not always beneficial to crop production, however. The shape and size of the clay minerals permit them to pack closely when a soil is tilled at too high a moisture content. The result, in fine textured soils, is the formation of hard and often large clods, and so a poor seedbed. Also, even a rather small percentage of colloids in a soil may result in the formation of a surface crust following a beating rain, which interferes with the emergence of seedlings. Quite impervious surface coatings, formed during the early part of a rain, also result in increased runoff with its consequent loss of water and greater erosion.

A considerable percentage of colloids in the subsoil may result in poor internal drainage and in insufficient aeration. The growth of plants with rather large and deep-growing tap roots, such as alfalfa and sweet clover, is often practiced in order to form drainage channels in such subsoils. In addition plow soles and claypans often develop in soils high in colloidal content.

Composition of Clay Minerals.[2] The crystals of clay minerals are made up of layers of aluminum oxide and silicon dioxide (Figs. 9

[2] *Advances in Agron.,* 1: 160, 1949.

and 10), in which the fundamental units of the crystal are chemically bound together by the sharing of certain oxygen atoms (commonly called oxygen ions in crystals) between aluminum and silicon atoms (ions). Some minerals, as montmorillonite and illite, contain two layers of silica with a layer of aluminum oxide in between. Kaolinite, halloysite, and similar mineral groups, on the other hand, contain only one

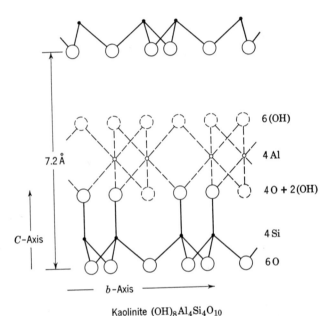

Kaolinite (OH)$_8$Al$_4$Si$_4$O$_{10}$

Fig. 9. Schematic presentation of the structure of a kaolinite crystal. After Grim, Cir. 49, Illinois State Geological Survey. Used with permission.

layer of silicon dioxide to each layer of aluminum oxide. Some of the three-layer crystals, as montmorillonite, are capable of absorbing water between the sheets and expanding; illite does not have this property.

Some of the oxygen ions on the aluminum oxide sheets are usually replaced by hydroxyl groups, as is illustrated in Figs. 9 and 10. This condition has much bearing on the quantity and kind of plant nutrients that the different clay minerals can retain, as is explained on page 58. Also, some of the silicon and aluminum ions in the sheets may be replaced by other ions of similar size but with different valence, and thus the capacity of the mineral to adsorb nutrient ions is affected, as is brought out on page 58. It is seen that different clay minerals have different properties, or, more properly, some minerals have certain properties to a much greater extent than do others. For example, montmorillonite and beidellite crystals are very small and have a high cation-exchange capacity (Table 5). The kaolinite group of minerals, on the other hand, occur as relatively large crystals with little cation-exchange capacity but are considered to have appreciable anion adsorp-

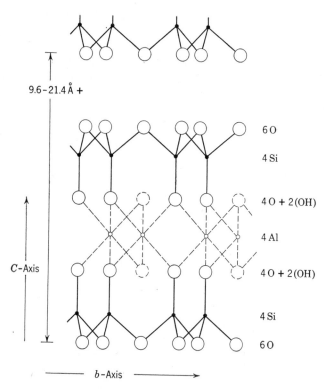

Montmorillonite $(OH)_4Al_4Si_8O_{20}$

Fig. 10. Schematic presentation of the structure of a montmorillonite crystal. After Grim, *Cir.* 49, Illinois State Geological Survey. Used with permission.

tion capacity. Accordingly, the kind of clay minerals in a soil, as well as the quantity of them, influences the productivity of the soil. It is of interest, therefore, to study the conditions under which the different minerals are formed and their distribution in the soils of different parts of the country.

Distribution of Clay Minerals.[3] Clay minerals are well distributed throughout the soils of the world, although there is not an even distribution of the different groups. There is evidence that the environ-

[3] This topic is discussed by Gieseking in *Advances in Agron.,* 1: 177, 1949.

mental conditions under which the different minerals develop vary considerably, although the information on this subject is far from complete. Kaolinite develops in soils from which the bases have been leached. Complete base removal may not be necessary, but at least a low concentration is essential. Kaolinite is a product of the weathering of sodium and potassium feldspars and of hydrous micas. It is a constituent of many sedimentary clays and of residual and sedimentary kaolin. It is more abundant in clays of warm humid climates but is quite widely distributed in other climatic zones including some semiarid soils of California. Nacrite and dickite, on the other hand, are seldom found in sediments. They are more abundant where hydrothermal alteration has occurred.

The occurrence of kaolinite in soils of warm climates, and especially in those which have been submitted to extensive leaching, would lead to the expectation of an above-average phosphorus-fixing capacity in soils of the southeastern part of the United States. The high content of hydrated iron oxide in these soils also contributes to this property.

Members of the montmorillonite group of minerals with high cation-exchange capacity are widely distributed but are especially abundant in soils of humid temperate regions. A relatively high content of organic matter in the soil appears to favor the development of minerals of this type. Grassland soils are reported to contain more of the montmorillonite minerals than timbered soils in the same climatic area. They are found in soils derived from igneous rocks, and sometimes in sediments. These minerals are formed in the presence of bases, magnesium appearing to favor their formation especially. Calcium feldspars, and the ferromagnesium silicates of basic igneous rocks, such as basalts, give rise to montmorillonite. Through the loss of sodium and potassium volcanic glasses may also produce these minerals.

Soils of the North Central states, particularly those with a natural grass vegetation, should have a high cation-exchange capacity because conditions are favorable for the development of montmorillonite and similar minerals, and also because of the above-average content of organic matter. These soils also should exhibit quite extensive expansion and contraction upon wetting and drying.

Illitic minerals are frequently associated with marine clays and are constituents of shales. Kaolinite and illite appear to be the main constituents of the clays of the Coastal Plains and the Gulf of Mexico. Illite is also abundant in the glacial deposits of the United States. Because of the ease with which this mineral undergoes alteration, it is not commonly found in residual deposits. These minerals are derived from micas to a large extent but can doubtless be formed by soil development processes. Halloysite minerals sometimes occur in association with kaolinite in some sediments and have been found in Atlantic sediments. The quantities, however, are small.

A study of the colloidal constituents of alkali soils by Kelley [4] et al. showed the presence of a mixture of montmorillonitic, kaolinitic, and mica-like minerals in white-alkali soils. On the other hand mica-like minerals made up the major part of the colloids in black-alkali soils.

TABLE 4. APPROXIMATE MINERAL COMPOSITION OF THE CLAY FRACTION OF SEVERAL SOILS

		Mineral Constituent, per cent				
Soil Type or Series	Loca-tion	Quartz	Kaolinite	Montmo-rillonite	Illite or Hydrous Mica	Iron Oxide
Huston clay loam *	Miss.	<5	20	55	26 †	‡
Oktibbeha clay loam *	Miss.	<5	20	60	20 †	‡
Susquehanna clay loam *	Miss.	<5	10	65	25 †	‡
Orangeburg sandy loam *	Miss.	<5	25	70	4 †	‡
Lufkin clay *	Ala.	<5	<5	80	15	<5
Cecil clay *	Ala.	0	90	<5	<5	10
Sarpy sandy loam *	Miss.	<5	10	50	35	<5
Norfolk sandy loam *	. . .	10	25	30	35	<5
Catalina clay *	Puerto Rico	0	100	0	0	. . .
Clarion	Iowa	. . .	15	60	25	. . .
Grundy	Iowa	. . .	5	65	30	. . .
Tama	Iowa	. . .	15	55	30	. . .
Webster	Iowa	. . .	0	85	15	. . .
Greenville	Ga.	. . .	80	0	0	15
Frederick	Va.		70	0	20	10
Hagerstown	Pa.		70	0	20	9
Hagerstown	Md.		50	0	40	8
Miami	Ind.		10	0	80	7
Barnes	S. Dak.		30	20	40	0
Desert soil	Cal.		20	70		2

* Fine clay only <0.2 μ.
† Determined from chemical analysis, assuming that mica contains 6% K_2O.
‡ Iron oxide removed before separation of clay.

Data from R. Coleman and M. L. Jackson, Mineral composition of the clay fraction of several Coastal Plain soils of southeastern United States, *Soil Sci. Soc. Amer. Proc.*, 10: 381; M. B. Russell and J. L. Haddock, Identification of the clay minerals in five Iowa soils by the thermal method, *ibid.*, 5: 90; and L. T. Alexander, S. B. Hendricks, and R. A. Nelson, Minerals present in soil colloids. II. Estimation in some representative soils, Soil Sci., 48: 273.

The percentage of several clay minerals in the colloidal fraction of a number of soils is given in Table 4.

[4] *Soil Sci.,* 51: 101, 1941.

PROCESSES OF ION ADSORPTION AND EXCHANGE

The process of ion adsorption by soil colloids plays a significant role in soil fertility. Were it not for this phenomenon the cations made soluble through the decay of organic matter and mineral decomposition would leach rapidly from the soil in humid regions unless absorbed by plant roots. Also, soluble cations added in fertilizers would be largely lost unless applied at a time when plants could take them up. Furthermore, replacement of the adsorbed ions from the colloids is an important part of the function of colloids in providing a reservoir of nutrients for plant use.

Adsorption of Ions by Clay Minerals. The positive and negative ions in clay minerals are bound together by electrostatic forces, and the negative and positive forces or valencies are equal. At the edges of the crystals, however, there will be some unsatisfied negative valencies from the oxygen ions, and hence a limited amount of cation adsorption is possible at these points. On the other hand, it will be noted in Figs. 9 and 10 that hydroxyl ions may be substituted to a greater or less extent for oxygen ions. When this occurs on the faces of the crystals the hydrogen of the hydroxyl may be replaced by some other cation. In addition it is possible for the entire hydroxyl group to be replaced by an anion. Not a great deal is known about anion adsorption, but it is noteworthy that kaolinite and similar minerals expose many more hydroxyl ions than do montmorillonite and illite, and hence the capacity of the kaolinite and similar minerals to adsorb PO_4 and other anions is theoretically much greater. McAuliffe [5] and associates have demonstrated the fixation and replacement of phosphate ions on the surface of kaolinite.

Another process by which clay minerals become capable of adsorbing cations is through the replacement of the silicon or aluminum of the crystal by ions with lower valencies. For example, if magnesium or ferrous iron were substituted for aluminum some of the oxygen valencies originally satisfied by the aluminum would be left free and hence could adsorb other cations. This replacement of silicon or aluminum by other cations is known as "isomorphic substitution," and the replacing cations must be similar in size to the ion replaced. Isomorphic substitution is much more extensive in some clay minerals than in others and, together with the difference in size of crystals, accounts for the higher base exchange capacity of some minerals, such as montmorillonite, than of others, as kaolinite.

[5] *Soil Sci. Soc. Amer. Proc.,* 12: 119, 1947.

There is also the possibility of the penetration of the crystal by ions sufficiently small to enter the interstices of the lattice. Too little is known of this phenomenon, however, to justify a discussion of it.

The capacity of soils or of fractions of soils to adsorb exchangeable ions is usually expressed in terms of milliequivalents (m.e.) per 100 grams of dry material. Recently the exchange capacity has sometimes been given in equivalents per million (e.p.m.). The cation-exchange capacity of several clay minerals is given in Table 5.

TABLE 5. APPROXIMATE SIZE, CATION-EXCHANGE CAPACITY, AND FORMULA OF SEVERAL CLAY MINERALS

Mineral	Size, microns	Exchange Capacity, milliequivalents (m.e.) per 100 grams	Formula
Kaolinite	0.5–2.0	3–15	$(OH)_8Al_4Si_4O_{10}$
Nacrite	5.0–15.0	3	$(OH)_8Al_4Si_4O_{10}$
Dickite	2.0–5.0	0	$(OH)_8Al_4Si_4O_{10}$
Halloysite	Rod shaped	6–10	
Metahalloysite	...	...	$(OH)_8Al_4Si_4O_{10}$
Montmorillonite	0.01–0.1	80–100	$(OH)_4Al_4Si_8O_{20} \cdot nH_2O$
Beidellite	0.05–0.5	60–80	$Al_2(Al_{0.33}Si_{3.66})O_{10}(OH)_2Na_{0.33} \cdot nH_2O$
Nontronite	...	55–70	$Fe(Al_{0.33}Si_{3.67})O_{10}(OH)_2Na_{0.33}$
Saponite	...	65–85	$Mg_3(Al_{0.33}Si_{3.67})O_{10}(OH)_2Na_{0.33} \cdot nH_2O$
Illite	0.1–1.0	30–40	$Al_2Si_4O_{10}(OH)_2(K)$

Adsorption of Nutrients by Materials Other Than Clay Minerals. The hydrated oxides of iron and aluminum also have ion-fixing capacity. This action is thought to be accomplished by replacing the hydrogen of the hydroxyl with another cation or by replacing the entire hydroxyl by an anion. These hydrated oxides are considered to be amphoteric, and their relative cation-anion exchange capacities are influenced by the pH of the system.[6] It has been shown that the OH groups may be replaced by the phosphate ion.[7]

The organic colloids also possess a high ion-fixing capacity. In fact, it is frequently from 4 to 7 times that of an equal weight of mineral colloids. The proportion of the ion-exchange capacity of soils that is due to organic colloids varies greatly, some workers reporting a minimum of 6.9 per cent and some a maximum varying from 40 to 60 or 80 per cent. In what structures of the organic matter the ion-fixing capacity resides has been the subject of much investigation and remains a disputed question.

Although it is usually considered that most of the ion-exchange capacity of a soil resides in the clay and humus fractions this is not always

[6] *Soil Sci.*, 30: 459, 1930.

[7] The fixation of phosphate ions is discussed fully by Dean in *Advances in Agron.*, 1: 391, 1949.

true. Fragments of some minerals of larger size than clay if relatively unweathered, or if recently crushed so that fresh surfaces are exposed, have an appreciable exchange capacity. For example Barshad [8] found the percentages of the total cation-exchange capacity of four prairie soils from California supplied by silt and sand varied from 16.8 to 42.9.

Exchange of Ions. Ions adsorbed or fixed on colloidal particles may be replaced by other ions having charges of similar sign. For example, if to a soil in which the colloids contain considerable calcium a potash fertilizer, as KCl, be added, the K ions will displace at least some of the Ca ions. The proportion of the Ca ions displaced will depend on the amount of KCl applied, or, in other words, on the concentration of the K ions in the soil solution.

The procedure by which this exchange takes place is of interest. It is understood that ions adsorbed on colloids are not held rigidly attached to the particle but move back and forth or oscillate through limited distances from the particle. The distances through which the ions move vary for the different ions. If an ion chances to be near the extreme of its oscillation distance another ion in the soil solution may move closer to the colloid and be attracted by the force of the oppositely charged surface of the colloid. Thus the new ion is held by the colloid and the original one is set free. It is of course impossible to determine exactly the procedure followed in ion exchange. Ions held within the crystal lattice are more difficult to replace because the replacing ion must penetrate the lattice.

Ions differ greatly in their replacing efficiency. Factors which seem to be most influential in determining the replacing power of ions are: (1) the degree of hydration or size of the water envelope, if any, surrounding the ion; (2) speed of motion; and (3) the charge carried by the ion. Usually the less hydrated ions are more effective in replacement phenomena than those with thick water envelopes provided the competing ions carry the same charge. Ions carrying the greater charge are more effective in replacement if other factors are equal. Thus bivalent ions will usually replace monovalent ions, and trivalent ions will replace bivalent ones. The hydrogen ion is the most effective in replacement of those commonly present in quantity, although it probably cannot replace aluminum or iron. The descending order of replacement of a number of common ions is reported as follows: [9] H, Sr, Ba, Ca, Mg, Rb, K, NH_4, Na, Li. It should be pointed out, however, that the

[8] *Soil Sci.,* 61: 423, 1946.

[9] *Cation Exchange in Soils,* by W. P. Kelley, p. 61. Reinhold Pub. Corp., New York, 1948.

effective order of replacement of various cations is governed in part by the nature of the colloidal complex.

ION FIXATION AND SOIL PRODUCTIVITY

It is difficult to overestimate the importance of ion fixation to soil productivity. Few if any soils contain enough of the various nutrient elements in a soluble state to satisfy the requirements of an average crop. Furthermore the rate of solution of mineral nutrients from soil particles, even from fragments of primary minerals of clay size, is too slow to meet the needs of rapidly growing plants. The necessity of a reserve supply of nutrients is therefore evident. Other factors being equal there is usually a close correlation between the ion-fixing capacity of soils and their productivity. Studies have indicated that it is not the quantity of nutrients in solution in a soil at a given time that indicates its productivity but rather the capacity of the soil to renew the supply when the nutrients in solution have been utilized. The cation-exchange capacity of soils from several locations in the United States is given in Table 6.

TABLE 6. CATION-EXCHANGE CAPACITY OF SEVERAL AMERICAN SOILS
Milliequivalents per 100 Grams

Soil Type or Series	State	Exchange Capacity	Soil Type or Series	State	Exchange Capacity
Cayucos sandy clay loam *	Cal.†	20.2	Cecil sandy loam	S. Car.‡	5.5
Los Osos sandy clay loam *	Cal.†	20.2	Norfolk sandy loam	Ala.‡	1.8
Gleason clay loam *	Cal.†	31.6	Susquehanna fine sandy loam	Ala.‡	4.1
Sweeney clay loam *	Cal.†	57.5	Norfolk sandy loam	Ala.‡	3.0
Grundy silt loam	Ill.‡	26.3	Greenville sandy loam	Ala.‡	2.3
Cory silt loam	Ill.‡	7.8	Cecil clay loam	Ala.‡	4.9
Delta light silt loam	Miss.‡	9.4	Susquehanna clay	Ala.‡	34.3
Colby silt loam	Wis.‡	13.3	Oktibbeha clay	Ala.‡	19.4
Miami silt loam	Wis.‡	7.8	Sassafras sand	N.J.**	2.0
13 fine sandy loams	N. Car.§	4.9	Sassafras loamy sand	N.J.**	2.7
9 sandy loams	N. Car.§	3.7	Colts Neck sandy loam	N.J.**	9.9
Minden	Iowa ‖	21.4	Collington loam	N.J.**	15.9
Edina	Iowa ‖	20.6	Gloucester loam	N.J.**	11.9
Clarion loam	Iowa ¶	19.1	Sassafras loam	N.J.**	7.5
Carrington silt loam	Iowa ¶	21.4	Hagerstown loam	N.J.**	16.5
Sac silty clay loam	Iowa ¶	35.1	Chester loam	N.J.**	10.6
Muck	Mich.	74.5	Penn silt loam	N.J.**	19.8
Muck	Mich.	84.7	Merrimac silt loam	N.J.**	10.2
Muskingum silt loam	Ohio	5.7	Bermudian silt loam	N.J.**	13.2
Keene silt loam	Ohio	9.3			

* Prairie soils. † *Soil Sci.*, 61: 423, 1946. ‡ *Soil Sci.*, 31: 99, 1931. § Data supplied by Dr. A. Mehlich. ‖ *Soil Sci. Soc. Amer. Proc.*, 15: 324, 1950. ¶ *Soil Sci. Soc. Amer. Proc.*, 12: 435. 1947. ** *J. Amer. Soc. Agron.*, 37: 217, 1945.

Some workers believe that virtually all the nutrients taken up by plants pass through the colloidal complex. That is, nutrients are ob-

tained by the colloids from the larger particles by slow solution processes, from organic matter by decay, and from added fertilizer materials,
and are then passed on to the plant through ion-exchange processes.
To what extent this theory is correct is difficult to establish, but it cannot
be denied that the colloidal fraction of soils plays a prominent part
in holding nutrients in reserve and delivering them to plants during
the growing season.

Under what conditions adsorbed nutrients are released to plants is
an interesting study and one which requires much more investigation.
The degree of saturation of the exchange complex has a bearing on the
release of nutrients. The release of a given ion is also affected by the
nature of the other ions held by the colloids, as well as by the nature
of the colloid itself. The action of the root and the requirements of
the plant may also have a bearing on the process. In productive soils
the order and quantity in milliequivalents of the cations commonly adsorbed on the colloids is as follows, according to Gieseking: [10] Ca, 15;
Mg, 5; H, 5; K, .25; NH_4, trace; and Na, trace. In alkali soils the
quantity of sodium is greatly increased.

REFERENCES

Barshad, I. A pedologic study of California prairie soils. *Soil Sci.,* 61: 423,
1946.
Buehrer, T. F., Robinson, D. O., and Deming, J. M. The mineral composition
of the colloidal fraction of some southwestern soils in relation to field behavior.
Soil Sci. Soc. Amer. Proc., 13: 157, 1948.
Coleman, R., and Jackson, M. L. Mineral composition of the clay fraction
of several Coastal Plain soils of southeastern United States. *Soil Sci. Soc.
Amer. Proc.,* 10: 381, 1945.
Gieseking, J. E. The clay minerals in soils. *Advances in Agron.,* I: 159. Aca-
demic Press, New York, 1949.
Gieseking, J. E., and Jenny, H. Behavior of polyvalent cations in base exchange.
Soil Sci., 42: 273, 1936.
Grim, R. E. *Clay Mineralogy.* McGraw-Hill Book Co., New York, 1953.
Harradine, F. F. The variability of soil properties in relation to stage of profile
development. *Soil Sci. Soc. Amer. Proc.,* 14: 302, 1949.
Hendricks, S. B. Lattice structure of clay minerals and some properties of
clays. *J. Geol.,* 50: 276, 1942.
Kelley, W. P. *Cation Exchange in Soils.* Reinhold Pub. Corp., New York, 1948.
Kelley, W. P. Modern concepts of soil science. *Soil Sci.,* 62: 469, 1946.
Kelley, W. P., Dore, W. H., and Page, J. B. The colloidal constituents of
American alkali soils. *Soil Sci.,* 51: 101, 1941.
Marshall, C. E. *Colloids in Agriculture.* Edward Arnold & Co., London, 1935.

[10] *Advances in Agron.,* 1: 190, 1949.

Marshall, C. E. *The Chemistry of the Silicate Minerals.* Academic Press, New York, 1949.

Ross, C. S. Minerals and mineral relationships of the clay minerals. *J. Amer. Ceram. Soc.,* 28, No. 7: 173, 1945.

Russell, E. J., revised by Russell, E. W. *Soil Conditions and Plant Growth.* Longmans, Green & Co., London, 1950.

Stout, P. R., and Overstreet, R. Soil chemistry in relation to inorganic nutrition of plants. *Ann. Rev. Plant Physiol.,* 1:305, 1950.

5

Soil Reaction and Liming

Soil reaction should be considered in productivity studies because soil structure, the solubility of minerals and availability of nutrients, the activities of microorganisms, and the intake of ions by crops are greatly influenced by the conditions accompanying different reactions in soils.

In regions having sufficient rainfall to carry soluble salts, primarily those of calcium and magnesium, out of the surface horizons of the soil, the development of acid soils is a natural result of the weathering process. On the other hand, when precipitation is not adequate for the removal of the basic products of weathering from the solum, alkaline soils develop. Also, some soils contain appreciable quantities of limestone and other basic rocks.

The unequal growth of various crops on soils having different reactions has been a matter of concern to students of agriculture since accounts of farming practices have been recorded. Early chemists as well as those of the present generation have studied the causes, methods of determining, and procedure for changing soil reaction. Some of the problems involved in soil reaction studies and the use of lime will be discussed under the following headings.

Discussion Topics

Causes and nature of soil acidity.
Development of saline and alkali soils.
Determination and expression of soil reaction.
Soil reaction and plant growth.
Changing the reaction of soils.

CAUSES AND NATURE OF SOIL ACIDITY

Hydrolysis and Base Solubility. Of the various chemical processes by which soil minerals are robbed of their basic constituents, hydrolysis is the most effective. The action of this process on minerals may be illustrated by the following type reaction in which calcium is used as a representative basic element:

$$\text{Mineral} \cdot \text{Ca}_x + y\text{HOH} \rightleftarrows \text{Mineral} \cdot \text{H}_x + y\text{Ca(OH)}_2$$

The hydroxide so produced may act immediately with CO_2 to form the carbonate or bicarbonate, or with traces of other acids as HNO_3 or H_2SO_4, or either the Ca or the (OH) or both may be adsorbed by colloids, or plant roots may absorb the cation. The important fact is that mineral particles lose their basic elements, and these are replaced by hydrogen. Direct solution also aids to a greater or less extent in this process of depleting minerals of bases.

Effects of Base Removal. The removal of bases from minerals renders them unstable in structure, and when the process has gone far enough the mineral disintegrates. The products of mineral decomposition may remain in part or entirely as substances containing replaceable hydrogen ions and hence be acid, or they may recombine to form the clay minerals. If the cations liberated during mineral decomposition have been largely removed from the zone of decay, the clay minerals will in turn contain many replaceable hydrogen ions and so be strongly acid. Furthermore, fragments of minerals may remain which are acid on the surface because of the substitution of hydrogen for the original cations, but which have not disintegrated because the substitution process has not gone far enough. The accumulation of these base-deficient products of mineral decomposition results in acid soils or soil material. In areas of low rainfall the salts formed by mineral decay may not be removed from the zone of decomposition, and hence the accumulated soil material will not be acid.

When lime is applied to an acid soil the calcium ions replace the hydrogen ions in the clay minerals and products of decomposition of the original minerals and correct their acidity. Then the process of base removal through hydrolysis and solution starts all over, and the limed soil is on the way to becoming acid again.

Organic matter decaying in the soil may also lose its basic constituents, and hence a humus may be produced which contains replaceable hydrogen ions. A portion of the soil acidity may, accordingly, reside in the organic soil fraction.

Nature of Soil Acidity. In most mineral soils a very large part of the acidity resides in the clay fraction. There are occasional soils, however, composed almost entirely of sand and humus, in which the acidity results largely from the humus. There are also a very few soils which contain a sufficient quantity of sulfides, usually of iron, so that an appreciable amount of sulfuric acid develops through oxidation.

Traces of other inorganic acids are also present, the quantities varying more or less with the season of the year.

The negative charges of the clay minerals arise primarily from isomorphic replacement in their crystal lattice and the dissociation of hydrogen from the edges of the crystals. As long as the negative charges of the clay are largely satisfied by basic ions the soil exhibits little acidity, but as the basic ions are lost through leaching or plant use and are replaced by hydrogen ions the soil increases in acidity.

It must be remembered that all the hydrogen ions around an acid clay particle are not held equally close to the particle surface. Some of them move in an oscillation volume which permits them to go out a considerable distance and so to mingle with other ions in the soil solution. These hydrogen ions constitute what is known as the "active" acidity, and their concentration is designated the "intensity" factor of acidity. On the contrary those hydrogen ions which remain in an exchangeable but unionized state make up the "reserve" or "potential" acidity. Both the active and reserve acidity must be included when considering the total soil acidity. As has been mentioned in Chapter 4 humus has a very high cation-exchange capacity, and, when depleted of its bases, adds to the acidity of the soil. Further, humus contains carboxyl groups from which hydrogen will dissociate, and so there may be small amounts of true organic acids present.

In organic soils the situation is reversed. Some clay may be present, but usually the quantity is small even in soils containing near the lower limit of organic matter required to place them in the organic group. As a result the acidity of organic soils resides largely in the humus material.

DEVELOPMENT OF SALINE AND ALKALI SOILS [1]

Alkaline Soils. Under climatic conditions that do not permit of their removal, the salts formed during mineral decomposition remain in the surface horizons. Such accumulations are sometimes added to by salts washed out of soils occupying higher elevations by torrential rains. Soluble salts are also carried into shallow lakes which later disappear leaving their salt-impregnated beds. Portions of ancient ocean beds often become arable land after being lifted above water level or becoming cut off from the ocean by higher land, and such

[1] This topic is discussed more fully in *Diagnosis and Improvement of Saline Soils,* U. S. Regional Salinity Laboratory, Riverside, Calif., by Kelley in *California Agr. Exp. Sta. Bull.* 617, 1937, and in "Diagnosis and Improvement of Saline and Alkali Soils," *U.S.D.A. Agr. Handbook* 60, 1954.

areas usually contain considerable concentrations of salts. Also ground waters bring salts to the surface by capillarity, and the evaporation of irrigation water frequently contributes much salt to the soil. Soils enriched in salts by one or more of the above-mentioned methods and having a strong but not excessively high alkalinity are usually designated as white alkali soils, or more properly saline soils. The salts that accumulate to the greatest extent are the chlorides and sulfates of calcium, sodium, and magnesium. Sometimes nitrates are present and small quantities of bicarbonates but not soluble carbonates. Frequently the carbonates of calcium and magnesium and calcium sulfate are present in considerable quantities. Sodium salts do not make up more than one-half of the total salt content, and this cation constitutes less than 15 per cent of the exchangeable bases. Soils in this group have pH values [2] of 8.5 or less.

Saline-Alkali Soils. Soils containing large quantities of salts accumulated as described in the preceding section, but in which sodium constitutes more than 15 per cent of the exchangeable cations, are placed in the saline-alkali group. These soils are somewhat more alkaline than saline soils but the presence of the large amount of calcium and magnesium salts prevents the adsorbed sodium from being particularly detrimental. The pH of this group of soils seldom exceeds 8.5.

Alkali Soils. In some soils the total accumulation of soluble salts is not so great as in the two soil groups just described, but there is a larger proportion of sodium on the adsorption complex (over 15 per cent). Because there are not the concentrations of other salts to counteract the effects of the sodium, soil structure and plant growth are detrimentally affected. These soils have an appreciably higher alkalinity than do those of the preceding groups due to the hydrolysis of the sodium from the adsorption complex. The pH values range from 8.5 to 10.0.

DETERMINATION AND EXPRESSION OF SOIL REACTION

Early Methods of Determining Acidity. Soil acidity received much more attention from early students of plant growth than did alkaline soils. Possibly this is true because chemistry developed among people living in relatively humid climates. Early literature mentions taste as a means of detecting soil acidity. The basis for this suggestion is not clear as the hydrogen-ion concentration in acid soils is not sufficient to affect the sense of taste. The first methods used widely to

[2] pH values are explained on pp. 70–71.

indicate acidity were of a qualitative nature involving color changes. Litmus paper, first tried by Thaer in 1856, was employed extensively for this purpose. Also considerable use was made of the fact that humus is more soluble when not saturated with bases. By shaking soil in a dilute solution of ammonium hydroxide a yellow or brown solution is obtained, the intensity of the color indicating to some extent the degree of acidity. This method was applied extensively by Dr. H. J. Wheeler, former director of the Rhode Island Experiment Station.

During the last few years of the past century and the early years of the present one, numerous methods were proposed for the quantitative determination of acidity or, as it was frequently designated, the "lime requirement" of soils. Among them those of Veitch, Hopkins, Jones, and Comber were employed as widely as any. In the Veitch method different quantities of saturated lime water were added to equal weights of soil in porcelain dishes. After thorough stirring the mixtures were evaporated to dryness and the residues supersaturated with distilled water. By adding phenolphthalein to the tests the quantity of calcium required to satisfy the base requirement of the soil was determined.

In the Hopkins method 100 grams of soil were shaken for 3 hours with 250 c.c. of normal KCl solution. After settling 125 c.c. of the supernatant liquid were drawn off, boiled, cooled, and titrated with standard NaOH solution using phenolphthalein as an indicator. Because the exchange reaction between the salt and the adsorbed hydrogen was not complete a factor was used in calculating results.

Jones recommended rubbing the soil gently in a mortar with sodium acetate solution. After filtering the liquid was titrated with standard alkali solution. It was necessary to use a factor in calculating results, as in the Hopkins method.

Truog brought out in 1915 the first method which could be used in the field. The procedure involved boiling a soil-water mixture, to which had been added ZnS and $CaCl_2$, in an Erlenmeyer flask over an alcohol lamp. A strip of filter paper, impregnated with lead acetate, was placed over the mouth of the flask. The degree of blackening of the paper resulting from the reaction of the liberated H_2S with the lead acetate indicated the lime requirement of the soil.

Comber's method (1920) involved shaking the soil in a test tube with an alcohol or other non-aqueous solution of potassium thiocyanate. After settling the intensity of the red color due to ferric iron was considered a measure of soil acidity.

The method of Spurway (1924), which involved the color change resulting from the contact of a neutral solution of brome thymol blue with the soil held in a waxed paper folded to make a trough, was one of the first simple methods adaptable for field use. The method required no washing of apparatus, and the entire outfit could be carried in a pocket conveniently. A modification of this method is still employed extensively, as are similar methods involving the use of dyes.

Newer Methods of Acidity Measurement. With the development of the hydrogen electrode work was immediately started to adapt it to the measurement of soil reaction. Rapid progress was made, and now small outfits are available which may be used wherever a 110-volt circuit is available. This assemblage uses a glass electrode which consists of a thin-walled glass tube containing $N/10$ HCl. The concentration of the hydrogen ions in the soil suspension, into which the electrode is thrust, sets up a potential through the glass membrane with the hydrogen ions in the electrode. By balancing the half-cell so produced against a standard calomel electrode the potential can be measured and the concentration of hydrogen ions in the soil determined. It is to be noted that this procedure measures the hydrogen-ion concentration of the soil solution and does not give the concentration of hydrogen ions held close to the colloidal surfaces. In other words the glass-electrode method measures the active but not the reserve acidity.

Also various factors affect the hydrogen-ion concentration of the solution of a given soil. For example a larger proportion of water to soil in the suspension results in a decrease in concentration of hydrogen ions, and the difference in concentration of these ions at the surface of the colloids and in the outer portions of the ionic swarm is magnified. This effect varies somewhat with different soils and with the soil-water ratio. For example, if the moisture content is reduced to the field capacity some soils show a greater acidity than they do with a soil-water ratio of 1:1, and others exhibit less acidity. At this low moisture content soils which are neutral or alkaline at higher moisture contents usually become acid or lower in alkalinity. Fortunately, the change in acidity of most soils from humid regions at the different moisture contents commonly used in measuring acidity is not large enough to influence the practical conclusions drawn from the determination. With alkaline and alkali soils, however, this may not be true.

On the other hand an increase in soluble salts in the soil solution tends to reduce the difference in concentration of hydrogen ions near the particle surfaces and in the solution farther from them. Salts containing cations of higher valence are more effective in this action than are salts containing low-valency cations. Therefore, by adding a neutral salt solution to a soil when measuring the acidity, a higher acidity is found and the measurement represents more nearly the concentration of hydrogen ions at the surface of the colloidal particles. It is evident, therefore, that some variation in the acidity of samples taken from a soil at different times during the year will be found because the salt content of soils has been shown to vary at different seasons. However, whether the use of a salt solution is advisable in determining the soil pH is questionable, especially since the strength of the solution will affect the results obtained. Many workers prefer to use water solutions for pH measurements.

Another factor influencing the results of soil acidity measurements is the concentration of carbon dioxide in the soil. As is well known the percentage of carbon dioxide in the soil air varies with aeration of the soil and with the activity of plant roots and of other organisms living in the soil. It has been shown by several investigators that the acidity of the soil increases with an increase in carbon dioxide content. If acidity determinations were commonly made in the soil as it occurs under field conditions the effect of carbon dioxide on the results of the measurements would be a matter to be given serious consideration. However, soil samples are usually quite well aerated before their acidity is determined, and the carbon dioxide content may then be ignored. It should be remembered, however, that, *in situ,* carbon dioxide may affect appreciably the reaction of a soil down to pH 6 and hence the soil-plant relationship. Below a pH of 6 the apparent influence of carbon dioxide on soil reaction is probably due to the formation of other and stronger acids. The quantity of carbon dioxide in the soil is especially significant in saline soils and frequently does materially alter the reaction and the intake of nutrients by the plant.

Expressing Soil Reaction. There is no adequate method of expressing the reaction of a soil. To say that a soil is medium in acidity, strongly acid, or slightly alkaline, etc., may suffice for some purposes, but the interpretation put on such terms by different persons renders them quite indefinite. Since the glass electrode has come into common use it has become customary to express soil reaction in terms of the hydrogen-ion concentration. If chemical procedure were followed the hydrogen-ion concentration at neutrality would be expressed in normality. At the neutral point concentrations of H and OH ions are equal and water represents this situation. Because 1 liter of water contains 0.000,000,1 gram of hydrogen ion it is 0.000,000,1 normal. Likewise a neutral soil would be 0.000,000,1 normal, a soil designated as strongly acid would be approximately 0.000,05 normal, and an alkaline one would be about 0.000,000,01 or less normal with respect to the hydrogen ion. Evidently to express the reaction of soils in terms of normality would be quite cumbersome. In seeking a simpler method of expression, it was suggested that the logarithm of the reciprocal of the hydrogen-ion concentration be used. Referring again to neutrality, at which point the hydrogen-ion concentration is 0.000,000,1 gram per liter, and taking the reciprocal of this number, the figure of 10,000,000 is obtained. The logarithm of this number is 7. It would be simple to say that the acidity of this soil or solution is 7, provided one knows what is meant. Following this system it is found that a soil 10 times as acid as one at neutrality would contain 0.000,001 gram of hydrogen per liter and that the logarithm of the reciprocal of this value is 6. It is seen then that the greater the acidity or the higher the normality of a solution the less is the number obtained by this new method of expression. The next step was to find a suitable designation for these numbers indicating degree of acidity. It was decided to call them pH values, the p to indicate that the value is a logarithm and the H to refer to hydrogen-ion concentration. Accordingly the pH scale was developed and has come into common use. In using pH values it should be remembered that they indicate the concentration of both the hydrogen and hydroxyl ions for, if the hydrogen-ion concentration of water is 0.000,000,1 gram per liter, the concentration of the hydroxyl ion must be of the same order. Then if a soil has a pH of 5, that is, the normality of the hydrogen ion is 0.000,01, the hydroxyl ion must be present at a normality of 0.000,000,001 or there would be 0.000,000,017 gram of hydroxyl ion per liter. Also a soil with a pH of 8 would be 0.000,001 normal in relation to OH^- and 0.000,000,01 normal in relation to H^+.

In using the pH scale it should always be remembered that the value expresses the active, and not the total, soil acidity. This determination is not sufficient therefore to indicate the quantity of base necessary to neutralize the soil or meet its lime requirement. It should also be borne in mind that pH values are logarithms and hence are not to be averaged. Likewise pH values move up or down by geometric progression, and so a relatively small change in pH represents a comparatively large change in soil reaction.

Determining the Lime Need of Soils. The term "lime requirement" is frequently used in referring to the quantity of lime to apply to a given soil. The expression is useful in discussing liming with farmers, but its meaning is quite indefinite as the term is used by different workers. For example, it may be used to designate the quantity of lime required to neutralize a soil. On the other hand, it may refer to the quantity of lime needed to bring a soil to a pH which is considered practical for the system of farming being followed. Occasionally the term is used in connection with liming for a special crop which may be best grown on a soil of medium acidity or on one which is alkaline. In

the following discussion the term is used to indicate the quantity of lime
needed to bring a given soil to a pH of approximately 7.0.

As previously pointed out the pH value of a soil gives something of
an average of the hydrogen-ion concentration of the soil solution, which
in turn varies greatly with the distance from the colloidal surface. How
accurately the pH value expresses this average is not known. Accordingly if these values are to be used as an indication of lime need, as they
commonly are, they must be interpreted on the basis of field experiments involving applications of different quantities of lime. In systems of general farming with crops which grow satisfactorily over a
fairly wide range of soil reaction, this procedure gives suitable results.
This is particularly true with heavy-textured soils on which overliming
is not likely to cause detrimental results. With sandy soils, however,
especially those that are very strongly acid, one must be more careful
because overliming may result in nutrient deficiencies and underliming
may not correct sufficiently the undesirable soil conditions accompanying acidity. Furthermore in dealing with the intensive production of
special crops, it is desirable to know more exactly the quantity of lime
needed to bring a soil to a given pH value.

Titration Methods of Measuring Lime Requirement. Several
methods of determining lime requirement by titration of the soil with a
standard base, usually $Ca(OH)_2$ or $Ba(OH)_2$, have been proposed.
One of these, proposed by Dunn,[3] consists of placing 10-gram samples
of soil in 250-c.c. Erlenmeyer flasks and adding different quantities of
0.04 N $Ca(OH)_2$ solution,[4] 3 drops of chloroform, and 100 c.c. distilled
water. After 4 days of standing with thorough shaking twice a day, the
pH values of the suspensions are determined with a glass electrode.
From the data curves are constructed using pH values as ordinate points
and tons of lime per acre on the abscissa. From these curves the tons
of lime needed to produce any desired pH value in the soil may be determined. Several investigators including Dunn have found that applying the quantity of solid lime [$Ca(OH)_2$ or $CaCO_3$] to a soil which the
titration curve indicates is needed to produce a given pH actually results
in a slightly lower pH in the soil. This result is obtained under both
laboratory and field conditions. To overcome this discrepancy a "liming factor" is obtained by dividing the tons of lime actually needed to
give a certain pH by the tons of lime indicated on the curve as needed
to produce that pH. This liming factor usually varies from slightly less

[3] *Soil Sci.,* 56: 341, 1943.
[4] Five cubic centimeters of this solution is considered equivalent to 1 ton
limestone per acre.

than 1 to about 2. Pierre and Worley [5] report an average of 1.5 for 77 soils. Although several causes may be responsible for the liming factor, results indicate that it is due primarily to the reaction of the applied calcium with material other than the exchangeable hydrogen.

The desirability of using a method such as outlined for lime-requirement determinations may be illustrated by the following example. A highly buffered soil with an exchange capacity of 20 m.e. per 100 grams may require 2 m.e. of calcium to neutralize it. In contrast, a very sandy soil with an exchange capacity of 4 m.e. may also need 2 m.e. for neutralization. One of the total acidity methods would indicate that each soil needed 2 m.e. of Ca per 100 grams. It would not, however, show that the highly buffered soil needed little if any lime while the sandy soil would need liming. A pH determination would indicate little need of lime for the one soil and a high, active acidity for the sandy soil, but it would not show how much lime was needed. However, a determination by the buffer or titration method would give the information needed for liming each of the two soils to a desired pH.

Lime Needs of Organic Soils. The reaction of organic soils varies widely. Some peat deposits have been reported to have a pH value as low as 3 and others as high as 8.3. Not only is there a wide variation in the reaction of different organic-soil areas, but it is not uncommon to find considerable difference in the pH of various parts of the same deposit. Slightly acid or alkaline areas in a strongly acid peat deposit may arise from burning or from the presence of springs of alkaline water.

That pH values are not dependable indices of the lime need of organic soils is well understood. For example, Schickluna and Davis [6] report maximum onion yields to have resulted from the application of 2 and 8 tons of calcium carbonate to soils which had pH values of 3.7 and 3.6, respectively. The same workers obtained a maximum onion yield from one soil at a pH of 4.2 and from another at a pH of 5.3. These data indicate that pH value is not always a dependable indication of the detrimental effect a soil may exert on crop growth. The determination of exchangeable calcium in addition to the pH has been found advisable in making lime recommendations for organic soils. Furthermore, a knowledge of the quantities of the different forms of manganese, particularly that which is either exchangeable or easily reducible, in the soil is useful in making lime recommendations.

Some workers consider that the total quantity of lime in a soil should be considered in recommending lime applications. Nygard [7] found that

[5] *Soil Sci.*, 26: 363, 1928.
[6] *Michigan Agr. Exp. Sta. Quart. Bull.* 34, No. 3, 1952.
[7] *Soil Sci. Soc. Amer. Proc.*, 18: 188, 1954.

lime-deficient peats contained less than 0.63 per cent CaO [8] in the dry material and that lime-sufficient peats contained 0.59 per cent or more of CaO. Although a pH value of 4.5 or below was not a reliable indication of lime deficiency, a pH value of 4.6 or higher indicated no lime deficiency. Apparently, there is no simple procedure for determining the lime need of organic soils, although it is usually considered that soils with a pH value of 4.6 or higher do not need lime.

SOIL REACTION AND PLANT GROWTH

Toxicity of Acidity to Plants. The reasons why many commonly grown crops do not thrive in strongly acid soils did not concern early investigators seriously. For many years it was generally assumed that the acids supposed to be present in the soil were harmful to the roots of plants. But as the nature of soil acidity came to be better understood more curiosity as to the causes of the inferior growth of plants in acid soils developed. The effect of hydrogen-ion concentration on plant roots and absorption of nutrients was carefully investigated by Arnon [9] and his associates. By growing plants in nutrient solutions of varying pH values it was determined that roots are definitely damaged at a pH of 3. At reactions between pH 4 and pH 8 many plants grew satisfactorily, however, and as relatively few soils have reactions exceeding these limits it is evident that some cause other than the effects of hydrogen ion is responsible for the poor growth of crops in acid soils.

Acid soils have been found to contain varying quantities of soluble aluminum, and because this element has been shown to be toxic to numerous plants the theory has been advanced that soluble aluminum is one cause of poor plant growth in acid soils. Appreciable quantities of soluble manganese may also occur in acid soils, and this element is toxic to some plants; Fig. 11 shows the effect of several soil treatments on the growth of potatoes in an acid soil containing considerable soluble Mn and Al. Not all crops are equally sensitive to soluble aluminum and manganese. In fact some plants are damaged by aluminum but are quite tolerant of manganese, for example, the sugar beet, and contrariwise certain crops are sensitive to manganese but relatively resistant to aluminum toxicity. The potato falls in this plant group. Oats on the other hand, and also rye and buckwheat, are tolerant of both aluminum and manganese.

A deficiency of available calcium is another explanation of the depressed growth of many crops on acid soils. In fact, certain plants grow

[8] The CaO content is determined in the acid solution of the soil ash.
[9] *Plant. Physiol.,* 17: 515, 1942.

quite well on acid soils if supplied with calcium from a neutral salt which would not influence acidity. Soybeans and lespedeza may be listed in this group.[10] The quantity of calcium used by a crop is not always a criterion of its tolerance or susceptibility to acidity. For example buckwheat uses considerable calcium and yet grows reasonably well in many acid soils. Phosphorus availability is also low in strongly acid soils, and a deficiency of this element may add to the depressed plant growth.

Fig. 11. Potatoes on an unproductive acid Connecticut soil which was high in soluble Mn and Al. Treatments that reduced the acidity were beneficial. Lime plus superphosphate produced normal growth. Treatments from left to right were: none, superphosphate, hydrated lime, and lime plus superphosphate. From *Soil Sci. Soc. Amer. Proc.*, 15: 242, 1950. Courtesy of B. A. Brown et al.

It should be remembered that all soils having the same degree of acidity are not equally deficient in available calcium and do not contain the same quantities of soluble aluminum or manganese. In consequence all soils with the same low *p*H value may not have equally detrimental effects on a given crop. Furthermore there may be constituents in acid soils, other than those mentioned, which are harmful to certain crops. Our knowledge of plant-soil relationships in acid soils is by no means complete. In general crops are more tolerant of acidity in moist and cool climates than they are in areas of higher temperatures and low precipitation. The reason for this is not clear.

Plant Preference for Acidity. Many plants which grow quite well in strongly acid soils do not grow in that environment through choice, but because they are better able to meet competition from other plants in such locations. A number of these plants will grow more luxuriantly in soils of a higher *p*H and sometimes in alkaline soils. There are some

[10] *Missouri Agr. Exp. Sta. Res. Bull.* 513, 1952.

plants, however, which grow satisfactorily in acid soils only. The full explanation of this phenomenon is not known, but it may be due to an intolerance of a high level of available calcium or to the high demand for iron which cannot be met in soils of higher pH, or to both.

Plant Growth in Alkaline Soils. Many crops grow poorly in highly alkaline soils, not because of the alkalinity or OH-ion concentration, but because the plants are unable to obtain an adequate supply of all nutrients. The nutrient elements most likely to be deficient in alkaline soils are manganese, boron, and sometimes iron. Unfortunately in an alkaline environment manganese and iron are highly oxidized and therefore insoluble, and phosphorus and boron form highly insoluble compounds. The use of acidifying agents such as sulfur has been found beneficial, and the addition to the soil of considerable quantities of organic matter which will decay rapidly and liberate carbon dioxide is helpful in overcoming the detrimental effects of alkalinity.

CHANGING THE REACTION OF SOILS

Reducing Soil Alkalinity. Through the presence of $CaCO_3$ well-aerated soils may attain a pH of 8.4. However, under water-logged conditions the pH may rise above this value. In drained soils a pH of more than 8.4 indicates that sodium is the predominant cation on the adsorption complex, and some sodium carbonate will be present in the soil solution.

The first step in reducing the pH of alkali soils is to change the sodium present in the complex or as sodium carbonate into a neutral salt such as the sulfate. This may be accomplished by adding finely ground calcium sulfate or sulfur. It is also desirable to have present a considerable quantity of soluble calcium, and this may best be assured by plowing under green manures or animal manure which liberate large volumes of carbon dioxide during decay with the resultant formation of calcium bicarbonate.

The second step in the reclamation of these soils is the removal of soluble salts by leaching. The chlorides and sulfates are the salts that it is most important to remove. Seldom are there sufficient nitrates to be detrimental to crop growth. It has been shown by Kelley [11] that leaching alone will remove the objectionable sodium and soluble salts from alkali soils especially if green manuring is practiced. Good drainage is necessary if leaching is to be successful. The use of gypsum or of sulfur, however, hastens the process. The quantity of calcium car-

[11] *California Agr. Exp. Sta. Bull.* 617, 1937.

bonate present is usually so large that it is impractical to remove it and hence to obtain a neutral or slightly alkaline reaction. But by the methods suggested the pH may be reduced sufficiently to permit of the intake of nitrate and phosphate by the plant.

Making Soils Acid. Frequently symptoms of nutrient deficiency are seen in crops growing on soils which are naturally about neutral or alkaline and on soils which have been limed excessively. The elements that are most commonly available in too small quantities in soils having higher pH values are manganese and boron. These deficiencies may be corrected temporarily by additions of soluble salts of the elements, and this procedure is recommended in general farming practice. In intensive crop production, however, on relatively small acreages, frequently a more practical and permanent method of correction of the soil condition is to reduce the pH. This is especially true if the pH is not greatly higher than is desired. The application of sulfur is the practice usually followed to reduce the soil pH.

In the growing of certain decorative plants which require an acid soil materials other than sulfur are often applied. Among them is aluminum sulfate and iron sulfate. The chief value of these compounds lies in the fact that they very quickly yield sulfuric acid through hydrolysis, although the supply of available iron is also increased if the iron sulfate is used. To calculate the correct amount of sulfur or of iron or aluminum sulfate needed to lower the pH of a soil to a given point it is necessary to know the quantities of calcium, magnesium, and sodium, if any, that are present as carbonates and also in replaceable form. With these data and the following facts the quantities needed can be determined: 640 pounds of sulfur, or 4,443 pounds of $Al_2(SO_4)_3 \cdot 18H_2O$, or 5,560 pounds of $FeSO_4 \cdot 7H_2O$ will be required per acre-foot of mineral soil for each milliequivalent of Na, Ca, or Mg per 100 grams of soil to render the soil completely unsaturated. For organic soils the quantities will be approximately one-fourth of the above amounts. Assuming that a cubic foot of dry mineral soil weighs approximately 100 pounds the quantities of the above materials required per 100 pounds of soil are 7.25 grams of S, 50.3 grams of $Al_2(SO_4)_3 \cdot 18H_2O$, and 63.0 grams of $FeSO_4 \cdot 7H_2O$. It should be remembered that all the replaceable calcium or magnesium need not be removed to obtain a strongly acid reaction. It is necessary, however, to neutralize all the carbonates and to remove an appreciable portion of the replaceable bases; perhaps from one-half to two-thirds will suffice to make most soils sufficiently acid for the growth of many plants that require an acid soil.

A simpler method of determining the quantity of any of the acidifying agents needed to reduce the alkalinity of a soil to a given point is to apply different quantities of the chemical to equal weights of the soil and determine the *p*H of the mixture after allowing a sufficient time for the reactions involved to take place.

Decreasing Soil Acidity. The decrease or correction of soil acidity by the addition of compounds of calcium or of calcium and magnesium is a common practice in humid climates. It should be emphasized that the purpose of the application of these basic substances is not so much the reduction of acidity as it is the correction of soil conditions which accompany an acid reaction.

The compounds most generally used to correct acidity are the carbonates and hydroxides of calcium and magnesium. Usually the proportion of calcium compound present is high, with the magnesium compound making up from a few to as much as 44 or 45 per cent of the mixture. Sometimes practically no magnesium is present. With carbonates or limestones the presence of magnesium makes the stone harder and more resistant to reaction with acids.

The quantities of different liming materials to be applied depend on many factors, some of which are: (1) the intensity of the soil acidity or the *p*H value; (2) the buffer capacity of the soil or its reserve acidity; (3) the percentage of base saturation in the exchange complex; (4) the type of crops to be grown; (5) the fineness of the limestone or other carbonates if these are used, and (6) the amount of easily reducible manganese present, especially in organic soils. Because of the danger from certain plant diseases, the causal organisms of which thrive in sweet soils, it is considered advisable to grow some crops in distinctly acid soils. This is true even though the yield may not be so high as it would be on more nearly neutral soils.

In a general farming system involving the production of grains, hay, and sometimes root crops it has usually been considered that a soil *p*H of around 6.5 was probably more desirable than one of 7.0. The possibility of a deficiency of some of the micronutrients at higher *p*H values was one of the reasons for this opinion. Also, desirable microorganisms are active at this soil reaction, and mineral nutrients have a relatively high availability. In the Central West the opinion appears to be growing, however, that a reaction of approximately *p*H 7 is more desirable because of the increased availability of phosphorus. On the other hand, in some states in which a high reserve of phosphorus has been built up in the soil through long-continued heavy applications of fertilizer, the increased availability of phosphorus resulting from a high *p*H is of little importance. Also, heavy annual applications of fertilizer are usually made in such areas, and furthermore a *p*H above 6.3 or 6.5 frequently results in a manganese deficiency with a number of crops.

Methods of determining the quantities of lime to apply have been discussed on pages 67–70.

Danger from Overliming. Experience has shown that additions of lime sufficient to bring the pH of a strongly acid soil near or above the neutral point may result in damage to some crops. All crops are not equally susceptible to damage from this practice. The detriment results from the reduction in availability of certain nutrients, especially manganese and boron, but sometimes potassium and possibly other elements. Damage is more likely to occur on well-drained sandy soils which have been submitted to extensive leaching. Heavy textured, more highly buffered soils usually have a greater reserve of these nutrient elements, and hence crops growing on them are not so likely to be damaged by heavy lime applications. Crops have been injured by overliming such soils, however.

Further, a crop may grow satisfactorily on soils which have a high pH value naturally but yet may be damaged by heavy liming when growing on a strongly acid soil. An explanation of this phenomenon lies in the fact that the naturally neutral or alkaline soil has not been submitted to such severe leaching and hence has not been depleted of its supply of available nutrients to the extent that the acid soil has. It is also possible that the original supply of these elements was greater in the non-acid soil.

It is usually more advisable to reduce the acidity of strongly acid sandy soils by steps, through several additions of moderate quantities of lime, than it is to make a very heavy application at one time. Also the danger of nutrient deficiency may be averted by applying fertilizer containing the elements thought to be in short supply.

REFERENCES

Brown, I. C. A rapid method of determining exchangeable hydrogen and total exchangeable bases in soils. *Soil Sci.,* 56: 353, 1943.

Chapman, H. D., Axley, J. H., and Curtis, D. S. The determination of pH at soil-moisture contents approximating field conditions. *Soil Sci. Soc. Amer. Proc.,* 5: 191, 1940.

Curry, A. S. Alkali soils and their management. *New Mexico Agr. Ext. Service Cir.* 105, 1931.

Dunn, L. E. Lime-requirement determination of soils by means of titration curves. *Soil Sci.,* 56: 341, 1943.

Keaton, C. M. A theory explaining the relation of soil-water ratios to pH values. *Soil Sci.,* 46: 259, 1938.

Kelley, W. P. The reclamation of alkali soils. *California Agr. Exp. Sta. Bull.* 617, 1937.

Lynd, J. Q., and Turk, L. M. Overliming injury on an acid sandy soil. *J. Amer. Soc. Agron.,* 40: 205, 1948.

Magistad, O. C., and Christiansen, J. E. Saline soils; their nature and management. *U.S.D.A. Cir.* 707, 1944.

McGeorge, W. T. Corrective measures for the salinity problem in southwestern soils. *Better Crops with Plant Food,* Amer. Potash Inst., June–July 1947.

McGeorge, W. T. Factors contributing to the reaction of soils and their pH measurement. *Arizona Agr. Exp. Sta. Tech. Bull.* 78, 1938.

Midgley, A. R. Overliming acid soils. *J. Amer. Soc. Agron.,* 24: 822, 1932.

Nygard, I. J. Identification of lime-deficient peat soils. *Soil Sci. Soc. Amer. Proc.,* 18: 188, 1954.

Peech, M., and Bradfield, R. Chemical methods for estimating lime needs of soils. *Soil Sci.,* 65: 35, 1948.

Pierre, W. H., and Worley, S. L. The buffer method and the determination of exchangeable hydrogen for estimating the amount of lime required to bring soils to definite pH values. *Soil Sci.,* 26: 363, 1928.

Puri, A. N., and Asghar, A. G. Influence of salts and soil-water ratio on pH values of soils. *Soil Sci.,* 46: 249, 1938.

Russell, E. J., revised by Russell, E. W. *Soil Conditions and Plant Growth* (eighth edition). Longmans, Green & Co., London, 1950.

Swanback, T. R., and Morgan, M. F. Seasonal fluctuations in soil reaction. *Connecticut Agr. Exp. Sta. Bull.* 311, 1930.

Schickluna, J. C., and Davis, J. F. The chemical characteristics and effect of calcium carbonate on the manganese status of five acid organic soils. *Michigan Agr. Exp. Sta. Quart. Bull.* 34, No. 3, 1952.

Staff of U. S. Salinity Laboratory. "Diagnosis and Improvement of Saline and Alkali Soils." *U.S.D.A. Agr. Handbook* 60, 1954.

Truog, E. "Soil Acidity and Liming," Soils and men. *U.S.D.A. Yearbook,* p. 563, 1938.

Whitney, R. S., and Gardner, R. The effect of carbon dioxide on soil reaction. *Soil Sci.,* 55:127, 1943.

6

Soil Organic Matter

The influence of organic matter on plant growth may be studied under two main headings, namely, its effects on the physical conditions of soils and the role of organic materials in supplying nutrients to plants. To understand these contributions of vegetable and animal materials to the phenomenon of plant growth it is essential to know something of the chemical and physical properties of the organic substances that accumulate in soils and of the crude or raw materials from which they are derived. These subjects will be considered briefly in the following pages.

Discussion Topics

Nature of materials which contribute to soil organic matter.
Chemical, biological, and physical properties of the organic fraction in soils.
Additions and losses of soil organic matter.

NATURE OF MATERIALS WHICH CONTRIBUTE TO SOIL ORGANIC MATTER

Definition of Soil Organic Matter. The term "organic matter" as used in a discussion of soils has a very broad meaning because it includes all materials of vegetable and animal origin developing in or applied to the soil regardless of the stage of decomposition. Thus the term includes the highly decomposed and colloidal soil fraction known as humus, as well as the roots and tops of plants containing much easily decayable carbohydrate and protein material, and in adidtion the bodies of microorganisms, worms, insects, and other animals, and also animal manures and similar materials applied to the soil. It is well understood, however, that the portion of the organic matter that has reached the humus stage is the fraction that contributes most to the chemical and physical soil properties of greatest significance in crop production. On the other hand the products of decay are important sources of available nutrients to crops.

81

Materials Contained in Plant and Animal Substances. Waksman and Starkey [1] divide the constituents of plant and animal matter into ten groups, somewhat as follows:

I. Carbohydrates.[2]
  A. Monosaccharides. Compounds with two or more carbon atoms. Commonest types are
    1. Compounds with six carbon atoms (hexoses), examples of which are the simple sugars, glucose, fructose, etc.
    2. Compounds with five carbon atoms (pentoses). Examples are arabinose and xylose.
  B. Oligosaccharides. Compounds formed by uniting two or more sugars with the elimination of a molecule of water (disaccharides). The sugars sucrose and maltose are the most common representatives of the subgroup of disaccharides. Raffinose is an example of a trisaccharide formed from three monosaccharides by the loss of two molecules of water.
  C. Polysaccharides. Compounds composed of a number of monosaccharides or uronic acids combined through the elimination of water molecules. Subgroups are
    1. Hexosans.
      a. Starch $(C_6H_{10}O_5)_n$. A series of α-glucopyranose units joined by an α-linkage of the first carbon of one unit to the fourth carbon of the next unit for the linear portion, or amylose. The branched portion, amylopectin, contains a branch at the sixth carbon.
      b. Dextrins, resulting from partial hydrolysis of starch. Inulin and glycogen are other examples.
      c. Plant cellulose. Compounds essentially characterized by the formula $(C_6H_{10}O_5)_n$, having a regular chain structure of β-glucose residues joined by a linkage at the fourth carbon.
    2. Hemicelluloses. Hemicelluloses are formed by a condensation of pentoses or hexoses, or a mixture of them with uronic acids. Uronic acids have the structure of a sugar with an aldehyde group on the first carbon and a carboxyl group on the sixth carbon. Because the

$$\underset{H}{\overset{O}{\|}}{C}-\underset{OH}{\overset{H}{|}}{C}-\underset{OH}{\overset{H}{|}}{C}-\underset{OH}{\overset{H}{|}}{C}-\underset{OH}{\overset{H}{|}}{C}-C\diagup^{O}_{\diagdown OH}$$

hemicelluloses are not uniform in composition there are large differences in the ease with which they are decomposed. In fact some of them are highly resistant to decomposition and are considered by some workers to be important in the formation of humus. This group of compounds may be divided into several subgroups, namely: (a) hexosans, (b) pentosans, and (c) those hydrolyzing into sugars and

---

[1] *Soil and the Microbe.* John Wiley & Sons, New York, 1949.

[2] The general grouping of materials is similar to that of Waksman and Starkey, but much of the explanatory material has been added. Credit is due Professor C. D. Ball, of Michigan State College, for assistance in preparing this material.

uronic acids. Hemicelluloses occur in considerable quantities in higher green plants.

3. Polyuronides. Pectic acid is an illustration (hydrolyzes almost completely into galacturonic acid).

II. Lignins. These are complex polymers most probably of a derivative of phenylpropane and are known to contain a benzene ring, several methoxyl (OCH_3) and hydroxyl groups, and an aldehyde group (CHO). In the plant, lignin is "associated" with cellulose. Although the structural tissue of young plants is composed largely of plant cellulose, as the plant matures a more intimate combination of lignin and cellulose takes place.

III. Tannins. These are complex compounds containing phenol groups in which have been substituted a number of hydroxy groups (polyhydroxyphenols) or derivatives of these compounds. Frequently complex ring structures are formed.

IV. Glycosides. These are compounds of sugar, frequently glucose, with a non-sugar group such as alcohol, phenols, and aldehyde attached to the first or potential aldehydic carbon of the sugar chain. Glycosides are widely distributed in nature in small quantities. They occur largely in fruit, bark, and roots, although they are found frequently in the leaves also.

V. Organic acids, salts, and esters. Some of the organic acids most commonly found in plants are oxalic, citric, malic, succinic, and tartaric. Probably calcium is the cation most frequently combined with these acids although potassium, sodium, and other ions are sometimes present.

VI. Fats, oils, waxes, and related compounds.

A. Non-volatile fats and oils.

1. Fats and oils, solid or liquid in nature, are essentially esters of the fatty acids with glycerol.

2. Waxes are frequently essentially esters of higher fatty acids with monohydroxy-saturated alcohols or sterols but usually contain free alcohols and hydrocarbons.

B. Volatile or essential oils. These are mixtures of aldehydes, alcohols, acids, esters, and are mostly derivatives of turpenes.

VII. Resins.

VIII. Nitrogen compounds.

A. Proteins. These are complex compounds which may be divided into several groups. For example, the simple proteins yield α-amino acids upon hydrolysis with acid or enzymes. Conjugated proteins consist of compounds of non-protein groups with simple proteins (nucleoproteins are combinations of one or more proteins with nucleic acid). Derived proteins include various decomposition products as peptones, proteoses, etc.

B. Amino acids. Organic acids containing an NH_2 group.

C. Amines. Organic bases.

D. Alkaloids. Complex plant chemical entities. They are oily or crystalline bases containing nitrogen and are physiologically active.

E. Purines. Pyrimidines.

F. Nucleic acids.

IX. Pigments.

A. Chlorophyll.

B. Carotenoids.

    C. Anthocyanins.
    D. Anthoxanthins.
X. Mineral constituents.
    A. Cations, principally Ca, Mg, K, Fe.
    B. Anions, largely phosphate, chloride, sulfate, and silicate.

The amounts of the various groups of substances in several plant materials are given in Table 7, and the decomposition of them is dis-

TABLE 7. COMPARATIVE COMPOSITION OF SEVERAL MATERIALS *

Per Cent of Dry Material

Constituent	Corn-stalks	Rye Straw	Oak Leaves	Alfalfa Plants	Old Pine Needles	Sheep † Manure	Cow † Manure
Ether- and alcohol-soluble	5.99	5.33	6.44	10.41	30.92	2.83 ‡	2.77 ‡
Hot- and cold-water-soluble	14.14	6.26	13.93	17.24	7.29	24.92	10.34
Hemicelluloses	17.63	21.10	12.93	8.52	18.98	18.46	18.57
Cellulose	29.67	38.62	13.78	26.71	16.43	18.72	25.23
Lignin	11.28	14.63	30.30	10.78	22.68	20.68	20.21
Crude protein	1.98	0.81	4.25	8.13	2.19	. . .	. . .
Total nitrogen	0.73	0.28	0.82	2.62	. . .	4.08	2.38
Ash	7.53	5.09	5.09	10.30	2.51	17.21	12.95

    * Compiled from Tables 9 and 27 in *Humus* by S. A. Waksman, Williams & Wilkins Co., Baltimore, and Tables 1, 3, 5, and 7 from article by F. G. Tenney and S. A. Waksman in *Soil Sci.*, 30: 143. Some of the data also published in *Trans. Second Comm. Intern. Soc. Soil Sci.*, 1929, and *J. Amer. Soc. Agron.*, 21: 795.

    † Litter-free, both solid and liquid excreta.

    ‡ Ether-soluble only.

cussed by Waksman.[3] During the process of humus formation the water-soluble substances, cellulose and hemicelluloses, are largely decomposed. On the other hand, the percentages of protein and lignin increase markedly, and the fats and waxes change little in percentage.

It is well known that in the early stages of growth plants are relatively rich in minerals, protein, and water-soluble substances, and that as maturity approaches the percentages of these materials decrease while the proportions of lignin and cellulose increase. This change in composition is important from the standpoint of rate of decay of the material if incorporated into the soil and the quantity of nutrients, especially nitrates, set free for crop use. The data in Table 8 illustrate this change in plant composition with age.

    [3] *Soil Microbiology*, p. 107. John Wiley & Sons, New York, 1952.

Table 8. Composition of the Rye Plant (Stems and Leaves) at Different Stages of Growth * (from Waksman and Tenney †)

Stage of Plant Growth	Fats and Waxes, per cent	Water- Soluble Substances, per cent	Pen- tosans, per cent	Cellulose, per cent	Lignin, per cent	Total Nitro- gen, per cent	Ash, per cent
10–14 in. high	2.60	34.24	16.60	18.06	9.90	2.50	7.66
Just before heads begin to form	2.60	22.74	21.18	26.95	11.80	1.76	5.90
Just after bloom	1.70	18.16	22.71	30.50	18.00	1.01	4.90
Mature plant	1.26	9.90	22.90	36.20	17.10	0.24	3.90

* Calculated on the dry basis.
† From *Soil and the Microbe* by Waksman and Starkey. John Wiley & Sons, New York, 1949. Used by permission.

Ease of Decay of Plant and Animal Constituents. Some of the groups of materials listed as constituents of plant and animal tissue decay readily when returned to the soil, and others are quite resistant to attacks of decay organisms. In the first group may be placed water-soluble substances, starches, hemicellulose, cellulose, and proteins. Lignins, tannins, waxes, and resins on the other hand decay much more slowly. It is recognized that the rate of decay of a given compound in the soil is not governed alone by the nature of the compound but is influenced by the chemical and physical properties of the soil, by temperature, by the numbers and kinds of microorganisms present, and by the substances associated with the compound.

It will be noted from the data in Table 8 that young plants contain relatively high percentages of the substances that decay readily and much smaller quantities of those materials that resist decay and hence tend to accumulate in the soil. As a result there is little accumulation of organic matter in the soil from the plowing under of young plants.

CHEMICAL, BIOLOGICAL, AND PHYSICAL PROPERTIES OF THE ORGANIC FRACTION IN SOILS

Results of Early Workers. The nature of the organic material that accumulates in soil (humus) as a result of the decay of the crude animal and plant materials added has been studied for well over a century. Efforts were made to isolate definite chemical compounds from humus and establish formulas for them. Mulder about 1840 stated that there were 7 different organic substances in soils, namely, ulmic acid ($C_{40}H_{14}O_{12}$) and ulmin, humic acid ($C_{40}H_{12}O_{12}$) and humin, gleic acid ($C_{40}H_{12}O_{14}$), crenic acid ($C_{24}H_{12}O_{16}$), and apocrenic acid ($C_{48}H_{12}O_{24}$). There was much disagreement among the early chemists as to the for-

mulas of the compounds that could be isolated from humus. For example, in 1871 Detmer gave humic acid the formula $C_{60}H_{64}O_{27}$. Studies
of this nature continued until the beginning of the present century,
although Van Bemmelen (1888) suggested that humic acid was not a
definite chemical compound and Bauman and Gully (1910) maintained
that the acidity of humus was due to adsorption compounds and not
to true organic acids.

Much work was also done, largely by Schreiner and Shorey of the
U.S.D.A., on the presence of compounds in humus which are toxic to
many plants. Of the compounds isolated dihydroxystearic acid and
picoline carboxylic acid are among those that received most attention.
From a group of 60 soils representing 11 states, 20 were found to contain dihydroxystearic acid, which is very toxic. Although the presence
of such poisonous substances has been proved in certain soils it is generally believed that these compounds will not accumulate in well-drained
soils, which are managed by accepted methods.

On the other hand the presence of some organic compounds which
are helpful to plant growth was maintained. Creatinine was isolated
from soil, and in solution cultures wheat seedlings were able to utilize it
as a source of nitrogen.

Later Studies Concerning the Constitution of Humus. The
study of the organic fraction of the soil has not diminished, but the emphasis has been shifted largely to an investigation of the relationship
among the main groups of materials in humus and to the causes for the
chemical and physical properties exhibited by it.

Because lignin and protein make up a large part, about 70 to 80 per
cent, of the organic materials in humus interest has centered on these
materials. Some type of combination between these substances is generally accepted by investigators, but the nature of the union is not fully
established. The fact that synthetic lignoproteins are similar to humus
in reactions and decomposition lends weight to the theory of a union
between the two materials. Also proteins become stabilized in the soil,
which indicates their combination with a substance of high carbon
content.

It is believed that there is an interaction between the clay minerals
and the constituents of humus. Evidence of this combination is the
change in cation-exchange capacity when decayed organic materials
react with clay. The cation-exchange capacity of the product is less than
the sum of the exchange capacities of the organic matter and clay. For
example, Myers [4] electrodialyzed the humus prepared from decomposed

[4] *Soil Sci.*, 44: 331, 1937.

alfalfa, corn stover, and straw and then allowed it to react with the electrodialyzed colloid from Putnam soil. Some of his results are given in Table 9. There is some difference of opinion as to the nature of

TABLE 9. EFFECT OF COMBINING ORGANIC AND MINERAL COLLOIDS ON THEIR EXCHANGE CAPACITIES *

Constituent Colloids	Sum of Exchange Capacities of Constituents, m.e. per 100 grams	Exchange Capacity of the Product, m.e. per 100 grams
H-Alfalfa + H-Putnam clay	114	87
H-Corn stover + H-Putnam clay	110	77
H-Straw + H-Putnam clay	130	91

* Prepared from data on p. 346, *Soil Sci.*, 44, 1937; used with permission.

the union of the organic matter and clay. Ensminger and Gieseking [5] have suggested that below the isoelectric point the proteins of humus are held by the clay. On the other hand Hendricks [6] believes that some of the large organic molecules are held by forces other than electrostatic attraction. There may be an H-type of bonding to the clay surface.

Polyuronides and polysaccharides containing uronic groups are also important constituents of soil organic matter. From a study of 20 soils, including representatives of Prairie, Gray-brown Podzolic, Podzolic, and Planosol soils, Norman and Bartholomew [7] concluded that from 10 to 15 per cent of the organic carbon of surface soils is present in uronide groups and that the percentage is higher in subsoils.

There is some variation in the proportions of the several constituents in humus from soils of the different Great Soil Groups, as might be expected. For example, in arid soils a higher proportion of nitrogen and ether- and alcohol-soluble substances is found than in soils developed in a colder and more moist climate. Likewise humus from Chernozems contains an intermediate percentage of nitrogen and of lignin and associated complexes. Table 10 gives the composition of humus from several mineral-soil groups.

The high nitrogen content of humus is significant both from the standpoint of the liberation of available nitrogen as decay occurs and from the viewpoint of replenishing or increasing the supply in soils. In humid climates the building up of the organic content of soils represents the

[5] *Soil Sci.*, 48: 467, 1939.
[6] *J. Phys. Chem.*, 45: 65, 1940.
[7] *Soil Sci.*, 56: 143, 1943.

TABLE 10. CHEMICAL NATURE OF HUMUS IN DIFFERENT SOILS *

Nature of Soil	Hori- zon or Depth	Reac- tion	Total Humus (C × 1.724)	Nitro- gen in Humus	Chemical Composition of Humus				
					Ether- and Alcohol- Soluble Sub- stances	Water- Soluble	Carbo- hydrates	Pro- teins	Lignin- Like Com- plexes
	Cm.	pH			Per Cent				
Podsol, Michigan	A$_1$	4.6	41.6	2.57	3.29	4.00	16.54	16.08	55.62
	A$_2$	5.1	1.1	4.73	4.58	6.36	10.28	27.82	46.32
Chernozem, Manitoba	A	...	7.4	5.34	1.30	...	11.37	33.36	42.83
Chernozem, Texas	A	6.9	2.29	5.68	2.03	2.36	13.88	35.50	35.81
Chestnut soil	0–15	6.8	1.93	5.23	3.14	2.58	11.97	32.70	39.95
Serozem, Arizona	0–15	7.2	0.28	8.03	7.63	3.50	4.34	50.22	34.76

* Taken from *Humus*, p. 160, by S. A. Waksman, 1938 (second edition). Williams & Wilkins Co., Balti-more, Md. Used by permission.

only means of storing nitrogen in the soil. Accordingly, unless nitrogen fertilizers are to be supplied in sufficient quantity and at suitable inter-vals to meet the needs of crops, or green crops, which decay rapidly and liberate available nitrogen, are incorporated into the soil in large amounts, it is essential that a reasonable quantity of organic matter be accumulated in the soil.

On the average, humus contains approximately 5 per cent of nitrogen. The proportion of nitrogen to carbon is significant and is designated as the nitrogen-carbon ratio. The ratio is usually between 1:9 and 1:12 although much wider ratios are sometimes found. The ratio tends to be lower in arid soils and in those developed in humid but hot climates. With uniform moisture relations the ratio is wider with lower tempera-tures. The nitrogen-carbon ratio will be discussed more fully when the problem of accumulating humus in the soil is considered.

Cation-Exchange Capacity of Humus. One of the most valuable chemical properties of humus is its capacity to adsorb nutrient cations and release them for plant use. Humus has been found to have a cation-exchange capacity ranging from about 4 to 7 times that of mineral colloidal material. For example, Myers [8] found the colloidal fraction from two mineral soils to have an exchange capacity of 62 m.e.[9] per

[8] *Soil Sci.*, 44: 334, 1937.
[9] M.e. refers to milliequivalents.

100 grams and that prepared by the decomposition of straw, corn stover, and alfalfa to have capacities of 344, 262, and 291 m.e., respectively. Humus extracted from the mineral soil had an exchange capacity of 314 m.e. per 100 grams. The percentage of the exchange capacity of soils which is due to the humus fraction varies greatly. In some sandy soils the exchange capacity may be due largely to organic colloids. On the other hand there are soils with low organic content in which humus plays a small part in the exchange reactions. As most arid soils are quite low in humus content this constituent is not of so much importance in cation-exchange processes in them as it is in many soils of the humid regions. The large exchange capacity of humus gives it a high buffering capacity, and hence soils containing medium to large quantities of this material are resistant to change in reaction.

There is much disagreement as to why humus has cation-exchange capacity. The property has been ascribed to (1) the phenolic hydroxy groups, (2) carboxyl groups, (3) nitrogen-free substances, and the protein linkage of the lignoproteinates. Regardless of the explanation the ion-exchange capacity of humus has much to do with the productivity of many soils.

Biological Relationships of Organic Matter. It is difficult to differentiate between the chemical and the biological relationships of soil organic matter. The processes by which the organic materials that are developed in or added to the soil are broken down into intermediate, and ultimately into the simple end products of decay, are largely biological. The constituents of humus are by no means all residues of plant constituents which have resisted decomposition, but some of them, particularly the proteins, are synthetic products of living organisms. In fact, the bodies of microorganisms may amount to some 3,000 pounds in the plow layer of a productive soil. Algae would increase this weight and earthworms may add from 200 to 1,000 additional pounds.

The soil organic matter serves as food for the heterotrophic bacteria, fungi, earthworms, actinomyces, certain of the nematodes, and the protozoa, although protozoa feed to some extent on bacteria. The number of microorganisms in a soil is materially influenced by the supply of readily decayable organic matter. If it were not for the soil organisms crude organic materials would remain practically undecayed in the soil with the nutrient elements they contain in an unavailable form as far as other generations of plants are concerned. This process of accumulation would continue until the available supply of one or more essential nutrients was exhausted. The role of soil organisms in keeping the supply of plant nutrients moving from an unavailable state in plant and animal tissue into available forms is not always fully recognized. The relation of microorganisms to soil properties and the growth of plants is discussed more fully in Chapter 14.

Physical Properties of Humus. The physical properties of humus which are most significant in regard to its effects upon the physical nature of soils and their crop-producing ability are its (1) structure, (2) volume weight, (3) adhesive and cohesive qualities, (4) water-holding capacity, (5) shrinkage with loss of water, and (6) coagulation by certain electrolytes. Color might be added to the list because in most soils the dark grays, browns, mahogany, and other darker shades are due to the modifying effect of humus on the colors of the minerals present. How important this color effect is on the productivity of the soil is open to question, although it is established that dark-colored soils warm up somewhat more readily than do light-colored soils of similar texture.

It is well known that the structure of humus varies with the kind of materials from which it was derived, with the state of decay, and various other factors, but it is always a very porous substance. Likewise it has a low volume weight compared to mineral soil material although this property also varies. Humus exhibits low cohesion and adhesion compared to mineral colloids. Nevertheless these forces do influence soil structure when an appreciable quantity of humus is present.

The capacity of humus to absorb large quantities of water is one of its outstanding characteristics. This property is due both to its physical make-up and to the chemical nature of its components, particularly cellulose and hemicelluloses. The water-absorbing capacity of humus derived from different materials varies, as has been shown by studies of various types of peat. The organic fraction of mineral soils is usually capable of taking up from 4 to 6 times its weight of water. The quantity of humus in most mineral soils is so small, however, that the amount of water absorbed by it has little influence on the total moisture content of the soil. On the other hand the modification of soil structure brought about by a medium amount of humus results in a considerable increase in moisture-retaining capacity. Upon absorption of water, humus swells greatly and shrinks again upon drying. This change in volume with water content is an influential factor in the alteration of the structure of soils containing appreciable quantities of organic matter.

Not only has it been shown, as previously mentioned, that some combination takes place between organic and inorganic colloids in the soil, but also the humus tends to surround or coat the soil particles, both large and small. The organic coating has considerable effect on the coagulation of the clay fraction by electrolytes. This effect varies with pH, but in general it can be said that organic colloids cause both a higher degree of aggregation and the formation of larger aggregates than would otherwise take place.

The beneficial effects of humus in improving soil structure are indicated by increased aeration, reduction in power requirement for plowing heavy soils, ease in preparation of good seedbeds, rapid germination of seeds, and a reduced volume weight. The Ohio experiment station has studied the increase in volume weight of a clay soil with the dissipation of organic content and a corresponding decrease in pore space. The data in Table 11 show these relationships.

TABLE 11. EFFECT OF 40 YEARS' CROPPING ON THE PHYSICAL PROPERTIES AND ORGANIC-MATTER CONTENT OF NAPPANEE SILTY CLAY LOAM IN PAULDING COUNTY, OHIO *

Depth, ft.	Weight of Soil, lb. per cu. ft.		Pore Space, per cent of soil volume		Organic-Matter Content, lb. per acre	
	Virgin	Cropped	Virgin	Cropped	Virgin	Cropped
0–1	65.5	81.7	60.3	50.5	132,000	89,400
1–2	70.3	86.7	58.1	47.6		
2–3	76.6	91.0	53.5	44.8		
Average	70.8	86.5	57.3	47.6		

* *Ohio Ext. Service Bull.* 175, 1941.

ADDITIONS AND LOSSES OF SOIL ORGANIC MATTER

Appreciation of the contribution that organic matter makes to the productivity of most soils has occasioned much study of the effect of soil cultivation and different cropping systems on the organic content of soils. Similarly, methods of maintaining or increasing the amount of organic matter have been given much attention. The quantity of organic matter in most soils is rather low, with the exception of organic soils, that is, when the organic content is expressed in percentage by weight. This fact is due in part to the low specific gravity of humus compared to that of the mineral fraction of the soil, but even when expressed as percentage by volume the humus content of soils in general is low. The effects which organic matter produces on the properties of representative soils are greater than would be anticipated from the quantities present.

Quantity of Organic Matter in Soils.[10] There is no method which determines accurately the percentage of organic matter in soil. Heating the soil to a sufficiently high temperature to burn the organic material

[10] Soils containing 20 per cent or more of organic matter are usually designated as organic soils.

present results in a loss of moisture from the mineral fraction and some-times the volatilization of salts and decomposition products of the mineral material and hence gives high results. Because of the approximately constant percentages of carbon and nitrogen in humus, methods based on these relationships are frequently used. For example, the percentage of organic carbon in a soil may be determined, and this is multiplied by the factor 1.724 to get the percentage of humus present. This procedure is based on the results of studies of the composition of humus which show it to contain approximately 58 per cent of carbon.

The nitrogen content of soil may be determined easily, and since humus has been found to contain about 5 per cent of this element the percentage of humus may be obtained by multiplying the nitrogen percentage by 20. In this procedure it is assumed that soil does not contain an appreciable amount of nitrogen except as a constituent of humus.

Various methods for determining the approximate amount of organic matter in soils from the intensity of color produced when it is oxidized

TABLE 12. PERCENTAGE OF ORGANIC MATTER IN SOILS FROM DIFFERENT AREAS IN THE UNITED STATES

Soil Type and Number of Samples	State	Organic Matter,* per cent	Soil Type and Number of Samples	State	Organic Matter,* per cent
16 Yolo loams	Cal.	1.34	29 Tama silt loams	Iowa	4.14
16 Zamora clay loams	Cal.	1.46	7 Clay loams on Black-		
16 Myers clay	Cal.	1.74	land prairie	Texas	2.39 ‡
1 Sweeney clay loam †	Cal.	5.37	13 Fine sandy loams on		
1 Gleason clay loam †	Cal.	3.54	Gulf Coast prairie	Texas	1.48 ‡
4 Clay loams	Ariz.	0.72	19 Fine sandy loams on		
6 Loams	Ariz.	0.53	timbered area	Texas	0.91 ‡
13 Sandy loams	Ariz.	0.55	10 Clay loams on Rio		
6 Brown silt loams (prairie)	Ill.	5.04 ‡	Grande plain	Texas	2.44 ‡
4 Black clay loams (prairie)	Ill.	7.23 ‡	18 Fine sandy loams on		
7 Yellow silt loams (tim-			Rio Grande plain	Texas	1.34 ‡
bered)	Ill.	2.02 ‡	5 Peats	Mich.	90.9
25 Soils from "bluegrass" re-			148 Virgin soils	Ore.	2.08 ‡
gion	Ky.	3.78 ‡	28 Loams	N. Y.	3.12 ‡
54 Soils derived from St.			30 Silt loams	N. Y.	4.28 ‡
Louis limestone	Ky.	2.11 ‡	5 Clay loams	N. Y.	6.06 ‡
33 Soils from western coal			18 Silt loams	E. Kans.	4.54
fields	Ky.	1.98 ‡	8 Silt loams	W. Kans.	2.33
36 Carrington loams	Iowa	3.81	11 Clay loams	W. Kans.	3.83
16 Webster loams	Iowa	5.71	25 Sandy loams	Ga.	0.83 †
36 Clinton silt loams	Iowa	2.59	7 Loams	Ga.	0.98 ‡
14 Marshall silt loams	Iowa	3.78			

* C × 1.724 or CO₂ × 0.471, unless otherwise indicated.   † Prairie soils.   ‡ N × 20.

Data from following sources:
Soil Sci. Soc. Amer. Proc. 14: 302.
U.S.D.A. Tech. Bull. 502.
Soil Sci., 61: 423, 1945.
Unpublished data by H. V. Smith, Univ. of Ariz.
Texas Agr. Exp. Sta. Bull. 549, 1937.

Kentucky Agr. Exp. Sta. Bull. 193, 1915.
Oregon Agr. Exp. Sta. Bull. 112, 1912.
Kansas Agr. Exp. Sta. Bull. 199, 1914.
Georgia Agr. Exp. Sta. Bull. 126, 228, 308.
Cornell Univ. Agr. Exp. Sta. Bull. 513, 1930.

with potassium dichromate have been proposed. The procedure recommended by Graham [11] is an example.

The data in Table 12 show the percentage of organic matter in soils from several sections of the United States. These data bring out the great variation in the humus content of soils from different portions of the country. They also show that soils from different locations in a given section of the United States may vary widely in percentage of organic matter. Soils from arid areas are usually quite low in organic

TABLE 13. ORGANIC-MATTER CONTENT OF SEVERAL SOILS AT DIFFERENT DEPTHS

Soil Type or Area and Number of Samples	State	Depth, in.	Organic Matter, per cent
7 Marshall silt loams	Kans.	0–7	2.7
		7–20	1.87
		20–40	0.75
6 Oswego silt loams	Kans.	0–7	2.60
		7–20	1.42
		20–40	0.57
6 Volusia silt loams	N. Y.	0–8	4.78
		8–24	2.08
13 Ontario loams	N. Y.	0–8	3.70
		8–24	1.43
		24–36	1.01
25 Soils from "bluegrass" region	Ky.	0–7	3.78
		7–20	2.32
6 Brown silt loams (prairie)	Ill.	0–6⅔	5.04
		6⅔–20	2.96
		20–40	1.16
7 Yellow silt loams (forest soil)	Ill.	0–6⅔	2.02
		6⅔–20	1.03
		20–40	0.80
1 Mohave loam	Ariz.	0–15	0.13
		15–28	0.11
1 Gothard clay loam	Ariz.	0–12	0.40
		12–21	0.35
1 Kelton sandy loam	Ariz.	0–9	0.17
		9–24	0.16
1 San Pedro clay	Ariz.	0–8	0.57
		8–36	0.66

[11] *Missouri Agr. Exp. Sta. Cir.* 345, 1950.

content.   On the other hand, the high humus content of some of the
northern prairies is shown by Shutt,[12] who reports an average organic
content of 7.86 per cent (based on N content) for 12 Saskatchewan
soils.   The percentage varied from 2.68 to 11.44.

The data in Table 13 show the much smaller amount of organic
material in the subsoil than in the surface horizon of a number of soils.
In most soils of the humid regions there is quite a marked decrease in
humus content immediately below the plowed layer.   This results from
the fact that the majority of the roots of crop plants are in the plowed
layer of soil and also that additions of manure and green manuring
crops are incorporated into the plow soil.   The decrease in humus
content between plow soil and subsoil is usually not so marked in sandy
soil profiles as in profiles of fine-textured soils.   Also there is a much
more even distribution of organic matter in the profiles of arid soils
than in those of soils in humid climates.

Soils developed under grass have a higher percentage of humus, and
the organic-rich horizon is much thicker than is true for forest soils.
Likewise soils originally covered with tall grasses (the humid Prairie
or Brunigra soils) are higher in organic content than soils developed
under medium and short grasses (Chernozem and Brown soils).   The
larger amount of humus in Prairie soils is one cause for their high
productivity and for their resistance to deterioration under a long-
continued and soil-depleting cropping system.

Organic-Matter Loss Due to Cropping.   It is well established
that the destruction of the native vegetative cover and tillage of soils
results in a rapid decay of the organic matter that has accumulated in
them over a long period of time.   This stimulated decomposition has
usually resulted in a rather rapid decrease in the organic content of
soils when they are placed in crop production.   Figure 12 shows the
average loss of organic matter from South Dakota soils as a result of
cropping.   The productiveness of soil also usually decreases more or
less in proportion to the supply of organic matter.[13]   The decrease in
productivity during the first years of cultivation is perhaps more marked
in timbered soils and especially in forested sandy soils than in prairie
soils.

On the other hand there may be some doubt as to whether many
timbered soils contain less total organic matter after a number of years
of cropping than when first put under cultivation.   It is true that the
organic material is distributed through a much thicker section of the

[12] *Can. Dep. Agr. Tech. Bull.* 44, 1925.
[13] *Missouri Agr. Exp. Sta. Bull.* 522, 1949.   Also, *Ohio Ext. Service Bull.* 175,
1941.

soil and hence does not appear in a very dark but thin layer at the surface. Likewise the original, very readily decayable organic matter has been decomposed and the humus now present is more resistant to decay. It is difficult to obtain accurate data on this subject because there is no way to sample a virgin timbered soil properly. No one knows how much, if any, of the forest litter should be included in the sample. Much of the litter is burned with the brush in clearing the land. The ash, rich in mineral nutrients, and the remnants of the

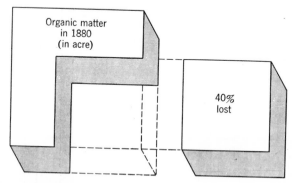

Fig. 12. South Dakota soils have lost 40 per cent of their organic-matter content in 65 years as a result of cropping. "Approximately one-half to three-fourths of a ton of organic matter is lost each year from cultivated soils." From *South Dakota Agr. Exp. Sta. Cir.* 92, 1952. Courtesy of L. F. Puhr and W. W. Worzella.

litter are plowed into the soil and so provide nutrients for the crops grown during the first few years. After a period of years most of the humus in the soil has developed from the roots and residues of the crops grown.

The same difficulties are not encountered in sampling cropped and virgin prairie soils. Studies on such samples show a marked decline of organic-matter content during the first few years of cropping, followed by a continuous but decreasingly less rapid loss until virtually an equilibrium is reached. A few examples of the loss of soil organic matter as a result of cropping which have been reported by investigators are as follows:

Snyder,[14] in Minnesota. A loss of one-third to one-half as a result of growing grain crops exclusively for 10 to 15 years.

Shutt,[15] in Canada. A prairie soil lost about 25 per cent of its humus content in 22 years of cropping.

[14] *Minnesota Agr. Exp. Sta. Bull.* 30, 1893.
[15] *Can. Dep. Agr. Tech. Bull.* 44, 1925.

Blair and Prince,[16] in New Jersey. A study of the soils on 19 farms in a county showed an average of 2.71 per cent of humus in the forested soils and 1.84 per cent in the cropped soils.

Russell,[17] in Nebraska. Reported the calculated loss of organic matter under dryland farming for different periods of time to be: 6.5 per

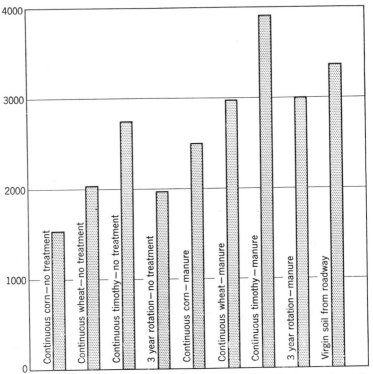

Fig. 13. Nitrogen content in pounds per acre in soil after 50 years under different cropping systems both with and without manure. The rotation consisted of corn, wheat, and clover. Manure was applied at the rate of 6 tons per acre annually. From Fig. 10, *Missouri Agr. Exp. Sta. Bull.* 458, 1942. Used with permission.

cent for 3–7 years, 12.4 per cent for 8–15 years, 26.8 per cent for 17–30 years, and 28.0 per cent for 45–60 years.

Jenny,[18] in Missouri. Calculated the loss of organic matter (expressed as nitrogen) to be 25 per cent during the first 20 years of cropping, 10 per cent for the second 20 years, and 7 per cent during the third 20 years. The effects of different crops and of a rotation, both

[16] *New Jersey Agr. Exp. Sta. Bull.* 604, 1936.
[17] *J. Amer. Soc. Agron.*, 21: 960, 1929.
[18] *Missouri Agr. Exp. Sta. Bull.* 324, 1933.

with and without applications of manure, on the nitrogen content of a Missouri soil are shown in Fig. 13.

General Principles of Organic Matter Accumulation. It has been pointed out previously that the nitrogen-carbon ratio in humus is usually from 1:9 to 1:12. In other words whatever the N:C ratio of the raw materials added to the soil, it must be brought to approximately the 1:9 to 1:12 level if organic matter is to accumulate. It is evident, therefore, that the proportions of nitrogen and carbon in organic materials left in the soil by crops or applied to it are of great importance in humus formation and that no more humus can be accumulated than the supply of nitrogen present provides for.

The determining role played by nitrogen in the production of humus from organic materials applied to the soil may be illustrated as follows: It is assumed that 35 per cent of the carbon in a substance is assimilated by the microorganisms involved in the decay process, the remainder being given off as CO_2. If a ton of straw contains 40 per cent, or 800 pounds, of carbon 280 pounds would be assimilated. If an average N:C ratio of 1:10 is assumed, 28 pounds of nitrogen would be needed for humus formation. As straw contains approximately 0.5 per cent of nitrogen there would be available only 10 pounds. Hence there would be a deficit of 18 pounds of nitrogen. If this were not supplied from the soil or some other source, there would be a much greater dissipation of the carbon as CO_2 and a correspondingly smaller quantity of humus produced.

For dry alfalfa, assuming a 40 per cent carbon and 3 per cent nitrogen content, there would be available 60 pounds of nitrogen. This would supply the needed 28 pounds for maximum humus formation and leave a balance of 32 pounds to be converted into nitrates or to be used in forming humus from other more carbonaceous material which might be present.

Also it has been stated that a considerable percentage of humus is made up of lignin and lignin-like compounds. It is essential therefore that such materials be present if humus is to be formed.

Given materials containing suitable quantities of protein and lignin, other factors such as temperature and moisture relations greatly influence the quantities of humus produced. In general, as shown by Jenny,[19] the quantity of humus accumulated in the soil decreases with an increase in temperature, if moisture conditions remain constant. On the other hand, with uniform temperatures the amount of humus in the soil increases with an increase in moisture supply. The problem

[19] *Missouri Agr. Exp. Sta. Res. Bull.* 152, 1930.

of maintaining the organic supply of the soil is, accordingly, more difficult in the southern states than it is in the northern states with similar
moisture relations.

Humus Formation from Crop Residues. The largest quantities
of organic matter supplied to soils under general farming conditions
consist of the roots and the stubble, straw, stover, or other top portions
of the crops grown on the land. These materials are all low in nitrogen
content unless they come from legumes, and even some of these plants
have a relatively low percentage of nitrogen when mature. Mature
plant residues on the other hand have a high content of lignin. It is
evident, therefore, that such materials must be supplemented with
nitrogen-rich substances if a larger percentage of the dry matter they
contain is to be converted into humus. As these residues decay some
nitrogen will be supplied through the decomposition of the humus in the
soil, but in most soils this is insufficient to convert a large percentage
of the carbon compounds in the residues into humus.

The application of manure, if not too rich in bedding, in conjunction
with crop residues is desirable as a source of nitrogen needed in the
humification process. Also leguminous, green-manuring crops are a
good source of nitrogen for this purpose.

It would seem logical to apply nitrogen fertilizer when working corn
stover or straw into the soil in order to supply the extra nitrogen needed.
This practice has been followed frequently and almost always results
in an appreciable increase in yield of the following crop. Unfortunately,
however, results on a field basis are insufficient to show that nitrogen
fertilizer so applied results in a greater accumulation of humus. But
under laboratory conditions the addition of nitrogen fertilizer to highly
carbonaceous plant materials has resulted in the formation of more
humus than was obtained without the fertilizer.

Manure as a Source of Humus. Manures are very effective in
increasing the humus content of soils. Unless an excessive amount of
bedding is used they have a relatively high nitrogen content and also
already contain a considerable amount of humus which has been produced by decay in the digestive tract of the animals. There are many
records showing an appreciable increase in the humus content of soils
which have received medium to large applications of manure over a
period of years. In considering such data it should be remembered
that part of the increase in organic matter has resulted from the greater
growth of roots and stubble of the crops grown. This is also a result
of the manure application, but the humus did not come directly from
the manure. Some data representative of that obtained from such ex-

periments are as follows: The Missouri station [20] grew wheat for 50 years, with the addition of fertilizer in one instance and of 6 tons of manure annually in another. At the end of the 50-year period the fertilized soil contained 1.99 per cent organic matter and the manured soil 2.99 per cent. The same station grew timothy with and without manure. At the close of a 50-year period the manured soil contained 3.91 per cent humus and that receiving no manure 2.70 per cent. One plot on the Broadbalk field of Rothamsted receives no fertilization and another one gets 14 tons of manure annually. Both plots have grown wheat continuously since 1843. The manured plot was recently found to contain 4.7 per cent of organic matter and the unfertilized plot only 2.0 per cent.[21] The Ohio experiment station [22] reported 29,650 pounds of organic matter per acre in a soil growing a rotation of corn, wheat, and clover for hay for 29 years. With the same rotation, including the application of 8 tons of manure per rotation, the organic content of the soil was 34,200 pounds per acre.

Green Manures as a Source of Humus. The term green manure, as used here, refers to young or growing plants which are incorporated into the soil. Such plant tissue is relatively high in nitrogen and mineral nutrients and low in lignin compared to the composition of the mature plant. The rate of decay of the plant substance when worked into the soil is rapid, and both mineral nutrients and nitrogen are liberated quite rapidly in available forms. However, because of the low content of lignin and similar substances the decay of the plant tissue is quite complete and there is little humus accumulation. Furthermore the quantity of dry matter added to the soil by an average green-manure crop is not large and hence no great amount of humus could be produced. When used in conjunction with mature crop residues, leguminous green manures should result in more humus formation than when the green crop is worked into the soil alone.

Fertilizers as Sources of Humus. Most fertilizers contain a very small amount of organic matter and hence add little directly to the humus supply of the soil. A few fertilizers, particularly some especially prepared for lawns and gardens, are derived largely from plant or animal products and hence contain considerable organic material. The quantities applied per acre, however, even when heavy applications are made for intensive vegetable production, are not sufficient to add significant quantities of humus to the soil.

[20] *Missouri Agr. Exp. Sta. Bull.* 458, 1942.
[21] *Soil Conditions and Plant Growth*, p. 284. Longmans, Green & Co., London, 1950.
[22] *Ohio Agr. Exp. Sta. Bull.* 605, 1939.

The application of fertilizers usually results in an increase in crop growth, and a corresponding increase in root development takes place. This additional root substance together with the larger amount of top growth, which may be used in manure production or returned to the soil directly, should lead to some increase in soil humus.

The Use of Sods to Supply Organic Matter. The high organic content of prairie soils indicates that sod-forming plants are very effective in building up the humus supply in soils. This fact has been demonstrated in rotation studies and in comparisons of the humus content of soil in fence rows with that of soils in adjoining fields which are cropped. Sods reduce both wind and water erosion and the fine fibrous roots of the grasses fill the soil with evenly distributed organic matter. The nature of the root system also enables grass to reduce losses of nitrogen and bases effectively by leaching. Thus the base status of the soil is kept at a higher level than would otherwise be true, and as is well known an ample supply of bases is conducive to humus accumulation. It has further been demonstrated that the granules produced in soils growing sods are more stable than those developed in soils not growing sod crops.

A number of legumes have root systems somewhat similar to those of grasses. Although these crops may not be designated properly as sod-forming they certainly produce a mat of roots in the soil similar to a sod. Such crops are also very effective in causing an accumulation of humus. Not only are their effects on erosion, leaching, and distribution of organic residues in the soil similar to those of grasses, but they also are richer in nitrogen and when inoculated add nitrogen to the soil. This larger amount of nitrogen is also valuable in humus formation. A mixture of grasses and fibrous-rooted legumes is an almost ideal type of vegetation for the development of humus in soil. This fact is demonstrated by the results of an experiment at the Rothamsted experiment station. Two areas of soil were left undisturbed for 20 years. One area was covered by vegetation containing 95.26 per cent grasses and 0.43 per cent of legumes. The other soil area grew a cover containing 59.64 per cent grasses and 25.31 per cent of legumes. The effect of the different types of vegetation on the organic content of the soil is shown by the data in Table 14.

A number of agronomists feel that it is essential to allow the legume to occupy the land for more than a year, that is, during 1 year of hay production, in order to get the full benefit of the crop in soil building. Other workers do not believe that allowing the crop to occupy the soil for a second summer greatly increases its contribution to soil improvement.

TABLE 14. EFFECT OF THE GROWTH OF GRASSES AND OF GRASSES PLUS LEGUMES ON THE ORGANIC CONTENT OF SOIL *

Organic Content of Soil (N × 20), per cent

Vegetative Cover	Grasses			Grasses plus Legumes		
Depth of samples, in.	0–9	9–18	18–27	0–9	9–18	18–27
At beginning of experiment	2.16	1.48	1.19	2.16	1.40	1.16
After 20 years	2.62	1.66	1.30	2.90	1.91	1.68
Difference	0.46	0.18	0.11	0.74	0.51	0.52

* *The Book of the Rothamsted Experiments.* John Murray, London. Used with permission.

Level of Organic Matter to Be Maintained in Soil. A pertinent question is how much organic matter should be maintained in the soil. From the foregoing discussion it can be seen that many factors have a bearing on this question. Soil texture, drainage, climatic conditions, and the cropping system followed are influential factors. Just as the original soil gradually increased in humus content until an equilibrium was established between additions and losses, so a soil maintained under a uniform cropping system will gradually attain an equilibrium in humus content determined by tillage operations and environmental factors. For general farming purposes it is usually unprofitable to increase the organic content of the soil above the equilibrium level. Losses by decay are excessive when an attempt is made to raise the level. As a result large quantities of organic matter must be added in order to increase slightly the humus content. For the production of high-value-per-acre crops an increase in humus may be warranted but not for general farming purposes.

If an increase in organic matter is considered essential, a change in the cropping system and in cultural practices should be made.

Some agronomists think that the humus content of the soil may be maintained or increased under a rather humus-depleting system of culture if large quantities of commercial nitrogen are applied. More experimental work is needed to establish this point, however.

In general it is not considered advisable to attempt an increase in the normal organic content of the soil if a reasonably good system of culture is being followed. Rather it is better to make frequent, even though fairly small, additions of fresh organic matter which will decay rapidly and thus benefit one or two crops without any permanent soil improvement. In the final analysis it is through decay that organic matter makes some of its greatest contributions to crop production.

REFERENCES

Albrecht, W. A. "Loss of Soil Organic Matter and Its Restoration," Soils and men. *U.S.D.A. Yearbook,* p. 347, 1938.

Alexander, L. T., and Byers, H. G. A critical laboratory review of methods for determining organic matter and carbonates in soil. *U.S.D.A. Tech. Bull.* 317, 1932.

Blair, A. W., and Prince, A. L. Some effects of long continued manure, fertilizer, and lime treatments on the composition of cropped soils. *New Jersey Agr. Exp. Sta. Bull.* 604, 1936.

Broadbent, F. E. Nitrogen release and carbon loss from soil organic matter during decomposition of added plant residues. *Soil Sci. Soc. Amer. Proc.,* 12: 246, 1947.

Browning, G. M. A comparison of dry combustion and rapid dichromate titration methods for determining organic matter in soils, *ibid.,* 3: 158, 1938.

Ensminger, L. E., and Gieseking, J. Absorption of proteins by montmorillonitic clays and its effect on base exchange capacity. *Soil Sci.,* 51: 125, 1941.

Gottlieb, S., and Hendricks, S. B. Soil organic matter as related to newer concepts of lignin chemistry. *Soil Sci. Soc. Amer. Proc.,* 10: 117, 1945.

Hendricks, S. B. Base exchange of montmorillonite for organic cations and its dependence upon adsorption due to Van der Waals' forces. *J. Phys. Chem.,* 45: 65, 1940.

Jenny, H. A study on the influence of climate upon the nitrogen and organic-matter content of soil. *Missouri Agr. Exp. Sta. Res. Bull.* 152, 1930.

Jenny, H. Soil fertility losses under Missouri conditions. *Missouri Agr. Exp. Sta. Bull.* 324, 1933.

Myers, H. E. Physiochemical reactions between organic and inorganic soil colloids as related to aggregate formation. *Soil Sci.,* 44: 331, 1937.

Norman, A. G., and Bartholomew, W. V. The chemistry of soil organic matter. I. Distribution of uronic carbon in some soil profiles, *ibid.,* 56: 143, 1943.

Norman, A. G. Problems in the chemistry of soil organic matter. *Soil Sci. Soc. Amer. Proc.,* 7: 7, 1942.

Russell, J. C. Organic-matter problems under dry-farming conditions. *J. Amer Soc. Agron.,* 21: 960, 1929.

Schollenberger, C. J. Determination of soil organic matter. *Soil Sci.,* 59: 53, 1945.

Shutt, F. T. Some characteristics of the western prairie soils of Canada. *Can. Dep. Agr. Tech. Bull.* 44, 1925. Also, *J. Agr. Sci.,* 3: 335, 1910.

Waksman, S. A. *Humus* (second edition, revised). Williams & Wilkins Co., Baltimore, 1938.

Waksman, S. A. *Soil Microbiology.* John Wiley & Sons, New York, 1952.

Waksman, S. A., and Starkey, R. L. *Soil and the Microbe* (third edition). John Wiley & Sons, New York, 1949.

Wilde, S. A. Rapid colorimetric determination of soil organic matter. *Soil Sci. Soc. Amer. Proc.,* 7: 393, 1942.

7

Nitrogen and Crop Production

Of the various nutrient elements commonly applied to the soil nitrogen is the most abundant in nature. Although the quantities of nitrogen in soils are seldom large the total natural supply is great when consideration is given to the nitrogen of the atmosphere and to that contained in plants and animals. If inexpensive methods were available to convert the 148,000 tons [1] of atmospheric nitrogen per acre of land area into compounds useful in agriculture and industry, the problem of supplying adequate nitrogen for maximum crop production would be simplified. However, much energy and expense are required to convert the elemental nitrogen of the air into useful compounds. Also, nitrogenous compounds are rather easily decomposed into gaseous or soluble compounds which may be leached from the soil or may escape into the atmosphere. Some of the problems encountered in meeting the nitrogen needs of plants are presented under the following five headings.

Discussion Topics

Nitrogen requirements of plants.
Nitrogen content of soils.
Loss of nitrogen from the soil.
Additions of nitrogen to the soil.
Nitrogen fertilizers.

NITROGEN REQUIREMENTS OF PLANTS

An excess or deficiency of nitrogen has very marked effects on plant growth. Insufficient nitrogen may reduce yields drastically and also decrease the quality of the product. On the other hand, an excess of the nutrient may lead to equally disastrous results.

Effects of Nitrogen on Plant Growth. As a constituent of protoplasm nitrogen is intimately involved in the activity of every living cell. Moreover excesses and deficiencies of nitrogen quickly affect the char-

[1] There are 36,000 tons of nitrogen over each acre of land and water surface.

103

acteristics of plant tissues and growth. For example an excess of nitrogen results in a stimulation of vegetative growth which may result in
delayed maturity and in extreme cases in a decrease in fruitfulness
because of the dropping of flower buds. Size of cells is increased with
a decrease in cell-wall thickness, because the increase in vegetative
growth causes too large a portion of the carbohydrates to be made into
proteins, thus not leaving enough to make strong cell walls which contain little nitrogen. As a result the tissues are more susceptible to
attack by disease organisms and with some vegetables and fruits there
is deterioration or breakdown during shipment or storage. Lodging
of small grains often results from the weakening of the cell walls of
the straw and the proportion of straw to grain is increased. The production of wheat with a high ratio of carbohydrate to protein, so-called
"yellow berry," is believed to be due to an excess of nitrogen in some
instances.

If the quantities of soluble nitrogen are greater than those which
produce stimulation of growth, a retardation of growth may occur with
a chlorosis and even a burning or necrosis of the foliage.

A deficiency of nitrogen results in a lighter green color of the foliage,
and further nitrogen starvation gives rise to the symptoms discussed on
page 261. Stunting of the top growth of plants is frequently the result
of a nitrogen shortage, but, oddly, roots are elongated according to
Heald.[2] Yields of crops are depressed by nitrogen deficiency, and a
decrease in quality of fruits, vegetables, and grains usually results. For
example, vegetables grown for their stems or leaves are stringy and
tough, instead of crisp and juicy, when not adequately supplied with
nitrogen. Also kernels of cereals are not large and plump.

Nitrogen Content of Plants. Young plants are much richer in
nitrogen than are those approaching maturity. This point is illustrated
by the data in Table 15. These data explain in part the high nutritive
value of pasture compared to hay or to mature plant tissue. The necessity of having an abundant supply of nitrogen in the soil during the
early stages of plant growth is also evident. It should be remembered
that plants continue to absorb nitrogen until virtually mature. Therefore, an adequate supply of available nitrogen in the soil should be
maintained throughout the growth period. As plants mature, however,
they accumulate carbohydrates at a greater rate than they do protein,
and hence the percentage of nitrogen in the plant will decrease even
though the quantity in the soil is abundant.

[2] *Introduction to Plant Physiology,* p. 361. McGraw-Hill Book Co., New York,
1937.

TABLE 15. EFFECT OF AGE ON THE NITROGEN CONTENT OF PLANTS

Plant and Stage of Growth	Nitrogen Content, per cent dry matter	Plant and Stage of Growth	Nitrogen Content, per cent dry matter
Alfalfa		Sudan grass	
Pre-bud	3.41	2 ft. high and under	3.25
In flower	2.08	4 to 6 ft. high	1.33
Barley		Early dough stage	0.77
21 days old	6.08	Timothy hay	
49 days old	1.95	Heads 50 per cent out	1.43 †
86 days old	0.59	Early dough stage	0.94 †
Kentucky bluegrass *		14 Everglades grasses	
Cut every 2 weeks	2.83	Prebloom	2.63
Cut when in bloom	1.72	Early bloom	1.79
Rye		Early seed	1.53
10–14 in. high	2.50		
Mature plant	0.24		

* Five-year average.   † On hay basis.

During the greater part of the season the greatest concentration of nitrogen is found in the parts of the plant where growth is taking place and in the seed or reproductive portion as these parts are developed and mature. That nitrogen is translocated from the older parts of a plant to the points of active growth is evidenced by the development of nitrogen-deficiency symptoms in the older leaves when the scarcity of this nutrient occurs. When the supply of nitrogen is adequate all parts of the plant contain a relatively high percentage of the nutrient. That is, it does not tend to accumulate in particular plant parts to the extent that some other mineral elements do.

NITROGEN CONTENT OF SOILS

Because plants, with the exception of legumes, obtain their nitrogen from the soil the content of this element in soils is significant from the standpoint of plant nutrient supply. Further, with the exception of small amounts, all the nitrogen in soils of humid climates is contained in and is an essential part of the humus, which plays an important part in the physical, chemical, and biological functions of the soil. The nitrogen content then is indicative of the humus content of a soil and of the soil properties dependent on the humus.

Variation in Nitrogen Content of Soils. In general nitrogen varies more in quantity in the soil than do the other elements essential for plant growth which are taken from the soil. This statement is not true always because there are young soils developing in material containing limestone which are very high in calcium percentage, and concentrations of phosphorus occur in some soils near phosphate deposits, etc. Nevertheless, in arable soils as a whole, nitrogen content is more variable than is the content of other nutrient elements. This variability is not confined to soils in different climatic zones nor to those having different vegetative cover although these are influential factors, as is shown by the data in Table 16. Within the limits of a climatic zone or

TABLE 16. AVERAGE NITROGEN CONTENT IN VARIOUS SOIL REGIONS OF THE UNITED STATES *

Soil Region	Approximate Area of Region, acres	Approximate Nitrogen in Surface 6 In., per cent	Average Nitrogen to Depth of 40 In., per cent	Average Nitrogen per Acre to Depth of 40 In., lb.
Brown forest	180,000,000	0.05–0.20	0.05	6,700
Red and yellow	150,000,000	0.05–0.15	0.03	4,000
Prairie	113,000,000	0.10–0.25	0.12	16,000
Chernozem and Chernozem-like	123,000,000	0.15–0.30	0.12	16,000
Chestnut	102,000,000	0.10–0.20	0.08	10,700
Brown	52,000,000	0.10–0.15	0.06	8,000

* From Soils and Men. *U.S.D.A. Yearbook*, 1938.

within the confines of a farm and often within a single field the soil nitrogen content fluctuates with drainage conditions, topography, and soil texture. Also in soils of similar texture, topography, and drainage situation the nitrogen content frequently varies with management practices. For instance, the Missouri experiment station [3] found the nitrogen content of the surface 7 inches of soil which had grown wheat continuously for 50 years to be 1,750 pounds per acre, and that of a similar soil cropped to a rotation of corn, oats, wheat, and clover for the same period to be 1,917 pounds per acre. No fertilizer was applied in either case.

Variation in Nitrogen Content with Soil Texture and Depth. The influence of texture on soil nitrogen content is illustrated by the data in Table 17. These data show a distinct decrease in nitrogen content as soil texture becomes coarser. The Iowa station reports similar results,

[3] *Missouri Agr. Exp. Sta. Bull.* 522, 1949.

Nitrogen and Crop Production

TABLE 17. VARIATION IN NITROGEN CONTENT OF SOILS WITH TEXTURE *

Pounds per Acre at Different Depths, in.

Soil Texture Groups	0–6⅔	6⅔–20	20–40	0–40
Black clay loams †	7,230	7,470	3,210	17,910
Brown silt loams	5,035	5,920	3,570	14,520
Brown loams	4,720	6,660	4,150	15,530
Brown sandy loams	3,070	3,920	4,160	11,150
Yellow fine sandy loams	2,170	2,610	2,730	7,510
Sand plains and dunes	1,440	2,070	3,100	6,610

* Average results from a large number of samples of Illinois soils reported in *Soil Fertility and Permanent Agriculture*, C. G. Hopkins, Ginn and Co., Boston, 1910. Used with permission.

† These soils occupy lower locations; hence inadequate drainage and erosion may have contributed to their nitrogen content.

as is shown by Fig. 14, and the data of Swanson [4] are in agreement for Kansas soils. Likewise some 26 sandy loams in Georgia [5] showed a

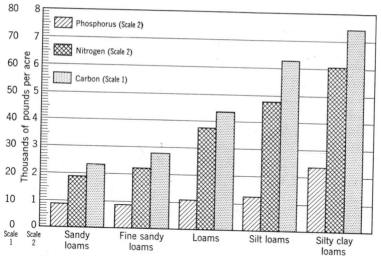

Fig. 14. The mean phosphorus, nitrogen, and carbon content in the surface 6⅔ inches of various textural groups of drift soils. *Iowa Agr. Exp. Sta. Res. Bull.* 203, 1936.

nitrogen content of 784 pounds in the surface soil, compared to 1,148 pounds in 10 clay loams. In considering the Illinois data it must be remembered that there is twice as much soil in the second depth as in

[4] *Kansas Agr. Exp. Sta. Bull.* 199, 1914.
[5] *Georgia Ext. Div. Bulls.* 126, 228, 308.

the first, and three times as much in the 20- to 40-inch layer as in the surface. It is interesting to note that the percentage of nitrogen does not decrease so rapidly with depth in the lighter textured soils as it does in those of finer texture.

Influence of Temperature and Moisture on Soil Nitrogen Content. Of the studies dealing with the effect of climatic conditions on the nitrogen content of soils that of Jenny [6] is outstanding. The nitrogen contents were determined in soils from a large number of counties in an area bounded by lines running south from approximately the southern tip of Lake Michigan and the western state line of North Dakota, respectively. A number of counties in states bordering the Atlantic were also included. Most of the soils studied were loams or silt loams, although some sandy loams were included from the eastern states, and there was a variety of textural classes in the soils from the semiarid area. In calculating the average nitrogen content of the soil in a county, the percentage of nitrogen in each soil group sampled was multiplied by the per cent of the county area occupied by that soil. The sum of the values so obtained for the soil groups of the county was then divided by the sum of the percentages of the county area occupied by the soils analyzed.

The soils were grouped according to topography and again on the basis of native vegetative cover (timber, prairie, shorter grasses). Another factor used in grouping the samples was based on moisture relations. For this purpose annual precipitation, altitude, annual temperature, and per cent annual, relative air humidity were taken into consideration. Using altitude and annual temperature the vapor tension for a given location was obtained from meteorological tables. Then the relative saturation deficit was obtained by subtracting the relative air humidity from 100 per cent. By multiplying vapor tension by relative saturation deficit the absolute saturation deficit was found. The annual precipitation divided by absolute saturation deficit gives the N.S. quotient, [7] which is the moisture-relation criterion used in sorting the soil samples on the basis of constant temperature with varying moisture supply and again on the basis of constant moisture supply with varying

[6] *Missouri Agr. Exp. Sta. Res. Bull.* 152, 1930.

[7] An example of the method of calculation, using Sheridan, Wyoming, as the location, is as follows: Annual temperature is 6.17° C. The corresponding vapor tension, according to the Smithsonian Meteorological Tables, is 7.06 mm. of mercury. The relative air humidity is 67.5%. The relative saturation deficit is $100\% - 67.5\% = 32.5\%$. The absolute saturation deficit is 7.06 mm. $\times$ 32.5% $= 2.29$ mm. The annual precipitation is 367 mm. The N.S. quotient is $367/2.29 = 160$. (Prepared from Jenny's data in *Missouri Agr. Exp. Sta. Res. Bull.* 152, p. 14, 1930.)

temperature. Three categories in relation to moisture supply were used, namely, semiarid, semihumid, and humid.

Some of the results obtained in this study are presented graphically in Figs. 15 and 16. The decrease in soil nitrogen content with an increase in temperature under similar moisture conditions presents a

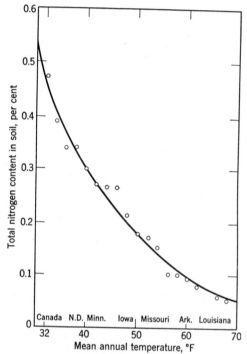

Fig. 15. Soil nitrogen content decreases with an increase in temperature when moisture supply is relatively constant. From *Missouri Agr. Exp. Sta. Res. Bull.* 152, 1930.

problem in soil management and explains in part at least the large use of nitrogen fertilizers in warm, humid climates. The value of rotations including a generous proportion of hay and pasture crops and an extensive use of cover crops is evident if the organic content of the soil is to be maintained or increased. Also the rapid decay of organic materials applied to soils in warm, humid climates accounts for the marked response in plant growth to the incorporation into the soil of green manures and leguminous crop residues.

The increase in soil nitrogen content as moisture supply increases, with temperature remaining constant, is noteworthy. This factor accounts for the higher organic content of the grasslands of the Prairie

Soil Fertility

and Chernozem belts compared to those lying farther westward. Evidently farmers of the North Central states have a better opportunity of maintaining a relatively high percentage of organic matter in their soils than do those farming either farther south or west. Even so, the problem of keeping the organic content of the soil at a desirable level under present cropping systems is a difficult one. Furthermore, the native productivity of soil in climates of moderate temperatures and reasonably

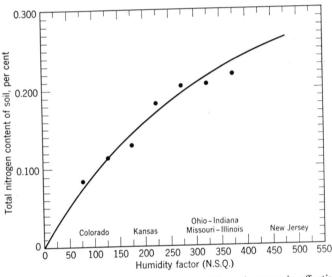

Fig. 16. The nitrogen content of soil increases with an increase in effective moisture supply if temperature is constant. The graph shows the relation between the nitrogen content of grassland soils and the humidity factor along the annual isotherm of 11° C. From *Missouri Agr. Exp. Sta. Res. Bull.* 152, 1930.

high precipitation is due in part to their relatively high organic content. The data of Jenny also bring out the effect of a grass vegetation on the accumulation of soil nitrogen.

Availability of Soil Nitrogen. From the standpoint of plant growth the availability of the nitrogen in the soil is fully as important as the total quantity present. Although there is a general relationship between total quantity of soil nitrogen and the amount of the element crops obtain from the soil, the amount of organic nitrogen a soil contains is not a reliable criterion of the quantity of the element plants can obtain during a given season. It is recognized that all nitrogen in the soil will pass into an available form in time; however, the unreliability of total amount as an index of rate of supply is illustrated by the growing need for and use of nitrogen fertilizers on the Prairie and Chernozem soils, which are far above average in total nitrogen content. In warm, humid climates the rate of organic-matter decay is rapid and hence there is a quick turnover of nitrogen with a high availability. On the other hand, organic matter accumulates in cold climates and the transformation of nitrogen from organic to available forms is slow. In climates with relatively cool summers and longer winters nitrogen becomes available at a moderate rate with much seasonal or periodic variation. For example, a cool spring may delay or slow down availability and an abnormal warm period may result in a high rate of nitrogen availability for a short time. Likewise a summer drought may materially reduce the rate of nitrogen transformation into available compounds.

Attempts have been made to predict the amount of nitrogen that will become available during a given season on the basis of soil organic-matter content. Hopkins [8] suggested an availability of 2 per cent of the total supply per year under average soil-management practices in the corn belt. Woodruff [9] reports a similar percentage from the results obtained by growing corn continuously for 33 years on Sanborn Field in Missouri. The percentage of the soil nitrogen contained in average yields of several crops grown continuously on this field are given in Table 18. It is considered that nitrogen absorbed by the corn repre-

TABLE 18. THE 33-YEAR AVERAGE NITROGEN CONTENT OF SEVERAL CROPS GROWN CONTINUOUSLY ON SANBORN FIELD AND THE PERCENTAGE OF THE TOTAL SOIL NITROGEN THIS REPRESENTS

Crop	Nitrogen in Crop, lb. per acre	Nitrogen in Soil, lb. per acre	Percentage of Total Soil Nitrogen in Crop
Corn	32.3	1,580	2.04
Oats	21.6	2,330	0.93
Timothy	20.2	2,670	0.76
Wheat	19.6	2,005	0.98

sents more nearly the amount made available from the soil humus because there was less nitrogen returned to the soil in stubble, second growth, and weed growth than was the case with the other crops.

The age of the organic matter in soils is related to the degree of decomposition it has undergone and so to the rate at which nitrogen will be liberated. Thompson [10] illustrated this point by comparing the rate of mineralization of the nitrogen in virgin and adjoining cropped soils

[8] Soil Fertility and Permanent Agriculture. Ginn and Co., Boston, 1910.
[9] Soil Sci. Soc. Amer. Proc., 4: 208, 1949.
[10] Soils and Soil Fertility, by L. M. Thompson. W. C. Brown Co., Dubuque, Iowa, 1950. Used with permission.

during a 30-day period at 35° C. An average of 299 pounds of nitrogen was mineralized in 6 virgin soils compared to 89.3 pounds in the corresponding cropped soils. The larger amount of nitrogen mineralized in the virgin soils is undoubtedly due in part to the larger quantity of organic nitrogen present, as well as to the stage of decomposition. The rate of mineralization of nitrogen in plant residues, green manures, and other organic materials applied to soils has been shown to be related to the carbon-nitrogen ratio. This point will be included in the discussion of green manures. It should be stated here, however, that nitrogen made available in the soil may be built into the bodies of microorganisms (immobilized) and hence be unavailable for plant use if an appreciable quantity of highly carbonaceous organic material is being decomposed in the soil.

Soil Nitrogen and Crop Yields. A number of studies have shown a close relationship between the content of organic nitrogen in the soil

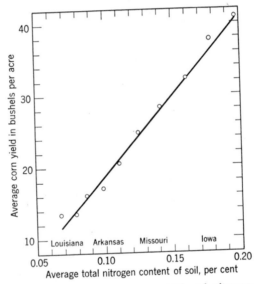

Fig. 17. Relationship between average corn yield and nitrogen content of the soil. From *Missouri Agr. Exp. Sta. Res. Bull.* 152, 1930.

and the yield of certain crops, primarily corn. Jenny [11] found a direct relationship between the average nitrogen content of upland loam and silt loam soils from central Iowa to Louisiana and average corn yields for these soils, as is shown by Fig. 17. North of central Iowa, however, lower temperatures interfered with this relationship and corn yields

[11] *Missouri Agr. Exp. Sta. Res. Bull.* 152, 1930.

decreased regardless of a higher soil nitrogen content. Klemme and Coleman also call attention to a close relationship between soil nitrogen content and corn yield on a number of soil types in Missouri, as is shown by the data in Table 19. These data indicate that about 1 bushel

TABLE 19. RELATION OF SOIL NITROGEN CONTENT TO CORN YIELDS *

Soil Series Silt Loams	Soil Nitrogen, lb. per acre 7 in.	Average Corn Yield, bu. per acre	Soil Series Silt Loams	Soil Nitrogen, lb. per acre 7 in.	Average Corn Yield, bu. per acre
Marshall	3,630	38.6	Cherokee	1,950	22.5
Grundy	3,370	32.0	Gerald	1,890	19.0
Eldon	3,160	31.2	Union	1,600	16.0
Crawford	2,840	25.4			
			Average	2,634	26.4

* *Missouri Agr. Exp. Sta. Bull.* 522, 1949.

of corn may be expected for each 100 pounds of nitrogen in the soil. Numerous studies have shown that 1 bushel of corn will be produced from each 1½ to 2 pounds of available nitrogen in the soil. Consequently if 2 per cent of the organic soil nitrogen is mineralized each year a yield of 1 bushel of corn for each 100 pounds of nitrogen in the soil could be expected. Although soils high in nitrogen content are usually considered productive for all crops a close correlation between soil nitrogen and crop yield has not been reported for crops other than corn. Such a correlation may exist but because corn takes up so large an amount of nitrogen the growth of the crop is more likely to be directly related to nitrogen supply than is that of other crops.

Effect of Soil and Climatic Condition on the Nitrogen Content of Crops. The composition of crops is primarily a matter of heredity, but environmental conditions do bring about some modifications in the percentages of various constituents present. This phenomenon is illustrated by the 4-year average composition of wheat from two Illinois soils.[12] The nitrogen content of the grain grown on Sable silty clay loam, a dark, grassland, productive soil, was 1.94 per cent and that grown on Cisne silt loam, which is light gray, poorly drained, and deficient in nutrients, was 2.28 per cent. The phosphorus content of the wheat grown on the two soils was the same. Thomas of the Ontario Agricultural College, in cooperation with the Department of Agriculture at Ottawa, made a study of the composition of several forage crops

[12] *Soil Sci. Soc. Amer. Proc.*, 5: 120, 1940.

grown on different kinds of soil in western Ontario. Some of the results showing the wide variation in crude protein and phosphorus
contents of the crops are presented in Table 20.

TABLE 20. VARIATION IN AND AVERAGE CRUDE PROTEIN AND PHOSPHORUS
CONTENTS OF SEVERAL CROPS GROWN ON DIFFERENT SOILS *

Per Cent on Moisture-Free Basis

Crop and Number of Samples	Crude Protein			Phosphorus		
	Highest	Lowest	Average	Highest	Lowest	Average
101 Alfalfa	29.5	12.7	18.5	0.407	0.131	0.195
103 Red clover	21.7	11.1	15.8	0.269	0.111	0.175
60 White sweet clover	21.2	11.6	16.6	0.243	0.103	0.177
103 Alsike clover	22.6	9.0	16.0	0.310	0.105	0.202
25 Trefoil	23.6	15.6	18.2	0.304	0.132	0.221
171 Timothy	14.9	5.3	7.9	0.285	0.053	0.175
77 Kentucky bluegrass	13.5	4.1	7.1	0.259	0.072	0.161
96 Canada bluegrass	11.6	4.7	7.1	0.245	0.058	0.141
23 Redtop	11.8	5.9	8.3	0.249	0.079	0.152

* Prepared from data in mimeographed release, 1939.

These data show the wide variation in composition of the same crop
when grown under different soil conditions and harvested about the
same time, the last week in June and first week in July. In considering
the data Thomas points out that plants grown on neutral loams contain
more protein than the same species grown on acid loams. Also the
content of crude protein, calcium, and phosphorus generally is higher
in plants grown on neutral, heavy soils than it is in the same species
grown on loam soils of neutral reaction. Thomas also concludes that
there is an increase in the phosphorus and protein content of the plants
studied with an increase in soluble soil phosphorus.

Nitrogen Fertilization and Protein Content of Crops. Additions of nitrogenous fertilizers have also led to diverse results in regard
to increased protein content of crops. Frequently yields have been increased without an increase in protein content, but not always.

Ohlrogge,[13] in discussing the results of some Indiana experiments,
concludes that large yield increases in relation to the quantity of nitrogen applied are usually accompanied by no change or a decrease in the
protein content of the crop. On the other hand small yield increases
in relation to the quantity of applied nitrogen result in an increased
protein content of the crop. Furthermore fertilizers other than nitrogen
which increase yield will tend to decrease protein percentage. In a study
of the response of corn to nitrogen applications on soils decidedly

[13] Victory Farm Forum. Chilean Nitrate Education Bureau, December 1949.

nitrogen-deficient, Krantz [14] found an increase in protein content of the gain of over 3 per cent in a large number of cases. However, the protein content of the grain was not increased very much when a great increase in yield occurred. Tyner [13] reports somewhat contradictory results. He increased oat yields from 52.8 bushels to 70.7 bushels and the protein content from 10.91 to 12.90 per cent by applying 40 pounds of nitrogen per acre, the P_2O_5 and K_2O applications remaining the same. Also a number of investigators, including Williams [15] and Lowry [16] et al., obtained an appreciable increase in protein content of wheat and also a considerably larger yield as a result of nitrogen applications.

It is generally considered that applications of nitrogen during the early part of the growth period of plants will increase plant size and yield unless a nitrogen deficiency develops later. Applications of nitrogen later in the life of the plant, however, are more likely to increase the protein content of the tissue with less probability of an increase in size. Also, it appears to be much easier to increase the protein content of the vegetative portions of plants than of the seed. At present there seems to be no definite basis for predicting an increase in protein content of a crop as a result of nitrogen fertilization. Such an increase is not likely to occur, however, unless an abundant supply of nitrogen is present. Considering the wide variation in the protein content of crops grown in different soils and with different fertilizer applications, and in view of the fact that before many years the composition of crops will probably be considered in determining their price, it is highly desirable that more accurate information be obtained regarding the factors that influence plant composition.

LOSS OF NITROGEN FROM THE SOIL

The fact that soils seldom contain more than a fraction of a per cent of nitrogen, even when appreciable amounts are added annually, indicates a considerable loss of the element. In fact the maintenance of a desirable quantity of nitrogen in the soil is one of the problems in good soil management. Several processes by which the element is lost from the soil will be discussed.

Removal of Nitrogen in Crops. Nitrogen is taken from the soil by grain crops in larger quantities than are any other of the essential elements. Forage and vegetable crops, on the other hand, with a few exceptions contain more potassium than they do nitrogen. Onion bulbs

[14] *North Carolina Agr. Exp. Sta. Bull.* 366, 1949.
[15] Master's Thesis, Kansas State College, 1952.
[16] *Nebraska Agr. Exp. Sta. Outstate Testing Cir.* 10, 1950.

and cauliflower heads are slightly higher in nitrogen than in potassium, and ears of sweet corn contain almost twice as much nitrogen as potassium. Tobacco plants are similar to vegetables in their nitrogen-potassium content, and cotton resembles the grain crop. The nitrogen, phosphorus, and potassium contents of average yields of a number of crops are presented in Table 21. The composition of leguminous crops are

TABLE 21. QUANTITIES OF NITROGEN, PHOSPHORUS, AND POTASSIUM IN SEVERAL CROPS *

Crop	Yield, bu.	N	P	K	Crop	Yield, lb.	N	P	K
Buckwheat	20	77.5	5.89	50.20	Cotton	500	68.0	10.26	28.38
Barley	35	42.8	7.47	27.38	Tobacco	1,500	67.0	5.46	92.59
Corn	50	78.4	12.05	45.80	Kentucky				
Oats	50	48.0	7.86	33.85	bluegrass	2,000	29.4	3.8	32.8
Flax	15	51.0	6.94	22.40	Timothy	2,000	19.6	3.0	31.4
Rye	20	29.1	7.00	19.66	Redtop	2,000	21.2	3.4	31.8
Wheat	25	42.5	7.25	17.42	Orchard grass	2,000	19.4	3.6	38.0
Potatoes	150	31.5	5.89	37.34	Bromegrass	2,000	29.8	3.4	44.3
Onions	300	39.3	6.72	31.20	Cabbage	20,000	60.0	8.7	66.4
Carrots	200	23.0	5.68	43.97	Cauliflower	15,000	42.0	6.6	41.5
Parsnips	267	26.4	10.48	64.72	Celery	10,000	25.0	8.7	62.2
Turnips	360	50.0	8.73	74.67	Beets	25,000	62.5	10.9	103.7
					Sweet corn	4,000	18.0	3.5	9.9

* Data for forage crops taken from *Illinois Agr. Exp. Sta. Bull.* 518. Results are average for 50 samples, except for orchard grass of which there were 30 samples. Data for other crops calculated from tables in *Fundamentals of Soil Science* (second edition), by C. E. Millar and L. M. Turk. John Wiley & Sons, New York, 1952.

† Nutrient content of above-ground portion of grain and forage crops and of harvested portion only of vegetables.

not given because the proportion of the nitrogen they contain that is taken from the soil is not known and undoubtedly varies greatly with soil conditions, inoculation, and other factors. It is well known that these crops contain considerably more nitrogen than they do potassium and that their phosphorus content is higher than that of most other commonly grown crops. It is evident that the quantities of nitrogen removed from the soil in crops are relatively large. Moreover, frequently a comparatively small proportion of the nitrogen in crops fed to livestock is returned to the soil, and of that in human food practically none is returned. The pounds of several nutrients contained in 1,000 pounds live weight of farm animals are shown in Fig. 18.

Loss of Nitrogen by Leaching. Lysimeter studies at several experiment stations have shown the loss of nitrates in drainage water to be considerable in humid climates. Little loss of ammonium salts occurs because the ammonium ion is readily adsorbed by the soil colloids and because it is rapidly oxidized into nitrates. Losses of nitrogen by leaching vary so much with amount and distribution of rainfall, length of time the soil is unfrozen, soil temperature and texture, the proportion of the growing season that there is no crop on the land, the organic content of the soil and the amounts of nitrogenous materials applied, tillage, and cropping system followed that actual data concerning losses under any given conditions are of little value. It is more advisable to center attention on practices which tend to decrease losses in drainage.

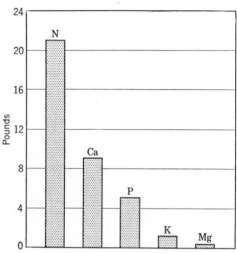

Fig. 18. Pounds of various nutrients contained in 1,000 pounds live weight of animals. Average for calf, steer, lamb, sheep, and swine. When livestock are sold much more nitrogen leaves the farm than other plant nutrients. Compiled from data by Lawes, as given by Bear in *Soils and Fertilizers,* John Wiley & Sons, New York, 1953.

The presence of a growing crop is one of the best methods of decreasing leaching losses. This point is illustrated by the data of Lyon [17] et al., which show losses of 822.2, 83.5, and 28 pounds of nitrogen per acre for a 10-year period from a silty clay loam soil carrying no crop, a rotation without legumes, and grass, respectively. The only soil treatment was five 10-ton applications of manure. The effectiveness of the rotation, which contained corn, two small grain crops, and two years of timothy, in conserving nitrogen is evident. Rotations containing more cultivated crops have been shown to permit of more leaching, and a continuous grass cover is known to be most effective in reducing losses in drainage. The decrease in nutrient losses under crops is due to both the intake of nutrients by the crop and the reduced amount of drainage because of transpiration. In rotations which permit the soil to be free

[17] *Cornell Univ. Agr. Exp. Sta. Memoir* 134, 1930.

of a crop for periods of several months, the use of cover crops is advisable to reduce leaching losses.

A reduction in the number of times a soil is worked with tillage implements also tends to decrease nitrogen losses in drainage water because tillage accelerates nitrate formation in many soils. With the perfection of methods now under investigation which provide for fitting and planting soil with only one or two operations, losses of nitrogen in drainage water during and before seedbed preparation should be reduced. With these methods weeds may be permitted to grow until seeding time and this vegetative cover will decrease nutrient losses.

Careful planning in the time of application of manures and nitrogen-carrying fertilizers will result in nitrogen conservation. When feasible it is best not to apply manures any great length of time before they can be incorporated into the soil. Furthermore, in warm climates it is desirable not to apply manure or nitrogen fertilizer very long before the soil is to be occupied by growing vegetation. For cultivated crops, especially in areas of high rainfall, it is better to apply part of the nitrogen as a side dressing during the growing season than to apply all of it at or before planting time.

Nitrogen Loss through Erosion. The great losses of nitrogen brought about by erosion are more fully appreciated now than in earlier years. Because soil erosion starts in the surface horizon, in which soil nitrogen largely occurs, the process necessarily results in much loss of this element. Also particles of organic matter and clay particles with organic matter adhering to them erode more easily than the larger mineral particles of the soil. The use of soil-management practices which have been shown to control erosion will reduce this nitrogen loss.

Volatilization and Other Nitrogen Losses. Under poorly aerated soil conditions many soil bacteria are capable of reducing sulfates, nitrates, and compounds of ferric iron and so obtaining the energy they usually derive from utilization of atmospheric oxygen. With nitrates the reduction may proceed until elemental nitrogen is produced which passes into the atmosphere. Conditions giving rise to this form of nitrogen loss are: (1) an accumulation of nitrates, (2) a supply of readily decomposable organic material, and (3) a limited supply of oxygen most generally resulting from excess water in the soil or excessive compaction. Even in well drained soils, however, there are innumerable very small areas with limited aeration in which reduction processes may occur and hence some, although small, losses of nitrogen. The actual loss of nitrogen that occurs through volatilization is not known, nor are all the conditions that facilitate the process fully understood. It is assumed, however, that with good soil aeration such losses are small because losses of nitrates in drainage water have been found approximately to equal losses in soil nitrogen when a soil is kept free of vegetation for many years.[18]

On the other hand a different situation may pertain when a growing crop is heavily fertilized with nitrogen. Under such conditions several workers have found a loss of nitrogen from the soil considerably in excess of that removed in the crops and in drainage water. For example, Bizzell [19] reports an unexplained loss during a 9-year period of 249 pounds of nitrogen per acre from a soil growing timothy and receiving 1,474 pounds of nitrogen. The nitrogen addition consisted of sodium nitrate plus that in rain. During the same time there was a nitrogen gain of 25 pounds when only 699 pounds of nitrogen in fertilizer and rain was applied. The loss of nitrogen in drainage water during the period was only 21 pounds for the soil receiving the heavy nitrogen application and 14 pounds for that receiving the small amount of fertilizer. There was no change in the nitrogen content of the subsoil during the experiment. Also a somewhat larger nitrogen loss was observed during an 11-year period under a rotation of corn, oats, and 2 years of timothy when a heavy application of nitrogen was made. With a lighter application a gain of nitrogen resulted. The greatest loss occurred from soil producing vegetable crops. During a 15-year period soil receiving 91 pounds of nitrogen in rain and 2,141 pounds in sulfate of ammonia lost 671 pounds of nitrogen. When nitrate of soda was substituted for the sulfate the loss was 609 pounds. Evidently the source of the nitrogen had little effect on the unaccounted-for loss.

Further evidence that the cropping system may have an influence on this unexplained loss of nitrogen is supplied by the results reported by Chapman [20] et al. During a 10-year period a soil cropped to barley for 6 years and sudan grass for 4 years, and treated with 200 pounds of nitrogen per year in fertilizer, gained 677 pounds of nitrogen when a winter cover crop of vetch was grown. However, when mustard was used as a cover crop the soil lost 523 pounds of nitrogen. This is a remarkable influence for a leguminous cover crop to exert on the nitrogen economy in a soil. The large loss of nitrogen from a cropped soil in addition to that removed in drainage and plant tissue is difficult to explain. Wilson [21] has offered as an explanation the loss of nitrogen known to result when compounds such as amines are oxidized to

[18] *Soil Conditions and Plant Growth,* by E. J. Russell, revised by E. W. Russell, p. 298. Longmans, Green & Co., London, 1950.

[19] *Cornell Agr. Exp. Sta. Mem.* 252 and 256, 1943 and 1944.

[20] *Hilgardia,* 19: 57, 1949.

[21] *Cornell Agr. Exp. Sta. Mem.* 253, 1943.

nitrites. He postulates the excretion of these substances by plants when abundantly supplied with nitrogen. This whole problem is a very interesting one and should be carefully investigated.

The influence of readily decayable organic matter on the loss of gaseous nitrogen from the soil is shown by the rapid decrease in nitrogen content of soils during the first few years they are under cultivation. Myers [22] et al. report a loss of 360 pounds of nitrogen per acre for the period 1931–1938 from a soil just put into cultivation. This is the average loss from seven plots in western Kansas and represents the soil loss in excess of the nitrogen removed in the wheat crop. During a 23-year period, in the same location, the nitrogen contained in the crops grown about equaled the soil loss of nitrogen. Apparently loss of nitrates by leaching in that area is negligible. Likewise Shutt [23] reported a loss of 1,403 pounds of nitrogen for a 4-inch soil depth and a 2,186-pound loss for the 8-inch depth during the 22-year period following the plowing of a prairie soil on the Dominion Experimental Farm at Indian Head, Saskatchewan. During the 22-year period the soil produced 6 crops of wheat, 4 of barley, 3 of oats, and was fallowed 9 years. Usually a fallow year followed a grain crop. No statement is given of the quantity of nitrogen contained in the crops harvested. A similar loss of nitrogen was found by Sievers and Haltz [24] from eastern Washington soils. Also the Missouri station [25] reported an average loss of 34.9 per cent of the nitrogen in 8 virgin soils after being put into cultivation.[26] Several other experiment stations have reported similar losses from soils when converted from a virgin to a crop-producing status. Data indicate that the losses of nitrogen are rapid during the first few years the soils are under cultivation and that the annual losses gradually decrease until something of an equilibrium is reached between nitrogen losses and additions. The nitrogen level at which this balance is attained is influenced by the soil-management system followed as well as by climatic conditions.

ADDITIONS OF NITROGEN TO THE SOIL

To offset the large loss of nitrogen from the soil there must be a correspondingly large addition of the element if soil productivity is to

[22] *Kansas Agr. Exp. Sta. Tech. Bull.* 56, 1943.

[23] *J. Agr. Sci.,* 3: 335, 1910.

[24] *Washington Agr. Exp. Sta. Bull.* 116, 1922, and *Bull.* 206, 1926.

[25] *Missouri Agr. Exp. Sta. Bull.* 522, 1949.

[26] Under the climatic condition of northern Missouri an appreciable loss of nitrates through leaching could be expected.

be maintained. Frequent applications of materials containing available nitrogen or compounds of the element that will shortly become available must be made also because of the difficulty in maintaining a sufficiently large store of organic nitrogen in the soil to insure an adequate supply of the nutrient in available form and offset the loss of soluble forms by leaching.

Return of Nitrogen in Crop Residues. With the wide adoption of combines and mechanical pickers there has been a considerable increase in the quantities of crop residues returned to the soil directly rather than as a component of manure. As a result a larger amount of nitrogen is now returned to crop land in these materials than formerly occurred. On an average the straw or stalk of grain crops contains slightly more than one-half as much nitrogen as does the grain. Soybeans present the greatest variation from this average, with a ratio of nitrogen in grain and straw of from 0.8 to 0.9. There is also more than one-half as much nitrogen in corn stover as there is in the ears. Wheat straw on the other hand contains less than one-half as much nitrogen as is present in the grain. The amounts of nitrogen that are returned to the soil in crop residues vary with the yield and the kind of crop. Considering yields commonly obtained the nitrogen content of the residues may vary from 10 to 60 pounds per acre. The figures presented do not include the nitrogen contained in crop root systems.

A number of studies of the effect of additions of crop residues on the accumulation of nitrogen in the soil have been made under laboratory conditions. However, studies of the increase in soil nitrogen content resulting from the application of crop residues under field conditions have not been numerous or too conclusive. Results of one of the more carefully conducted investigations are reported by Haltz and Vandecaveye.[27] They found, under annual cropping to wheat, that yearly applications of alfalfa, alfalfa + straw, straw + $(NH_4)_2SO_4$, and manure resulted in increased soil-nitrogen contents over a 14-year period. On the other hand, untreated soil and soil receiving straw alone and $NaNO_3$ alone lost nitrogen. Also, under a cropping system consisting of alternate wheat and fallow, all treatments resulted in a loss of soil nitrogen. The effect of the return of crop residues on yields of subsequent crops is discussed in Chapter 15.

Nitrogen Supplied in Manures. On some farms and in some states the nitrogen applied in manure represents the return of a portion of the nitrogen removed from the soil in crops. On some farms and in some states, however, much of the nitrogen in manure was derived from

[27] *Soil Sci.,* 45: 143, 1938.

purchased feed, and its application to the soil represents a direct addition to the soil's nitrogen supply. For example, it is estimated that Vermont farmers purchase approximately 187,250 tons of a protein ration to be fed to dairy cows. This feed is made from materials grown outside of the state. If this ration contains 51.74 pounds of nitrogen per ton, and 75 per cent of the nitrogen consumed is excreted by the cattle, some 3,633 tons of nitrogen are contained in the manure produced from feed brought into the state.

Manure as voided varies greatly in composition, even manure from the same kind of animals. When this variability is accentuated by the differences in amounts and composition of bedding used on individual farms and by the length of time and conditions of storage, the quantities of nutrients supplied to the soil by average manure applications become very uncertain. The highest, lowest, and average number of pounds of nitrogen found in a ton of mixed manure are reported by Van Slyke [28] to be 16, 8, and 10, respectively. It is evident that with manure applications of 10 or more tons per acre large quantities of nitrogen are supplied to the soil, and results of many experiments indicate that with frequent manuring the supply of organic nitrogen in the soil is increased unless an unusually soil-depleting cropping system is followed. Of the animal manures, that from poultry is the highest in nitrogen content, varying from around 1.0 to 1.5 per cent. Sheep manure ranks second, with the nitrogen content of the feces being from 0.7 to 0.8 per cent, of the urine 1.3 to 1.4 per cent, and of the mixed solid and liquid portions approximately 0.9 to 1.0 per cent.

Symbiotic Nitrogen Fixation.[29] Quantities of nitrogen added to the soil through the activities of organisms living in symbiosis with leguminous crops are extremely variable both for different crops and for the same crop under different conditions. The production of many nodules on the plant roots is not always a safe indication of abundant nitrogen fixation, and a large supply of nitrogen in the soil may decrease fixation of the element. It is very difficult to determine the quantity of nitrogen obtained from the air by these organisms under field conditions, but the following discussion may be helpful.

Some examples of the quantities of nitrogen fixed by symbiotic bacteria under given conditions may serve as a basis for estimating the amount of fixation in other situations. The oldest study of this type that has come to the attention of the writer was at the Rothamsted experi-

[28] From *Fertilizers and Crop Production*, by L. L. Van Slyke. Orange Judd Publishing Co., New York, 1932. Used with permission.

[29] A discussion of the organisms that fix nitrogen symbiotically and of the soil conditions that affect their activity is given on pages 294–297.

ment station. Two soil areas were left in sod for 20 years. In one area the vegetative cover contained 25 per cent leguminous plants, and in the other practically no legumes were present. The changes in nitrogen content of the soil in the two areas are presented in Table 22. It is as-

TABLE 22. ACCUMULATION OF NITROGEN IN THE SOIL RESULTING FROM THE GROWTH OF LEGUMES *

Type of Vege-tation	Soil Depth, in.	Nitrogen Content of Soil, lb. per acre			
		At Be-ginning	After 20 Years	In-crease	Total Increase
Sod, no legumes	0–9	2,219	2,837	618	
	9–18	1,995	2,238	243	
	18–27	1,612	1,760	148	
				——	1,009
Sod, 25 per cent legumes	0–9	2,924	3,920	996	
	9–18	1,898	2,579	681	
	18–27	1,569	2,265	696	
				——	2,373
Increase due to legumes					1,364

* *The Book of the Rothamsted Experiments.* John Murray, London, 1905. Used with permission.

sumed that the greater gain in nitrogen of the soil growing 25 per cent legumes was due to the nitrogen fixed by symbiotic organisms. It is interesting to conjecture what the nitrogen accumulation would have been if the vegetative cover had been entirely leguminous.

A careful study of nitrogen fixation by legumes was undertaken by Lyon and Bizzell.[30] Several legumes commonly grown for hay were seeded in a small grain crop, harvested for hay the next season, and then the soil was plowed for the next small grain. Also, three legumes for seed production were grown in 2-year rotations with a small grain. And finally peas and vetch were seeded in a small grain, harvested for seed, and then followed the next year by a small grain. All crops were analyzed for nitrogen content and the total nitrogen they contained was computed. The soil consisted of 60 per cent silty clay loam and 40 per cent sand, thus permitting of good aeration. The nitrogen content of the soil was determined at the beginning and at the close of the 10-year period covered by the experiment. Losses of nitrogen in drainage and by volatilization were considered to be about equal to additions in rain and in the rainwater used to water the crops. The data obtained

[30] *J. Amer. Soc. Agron.*, 26: 651, 1934.

are presented in Table 23. In this experiment no account appears to have been taken of the nitrogen fixed by non-symbiotic organisms. That

TABLE 23. NITROGEN ACCUMULATION UNDER DIFFERENT CROPPING SYSTEMS DURING A 10-YEAR PERIOD

| | | | Lb. of Nitrogen per 2,500,000 Lb. of Soil | |
| Cropping System | Nitrogen in Crops, lb. per acre | Change in Nitrogen Content of Soil | Apparent Fixation of Nitrogen | |
			For 10 Years	Per Year
Red clover: grain *	868	532	1,400	140
Alsike clover: grain	830	595	1,425	143
Alfalfa: grain	1,804	607	2,411	241
Sweet clover: grain	1,214	420	1,634	163
Vetch and wheat: grain	549	97	646	65
Red and alsike clover: grain	1,050	577	1,631	163
Sweet clover and vetch: grain	1,155	410	1,565	157
Soybeans: grain	1,058	−42	1,016	102
Peas and oats: grain	493	−32	461	46
Field beans: grain	672	−100	572	57
Barley, rye, or oats each year	220	−52	171	17
Alfalfa continuously	2,179	505	2,684	268

* The small grain crop grown in alternate years was either barley or rye.

this process was active is evidenced by the gain in nitrogen content of the soil growing non-legumes exclusively. According to these data alfalfa was the most effective crop in fixing nitrogen, with sweet clover and a mixture of red and alsike clovers ranking second. In considering these data it should be borne in mind that the nitrogen content of the soil at the beginning of the experiment was only 0.084 per cent.

Increase in Soil Nitrogen through Legume Growth. In the experiments cited in the preceding section a substantial increase in soil nitrogen content resulted from the growing of legumes. It must not be assumed, however, that this will always occur. When the nitrogen content of the soil is low, nitrogen accumulation is likely to occur if legumes, especially those which have a sod-like habit of growth, occupy the soil frequently or for a period of several years. On the other hand, there is ground for the opinion that a soil high in nitrogen may change little in its content of this element and may even lose nitrogen while growing a legume. Lyon and Bizzell point this out by showing that the sand and soil mixture used in the experiment cited previously, which contained only 0.084 per cent nitrogen made an average annual acre gain of 50 pounds of nitrogen while growing alfalfa continuously for 10 years, but the undiluted soil containing 0.12 per cent nitrogen gained only 19 pounds per year.

Likewise Swanson [31] found that eight soils in the humid and semi-humid portions of Kansas contained an average of 0.192 per cent nitrogen after growing alfalfa for 20 or more years, compared to a nitrogen content of 0.213 per cent in eight similar soils growing native grass, which was either pastured or cut for hay. In the semiarid portion of Kansas, however, the reverse situation obtained. Seven soils which had grown alfalfa 20 or more years contained 0.185 per cent nitrogen compared to 0.147 per cent for the corresponding soils growing grass.

It appears that little or no accumulation of nitrogen in the soil may result from the growth of legumes for hay under some conditions, especially if the land is not manured. Nevertheless, under the soil-depleting cropping systems usually followed under irrigation and in humid climates, it is generally considered that the growth of legumes for hay will increase the nitrogen supply in the soil. The assurance of nitrogen accumulation in the soil is greater if the manure produced from feeding the hay is returned to the soil. Some investigators believe that a legume should occupy the soil for at least 1 year of hay harvest in order to realize the greatest benefit from nitrogen fixation. Other workers, however, consider that nitrogen addition from a legume seeded in a small grain and plowed under the following spring is almost as great as when the crop is left for hay.

There is little evidence that a legume planted in rows, cultivated, and harvested for seed leaves a soil richer in nitrogen. In fact, as shown in Table 23, a loss of nitrogen may result. If the straw is returned to the soil, as is usually done with soybeans, the chances of averting a nitrogen loss are increased.

Non-Symbiotic Nitrogen Fixation. The organisms that fix nitrogen non-symbiotically and the soil conditions that influence their activity are discussed on pages 292–294.

The quantities of nitrogen fixed by non-symbiotic organisms is a pertinent consideration in planning soil-management systems. An accurate determination of the nitrogen fixed by these organisms is difficult because of the unknown losses of the element through volatilization and leaching. The cropping system followed, as well as climatic conditions and soil properties, undoubtedly influences the activities of these as well

[31] *J. Amer. Soc. Agron.*, 9: 305, 1917.

as of other soil organisms. The annual gain in nitrogen of 50 pounds reported in Table 22 for the field at the Rothamsted experiment station, carrying a non-leguminous vegetation, may be considered due largely to non-symbiotic fixation. Likewise the Cornell [32] experiment station reports an annual gain of 41.5 pounds of nitrogen by soil left in grass for 10 years without addition of nitrogen fertilizer. Each year the grass was cut and allowed to remain on the ground. In this record it is assumed that leaching and volatilization losses equaled if they did not exceed additions of nitrogen from precipitation.

Estimates of nitrogen fixation such as those cited were obtained under conditions especially favorable for the process because of the return to the soil of considerable quantities of organic matter with a wide carbon-nitrogen ratio. Few experiments involving commonly used crop rotations were conducted in such a way as to give a reasonably accurate estimate of non-symbiotic nitrogen fixation. Estimates have varied from 10 to 50 pounds per acre annually. Although information concerning the quantities of nitrogen added to the soil by this process is so indefinite, there is a general opinion that it is an important factor in the nitrogen economy of soils.

Additions to Soil Nitrogen through Precipitation. Many studies have been made of the quantities of nitrogen brought to the soil by precipitation. Results show that most of the combined nitrogen in the atmosphere comes from the combustion of fuel. Consequently the quantities brought to the earth in precipitation are greater near centers of population and industrial areas. In addition to the ammoniacal and organic nitrogen expelled through decay or combustion there is in the air a small amount of the element in an oxidized state, which is supposed to have been formed through the action of lightning. The quantities of oxidized nitrogen will vary, accordingly, with the frequency and intensity of electrical storms. The total quantity of nitrogen brought to the earth in precipitation varies from around 2 to about 20 pounds per acre per year. The average for localities not very close to cities or industrial cites has been found to be around 4 to 6 pounds.

NITROGEN FERTILIZERS [33]

Many years of experience as well as of experimentation have shown that the nitrogen supplied to the soil by natural processes and by appli-

---

[32] *Cornell Agr. Exp. Sta. Mem.* 15, 1928.

[33] A detailed discussion of nitrogen materials and the preparation of nitrogen fertilizers is given in Fertilizer technology and resources, *Agronomy,* III: 15. Academic Press, New York, 1953.

cations of manure is seldom sufficient to produce satisfactory yields of crops. Accordingly, more and more reliance has been placed on nitrogen fertilizers. Also the general use of processes of fixing atmospheric nitrogen has increased supplies of fertilizers containing this nutrient.

Classes of Nitrogenous Fertilizers. Nitrogen fertilizers or nitrogen "carriers," as they are often called, may be divided into two groups, namely, organic and mineral or inorganic. Each of these groups may be subdivided on the basis of origin into natural and synthetic products. It is also possible to make a third division of nitrogen compounds, which overlaps those mentioned but contains substances having additional characteristics. This group would include substances containing nitrogen in chemical combination with phosphorus or phosphorus and potassium. The most commonly used nitrogen fertilizers with their content of nitrogen and of phosphoric acid and potash, when present, are listed in Table 24.

Preparation of Nitrogen Fertilizers. The recovery of ammonia during the coking of coal and its conversion into ammonium sulfate is an old but very important process. Likewise the refining of nitrate of soda from the caliche obtained from Chilean deposits is one of long standing. However, processes which involve the fixation of atmospheric nitrogen are a comparatively recent development and have contributed much toward the greatly increased use of nitrogen fertilizers. Synthetic nitrogen production in 1952 amounted to 1,689,609 tons, and during the year ending June 30, 1952, only 1,424,780 tons of nitrogen were applied as fertilizer. A considerable part of the synthetic nitrogen is taken by chemical industries. The quantity used in fertilizers will undoubtedly increase as plants under construction for the fixation of nitrogen and its conversion into various products are completed and new ones are erected. Accordingly a brief discussion in this book of some of these processes of nitrogen fixation and fertilizer preparation is justified.

Two processes [34] for combining atmospheric nitrogen with other elements are of importance in the United States. The cyanamide process is the older, having been developed in Germany about the turn of the century. It consists of preparing calcium carbide (CaC_2) by heating coal or coke with CaO and then combining nitrogen with it at a temperature of $1,000°$ C. The nitrogen is obtained by the distillation of liquid air. The end-product contains 22 per cent nitrogen and 25 per cent of $Ca(OH)_2$. In moist soil the material hydrolyzes into urea and calcium hydroxide.

[34] See *Commercial Fertilizers* by Collings for a more detailed description of these and other processes. Blakiston Co., Philadelphia, 1950.

TABLE 24. NITROGEN FERTILIZERS AND THEIR NUTRIENT CONTENT

Organics of Natural Origin *

Material	Nitrogen, per cent	Phosphoric Acid,† per cent	Potash,† per cent
Dried blood	8.0–14.0	0.3– 1.5	0.50–0.80
Animal tankage	5.0–10.0	3.0–13.0	Small amounts
Garbage tankage	2.0– 4.0	1.0– 3.0	0.50–1.5
Process tankage	6.5–10.0	Variable	Small amounts
Fish scrap, dried	6.5–10.0	4.0– 8.0	Small amounts
Sewage sludge, ordinary	1.6– 3.3	1.0	Small amounts
Sewage sludge, activated	4.1– 7.5	2.5– 5.0	0.75
Cottonseed meal	6.0– 9.0	2.0– 3.0	1.0–2.0
Bone meals	0.7– 5.3	17.0–30.0	. . .
Castor pomace	4.0– 7.0	1.0– 1.5	1.0–1.50
Cocoa shell meal	2.5	1.0	2.5
Tobacco stems	1.3– 1.6	0.9	4.0–9.0
Sheep or cow manure, dried and pulverized	1.2– 2.0	1.0– 2.0	2.0–3.0
Poultry manure, dried and pulverized	5.0– 6.0	2.0– 3.0	1.0–2.0

Organics of Synthetic Origin

	Nitrogen, per cent	Remarks
Urea, $CO(NH_2)_2$	42–45	Sold under the trade names of "Uramon" and "Nu Green"
Calcium cyanamide ($CaCN_2$)	20–22	Sold under the name "Cyanamid"

These two compounds are classed as non-proteid organic nitrogen.

Mineral Carriers of Mainly Synthetic Origin

	Nitrogen, per cent	Remarks
Sulfate of ammonia $(NH_4)_2SO_4$	20.5	A large part of the output is a by-product from coke ovens
Nitrate of soda ($NaNO_3$)	15.5–16.5	Most of this material comes from a natural deposit in Chile‡
Calcium nitrate, $Ca(NO_3)_2$	13.0–15.5	Nitrate of lime
Cal-Nitro	16.0–20.5	A mixture of NH_4NO_3 and $CaCO_3$
Calurea	34.0	A compound of $Ca(NO_3)_2$ and $CO(NH_2)_2$
Ammonium sulfate-nitrate	26.0	A double salt of $(NH_4)_2SO_4$ and NH_4NO_3

TABLE 24. NITROGEN FERTILIZERS AND THEIR NUTRIENT CONTENT (*Continued*)

Mineral Carriers of Mainly Synthetic Origin (Cont.)

	Nitrogen, per cent	Remarks
Ammonium nitrate	33.0–35.0	Conditioned to resist absorption of moisture
Ammonium chloride	26.2	Small amounts used
Anhydrous liquid ammonia	82.2	Used for ammoniating purposes and for direct application
Ammonia liquor (B)	24.7	Ammonia absorbed in water
Urea-ammonia liquors § (UAL—A, B, C, D)	37.0–45.5	Solutions of urea in ammonia liquor
UAL solution 37	37.1	Contains 7.4% insoluble nitrogen
Ammonium nitrate-ammonia liquors	37.0–49.0	Solutions of NH_4NO_3 in ammonia liquor
Crude nitrogen solution	44.0	$NaNO_3$ and NH_3 in water

Chemical Compounds of Nitrogen with Phosphoric Acid or Potash or Both

	Nitrogen, per cent	Phosphoric Acid, per cent	Potash, per cent	Remarks
Potassium nitrate	14	0	45.0	Small natural deposits
Potassium ammonium nitrate	16	0	27.0	Essentially a mixture of NH_4NO_3 and KCl
Nitrate of soda potash	14–15	0	10.0–13.0	Occurs with Chilean deposits
Monoammonium phosphate	12	61.0	0	Sold largely as an ingredient of 13-13-13
Diammonium phosphate	21	53.0	0	Stable when made from relatively pure phosphoric acid and ammonia
Ammoniated superphosphate ‖	3–5	16.0	0	
Nitrated superphosphate ‖	5–6	16.0–17.0	0	Superphosphate treated with nitrogen solution II
Ammo-Phos A	11	45–48	0	Largely a mixture of ammonium phosphate and ammonium sulfate
Ammo-Phos B	16.5	20	0	
Ammo-Phos Ko ¶	12	24	12	A mixture of Ammo-Phos and K_2SO_4
Nitrophoska ¶	15	30	15	Several grades
Nitric phosphates **	14	14	14	Several grades

TABLE 24. NITROGEN FERTILIZERS AND THEIR NUTRIENT CONTENT (*Continued*)

Chemical Compounds of Nitrogen with Phosphoric Acid or Potash or Both (*Cont.*)

	Nitrogen, per cent	Phosphoric Acid, per cent	Potash, per cent	Remarks
Leuna-Phos	20	20	0	Essentially a mixture of $(NH_4)_2HPO_4$ and $(NH_4)_2SO_4$
Leunaphoska	10	10	13	A mixture of Leuna-Phos and a potassium salt

* From *Fundamentals of Soil Science* (second edition), by C. E. Millar and L. M. Turk. John Wiley & Sons, New York, 1952.

† Phosphoric acid (P_2O_5) may be converted into phosphorus by multiplying by 0.437, and potash (K_2O) may be changed to potassium by use of the factor 0.83.

‡ Also manufactured in this country.

§ Solutions of somewhat different nitrogen contents may be manufactured by other companies.

‖ These materials are mixtures rather than chemical compounds.

¶ Trade name for a series of highly concentrated complete fertilizers.

** Made by treating rock phosphate with HNO_3, or a mixture of HNO_3 and H_2SO_4, and adding potassium salts.

A somewhat later development was the formation of ammonia by combining nitrogen and hydrogen directly. The process, as modified by Haber and Bosch, is now used more extensively than any other. The first operation in the process is the preparation of free hydrogen by passing superheated steam over red-hot coke. The resultant CO and H_2 and remaining steam then pass over a catalyst, which causes the CO to react with the steam, forming H_2CO_3 and more H_2. These gases, which include air, are compressed, heated to 500–700° C., and submitted to the action of a catalyst. The result is a low yield of NH_3. After absorption of the NH_3 in water the remaining gases, mixed with a fresh supply, are passed over the catalyst again. The ammonia produced may be liquefied to produce anhydrous ammonia, it may be dissolved in water and the solution used alone or as a solvent for other nitrogen carriers, it may be oxidized to produce nitric acid, or it may be used in the preparation of urea and ammonium nitrate.

Urea is obtained by first making ammonium carbamate (NH_2 $COONH_4$) through the combining of CO_2 and NH_3 under high pressure. The carbamate then looses a molecule of water leaving urea [$CO (NH_2)_2$] in solution. After concentration by evaporation under vacuum, granules of urea are formed by spraying the solution into a chamber. The granules are coated with various inert materials to reduce their tendency to absorb moisture, and the product is then ready for sale as a 42 per cent nitrogen fertilizer.

Ammonium nitrate is prepared by passing ammonia gas into nitric acid. There are several processes of granulating the material. The granules are so hygroscopic, however, that they must be mixed with a conditioning agent such as clay, plaster of paris, tricalcium phosphate or other inert material. Also, they are sometimes coated with a water-repellent material and the bags in which the product is marketed must be waterproofed. This fertilizer has met with much favor and the production of it is increasing. One-half of its nitrogen content is in the form of ammonia and one-half is present as nitrate. This combination is considered especially desirable under some conditions.

Fixed atmospheric nitrogen is also used to a limited extent in the preparation of nitrate of soda, nitrate of lime, sulfate of ammonia, and various combinations of ammonia with phosphoric acid, and phosphoric acid and potassium. Large quantities are consumed in the ammoniation of superphosphate. In fact most manufacturers of mixed fertilizers add as much anhydrous ammonia or various solutions of nitrogen carriers in ammonia liquor as they consider consistent with the preparation of a good quality of product because these materials are cheaper than other forms of nitrogen.

Various solutions containing nitrogen have come into extensive use in the last few years, both for direct application and in ammoniating superphosphate, as was just mentioned. These are primarily solutions of ammonia which have been obtained by direct fixation or as a by-product and which contain either urea or ammonium nitrate (or both) and sometimes sodium nitrate. In addition, some attempts have been made to include a water-insoluble compound of nitrogen in the solution of urea and ammonia. A solution of ammonia alone is also frequently used. These solutions contain from approximately 25 per cent nitrogen up to about 46 per cent. Liquefied ammonia gas or anhydrous ammonia contains approximately 82 per cent of nitrogen.

Use and Application of Synthetic Nitrogen Fertilizers. Dry forms of synthetic nitrogen fertilizers are applied in the same way as are other solid nitrogen carriers. Because of its comparatively high nitrogen content, ammonium nitrate has become very popular. In some areas calcium cyanamide is preferred by the farmers. Its content of $Ca(OH)_2$ is considered a distinct advantage under some conditions.

This product in a powdered form serves as a defoliating agent on cotton to facilitate picking and as a herbicide to control a number of broadleafed weeds in small grains. Because of the toxic effects of cyanamide prior to the conversion of its nitrogen content into available form, the material should be applied from several days to a week or more before seeds germinate or roots become active. A longer period is required for the decomposition of the cyanamide in sandy soils and in those low in organic content than in more productive soils. Calcium cyanamide is prized as an ingredient of mixed fertilizers because it gives a product of good drilling quality.

The limited supply of urea has restricted its direct application as a fertilizer. It is used in ammonia solutions, as a non-protein animal feed, and for spraying plant foliage to provide quickly usable nitrogen.

The direct application of ammonia solutions has increased at an amazing rate. Anhydrous ammonia has been used to a certain extent, but the expense of the necessary tanks and distributing equipment that will resist the high pressures of the liquid has limited the utilization of this cheap source of nitrogen. It must be applied at a depth of several inches in order that the ammonia may be adsorbed by the soil.

Solutions of ammonia and other nitrogen compounds are sprayed on small grains, pastures, and hay crops, and on row crops in large quantities. The equipment needed is not expensive and the solutions do not need to be placed in the soil to avoid loss of ammonia gas. The solutions are, however, quite corrosive to metal in the distributing apparatus.

Utilization of Different Nitrogen Fertilizers by Plants. Nitrogen in the nitrate form is readily absorbed by most crops, and in general it is considered the most available of the nitrogen salts. Ammoniacal nitrogen can also be used by a number of crops, especially during the earlier periods of growth, but does not appear to be quite so satisfactory as the nitrate form when there is a limitation in air supply. This result may be explained by the utilization of some of the oxygen in the nitrate to replace some of that normally obtained from air. Some workers believe that crops especially rich in carbohydrates utilize ammonia more readily than crops relatively rich in protein. Under field conditions it is assumed that much of the ammonia is converted into nitrate before being absorbed by plants.

It has also been shown that plants can utilize nitrite nitrogen, which was to be expected because it is one of the products of the reduction of nitrates in the plant. However, even relatively low concentrations of NO_2 in the growth medium have been found toxic to most plants. Furthermore, in soils sufficiently aerated to permit of a satisfactory growth of many crops, nitrites are quickly oxidized to nitrates. It is assumed, accordingly, that crops commonly utilize very small quantities of nitrite if any.

It has also been demonstrated that amino acids and urea can be absorbed by plant roots. On the other hand, the large size of protein molecules apparently prevents their passage through the membranes of root cells. Also, some amino acids may be utilized within the plant to a certain extent although most of these compounds are quite toxic. Undoubtedly organic nitrogen fertilizers, particularly those derived from plant and animal sources, are broken down with the formation of ammonium and nitrate compounds before being absorbed by crops to an appreciable extent. This change is facilitated by urease, which is found in soils and plant roots, and converts urea into ammonia. The extent to which urea may be used directly by plants is not yet fully demonstrated although it is known that this compound can be absorbed through the leaves and so utilized. In the soil $CO(NH_2)_2$ is hydrolyzed by enzymatic action into NH_3 within a few hours under favorable conditions of moisture and temperature. It is known that $CaCN_2$ goes through extensive changes before being utilized as a nutrient. The danger of damage to growing plant tissue before these changes are completed is discussed on pages 131–132.

Virtually all nitrates and ammonium salts are soluble. As a result nitrates are subject to extensive loss by leaching in humid climates when applied to a soil not occupied by growing plants. Ammonium compounds would also be lost under similar conditions were it not for the fixation of the NH_4 ion by soil colloids. Nevertheless, when ammonium salts are applied to sandy soils in considerable quantities there is probably appreciable loss in drainage water unless absorption by plants is rapid. The natural organic forms of nitrogen have the advantage of not being subject to leaching loss. This property offsets to some extent the uncertainty as to the time in which they become available. It is generally considered that about one-third of the nitrogen in organic fertilizers does not become available to crops during the first year.

Although several nitrogen fertilizers have been given different availability ratings under specified test conditions, it is generally recognized that all the commonly used nitrogen carriers give satisfactory results with most crops when they are applied properly and in suitable amounts. The choice of a nitrogen fertilizer, therefore, becomes a question of the cost of a pound of nitrogen applied to the soil and of the greater convenience one carrier may have for the individual farmer.

The effect which a nitrogen fertilizer has on the yield and growth characteristics of a plant are determined largely by the rate of application, the nitrogen content of the soil, the time in the life cycle of the plant that the application is made, and on the availability of the fertilizer. The effect of applied nitrogen on the number and size of corn ears produced in a nitrogen-deficient soil is shown in Fig. 19.

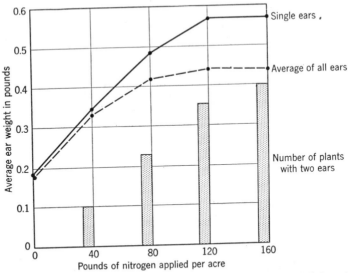

Fig. 19. Applications of nitrogen fertilizer to soils markedly deficient in this nutrient result in an increase in size of corn ears up to a certain point. It is interesting to note that single ears increased in weight much more than the average for all ears because the number of plants producing two ears increased with addition of nitrogen, as is shown by the height of the bars. Prepared from figures in *North Carolina Agr. Exp. Sta. Bull.* 366, 1949.

Effects of Nitrogen Fertilizers on the Soil. Organic carriers of nitrogen, as well as mineral compounds containing NH_3, NH_4, NH_2, and sulfur, require a supply of cations to neutralize the acid produced through decay processes, unless the fertilizer contains sufficient basic material to meet this requirement. Through biological action the nitrogen of these compounds is converted into nitrous and ultimately nitric acid and the sulfur into sulfuric acid. The quantities of $CaCO_3$ required to neutralize the acidity produced from 100 pounds of several of these materials are given in Table 25.

With soils having a low buffer capacity, and especially when large quantities of nitrogen fertilizers are applied, the tendency to increased soil acidity becomes important in crop production. In consequence, fertilizers sold in areas where these conditions are prevalent frequently contain a sufficient quantity of dolomite to neutralize the acid that will be produced. Such fertilizers are designated as "neutral." Under general farming systems in which periodic applications of lime maintain a *p*H

TABLE 25. EQUIVALENT ACIDITY OR BASICITY OF SEVERAL NITROGEN FERTILIZERS *

Fertilizer Material	Nitrogen, per cent	Equivalent Acidity or Basicity, lb. of CaCO₃	
		Per Unit of Nitrogen	Per 100 Lb. of Fertilizer
Sulfate of ammonia	20.5	107	110
Ammo-Phos	11.0	107	59
Anhydrous ammonia	82.2	36	148
Cal-Nitro	20.5	0	0
Calcium nitrate	15.0	27 †	20 †
Crude nitrogen solution	44.0	24	53
Nitrate of soda	16.0	36 †	29 †
Urea ammonia liquor	45.5	36	82
Calcium cyanamide	22.0	57 †	63 †
Cottonseed meal	7.0	29	10
Dried blood	13.3	35	23
Milorganite	6.0	30	10
Garbage tankage	2.5	50 †	7 †
Animal tankage	6–10	30 ‡–30 †	15 ‡–12 †

* From *Fundamentals of Soil Science* (second edition), by C. E. Millar and L. M. Turk. John Wiley & Sons, New York, 1952. Used with permission.
† Basicity.   ‡ Acidity.

approaching neutrality the quantities of acid-forming nitrogen fertilizers ordinarily used will have no significant effect on soil reaction. It should be recognized, however, that some of the applied lime is utilized in correcting the acids produced from the fertilizer.

On the other hand, several fertilizers contain sufficient base to neutralize all the acid produced and leave an excess which creates a slightly alkaline reaction. For example, calcium cyanamide contains a considerable excess of Ca, in the form of $Ca(OH)_2$, above that required to neutralize the acid produced from the nitrogen contained in it. This excess of $Ca(OH)_2$ will help to correct the acidity caused by acid-forming nitrogen fertilizers if such are applied. In addition, with some compounds such as $NaNO_3$ the anion is absorbed by plants to a much greater extent than is the cation. The result is a residue of cations which creates some basicity. These compounds are said to be "physiologically basic." Long-continued use of large quantities of $NaNO_3$ may cause the colloids to become impregnated with sodium and hence result in disintegration of the granules under conditions of limited rainfall.

Use and Cost of Different Nitrogen Fertilizers. Several factors determine the relative quantities of the different nitrogen fertilizers used in a given community or region. Among them are custom or habit, supplies available, kinds of crops grown, ease of application, and cost. There is considerable difference in the initial cost of the nitrogen in different carriers. For example, the average wholesale price per unit of nitrogen in bulk car lots at producing points or ports in 1952 was as follows: ammonium sulfate $2.06, anhydrous ammonia $0.97, calcium cyanamide $3.11, sodium nitrate $3.34, nitrogen solutions $1.20, and urea $3.03.

The retail prices of the different materials at any given point would, of course, not bear the same relation to each other as do the prices quoted. Furthermore, both wholesale and retail prices may change materially. However, the comparatively low cost of the nitrogen in anhydrous ammonia and nitrogen solutions is of interest.

Accumulation of Soil Nitrogen from Fertilizers. The application of nitrogen fertilizer does not contribute directly to a permanent increase in soil nitrogen content. Available forms of nitrogen are leached out unless used by soil organisms or plants, and the organic materials are converted into available forms fairly rapidly if they are of value as fertilizers. By increasing root growth nitrogen fertilizers may cause a small increase in organic matter, and an increase in crop yield opens the way for a greater addition of nitrogen in the form of residues and manure. A stimulation of the activity of microorganisms may also lead to a larger microbial cell accumulation. It is also reasonable to assume that a greater supply of nitrogen in the soil will lead to a larger production of humus from the decay of carbonaceous crop residues.

TABLE 26. QUANTITIES OF NITROGEN CONTAINED IN 100 PRINCIPAL CROPS IN DIFFERENT REGIONS OF THE UNITED STATES AND THE QUANTITIES APPLIED IN FERTILIZERS IN 1947 *

		Lb. of Nitrogen per Acre	
	Millions of		
	Acres in Har-	Contained	Returned
Region	vested Crops	in Crops	in Fertilizer
New England	3.6	29	13.0
Middle Atlantic	16.4	22	7.0
South Atlantic	24.0	15	20.0
East North Central	59.8	21	2.0
West North Central	133.7	20	0.3
East South Central	22.9	15	11.0
West South Central	52.8	16	2.4
Mountain	24.6	22	1.0
Pacific	15.1	27	15.0

* From *Agr. Chemicals*, October and November 1949. Used with permission.

Unfortunately there are few experiments on a field basis that afford any reliable data concerning the influence of nitrogen fertilization on the accumulation of nitrogen in the soil. Unquestionably climatic conditions as well as the cropping system followed will exert a determining influence on the accumulation of organic nitrogen in the soil.

Nitrogen Added to Soil in Fertilizers. The quantity of nitrogen added to soils annually in fertilizers varies greatly, as is seen by the data presented in Table 26. It will be noted that in the South Atlantic states more nitrogen is applied in fertilizers than is removed in crops. In contrast, in the West North Central states, which contain the largest acreage of harvested crops, only 0.3 pound of fertilizer nitrogen is applied for each 20 pounds contained in crops. It is of interest, however, that the use of nitrogen fertilizers is increasing rapidly in both the West and East North Central states.

REFERENCES

Albrecht, W. A. Methods of incorporating organic matter with the soil in relation to nitrogen accumulation. *Missouri Agr. Exp. Sta. Res. Bull.* 249, 1936.

Albrecht, W. A. The nitrate nitrogen in the soil as influenced by the crop and the soil treatment, *ibid.*, 250, 1937.

Brown, E. M. Seasonal variations in the growth and chemical composition of Kentucky bluegrass, *ibid.*, 360, 1943.

Chapman, H. D., Liebig, F. F., and Rayner, D. S. A lysimeter investigation of nitrogen gains and losses under various systems of cover cropping and fertilization, and a discussion of error sources. *Hilgardia*, 19, No. 3, April 1949.

Curtis, O. F., and Clark, D. G. *An Introduction to Plant Physiology.* McGraw-Hill Book Co., New York, 1950.

Haltz, H. F., and Vandecaveye, S. C. Organic residues and nitrogen fertilizers in relation to the productivity and humus content of palouse silt loam. *Soil Sci.*, 45: 143, 1938.

Lyon, T. L., and Bizzell, J. A. A comparison of several legumes with respect to nitrogen accretion. *J. Amer. Soc. Agron.*, 26: 651, 1934.

Myers, H. E., Hallsted, A. L., Kuska, J. B., and Haas, H. J. Nitrogen and carbon changes in soils under low rainfall as influenced by cropping systems and soil treatment. *Kansas Agr. Exp. Sta. Tech. Bull.* 56, 1943.

Neller, J. R. Factors affecting composition of Everglades grasses and legumes. *Florida Agr. Exp. Sta. Bull.* 403, 1944.

Russell, E. J., revised by Russell, E. W. *Soil Conditions and Plant Growth.* Longmans, Green & Co., London, 1950.

Salisbury, G. W., and Morrison, F. B. Early-cut, nitrogen-fertilized timothy hay as compared with alfalfa hay for feeding dairy cows. *New York Agr. Exp. Sta. (Cornell) Bull.* 694, 1938.

Strubblefield, F. M., and De Turk, E. E. The composition of corn, oats, and wheat as influenced by soil, soil treatment, seasonable conditions, and growth. *Soil Sci. Soc. Amer. Proc.*, 5: 120, 1940.

Tidmore, J. W., and Volk, N. J. The effect of plowing under and time of plowing under legumes on the conservation of nitrogen. *J. Amer. Soc. Agron.*,
37: 1005, 1945.

Tidmore, J. W., and Volk, N. J. Effect of different sources of nitrogen on soil
reaction, exchangeable ions, and yields of crops. *Soil Sci.*, 61: 477, 1946.

Weeks, M. E., and Fergus, E. N. Effects of soil, soil treatment, seasonal variation, and variety on yield and composition of corn crops grown on Kentucky
soil fertility plots. *Kentucky Agr. Exp. Sta. Bull.* 485, 1946.

8

Phosphorus

Although the element phosphorus was discovered in 1669 it was not recognized as an essential nutrient for plants until many years later. When scientists began to study the response of crops to applications of different nutrients it was at once discovered that many soils are deficient in supplies of available phosphorus. Analyses of soils also showed the total quantity of phosphorus in most soils to be low. Much study has been given to the chemical compounds of phosphorus in the soil, the fixation of soluble phosphates when applied to the soil, the absorption of the nutrient by plants, and the functions of the element in plant nutrition. Pertinent points concerning the relationship of phosphorus to soil productivity will be discussed under the following general headings.

Discussion Topics

Phosphorus content of soils.
Removal of phosphorus from the soil.
Return and addition of phosphorus to the soil.
Phosphorus fertilizers.

PHOSPHORUS CONTENT OF SOILS

The type of material from which soils were derived and the climatic conditions under which they developed, the degree of weathering, and their organic-matter content are some of the factors that have influenced the phosphorus content of soils. The quantity of phosphorus in soils of different texture and from different regions will be discussed from the standpoint of the total amount present, the combinations or forms in which it occurs, and its availability for plant use.

Total Phosphorus in Mineral Soils. Great variability is a characteristic of the phosphorus content of soils. For example, Marbut [1] shows the amount of phosphorus in the A_1 horizon of sandy loams of podzolic origin to vary from a trace of 0.28 per cent and of silt loams

[1] *Atlas of American Agriculture,* Part III.

139

from a trace to 0.14 per cent. Also fine-textured soils in general contain more phosphorus than sandy soil developed under the same climatic conditions. This fact is illustrated by an average percentage content of the element in the A horizon of 0.039 for 15 sandy loams, 0.073 for 5 silt loams, and 0.10 for 8 clay loams of Eastern United States. Furthermore, the Iowa experiment station reports the phosphorus content of the surface $6\frac{2}{3}$ inches of 11 sandy loams, 19 loams, 24 silt loams, and 19 silty clay loams, derived from glacial till, to be 864, 1,205, 1,288, and 3,089 pounds per acre, respectively. It should be remembered, however, that there are many exceptions to this generalization.

That a loss of phosphorus has occurred in the A_2 horizon of podzolic soils is evident from the data in Table 27, as is also the fact that in

TABLE 27. PHOSPHORUS CONTENT OF SOIL GROUPS, PER CENT [*]

Podzolic Soils

	Sandy Loams 15 Soils		Silt Loams 5 Soils		Clay Loams 8 Soils	
Horizon	A	B	A	B	A	B
	0.039	0.092	0.073	0.093	0.103	0.068

	27 Soils			11 Soils		
Horizon	A_1	A_2	B	A_1	A_2	B
	0.037	0.030	0.084	0.079	0.059	0.064

Chernozems

	Silt Loams 6 Soils				Clay Loams 4 Soils		
Horizon	1	2	3	4	1	2	3
	0.105	0.100	0.083	0.087	0.052	0.035	0.052

Dark Brown and Brown Soils

	Sandy Loams 3 Soils			Silt Loams 5 Soils		
Horizon	1	2	3	1	2	3
	0.070	0.061	0.057	0.079	0.065	0.083

[*] Compiled from data in *Atlas of American Agriculture*, Part III.

sandy soils of the region there is some concentration of the element in the B horizon. Toth and Bear,[2] however, found no concentration of phosphorus in the B horizon of 17 New Jersey soils, most of them loams,

[2] *Soil Sci.*, 64: 198, 1947.

as the average content of the element was 0.043 per cent in the A horizon compared to 0.034 per cent in the B horizon and 0.032 per cent in the C horizon.

Soils of the semiarid regions are usually richer in phosphorus than are those of similar texture in humid areas, and also there is less variation in the amount of the element in different horizons. Fuller and

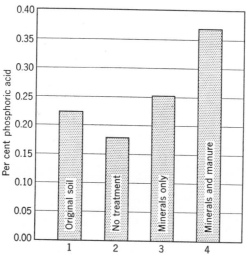

Fig. 20. Changes in the P_2O_5 content of a soil during 35 years of cropping to a rotation of corn, oats (2 years), wheat, and timothy. The mineral application consisted of 320 pounds of 16 per cent superphosphate and 160 pounds of muriate of potash applied annually. The annual application of cow manure was 16 tons. The soil was contained in cylinders. From *New Jersey Agr. Exp. Sta. Bull.* 604, 1936. Used with permission.

McGeorge,[3] however, found considerable variation in the amount of phosphorus in different depths of 7 calcareous soils from Arizona. In most cases the phosphorus content of the surface 6 inches was appreciably greater than that in lower depths, but in one instance the soil from 12 to 24 inches contained more of the element than the surface soil.

According to Marbut's data, soils of the Prairie contain about the same quantity of phosphorus as do the silt loams of podzolic origin. The 6 samples analyzed averaged 0.051 per cent phosphorus in the A horizon and 0.059 per cent in the B horizon. It is unfortunate that a larger number of samples were not taken. Data from the Iowa station, however, show the average phosphorus content of the surface soil of 79 Prairie silt loams derived from loess to be 0.058 per cent.

[3] *Soil Sci.,* 71: 315, 1951.

An appreciable change has taken place in the phosphorus status of soils long under cultivation. For example cropping has reduced the total phosphorus content of the plow layer of soils in areas of limited rainfall by somewhat less than 10 per cent according to Parker.[4] On the other hand the quantity of available phosphorus has increased because of the decay of organic matter. Figure 20 shows the change in phosphorus content of a New Jersey soil during a 35-year cropping period.

There has also been an increase in the supply of available phosphorus in soils devoted to the production of special crops in certain humid areas. This phenomenon has come about through heavy fertilization and is illustrated by the results of soil tests in North Carolina, as shown in Table 28. In the Southeastern states there is approximately 5 to 10

TABLE 28. EFFECT OF HEAVY FERTILIZATION ON AVAILABLE PHOSPHORUS SUPPLY IN SOILS AND RESPONSE TO ADDITIONS OF PHOSPHATE *

Cropping System	Quantity of P_2O_5 Usually Applied, lb.	Percentage of Soils Tested Ranking High or Low in Available P_2O_5		Percentage Increase from Application of 40 Lb. P_2O_5
		Low	High	
Tobacco and potatoes	115–120	11–13	82–84	0
Corn and cotton	27–55	20–40	43–81	4–7
Hay and pasture	1–19	66–76	16–24	48–82

* Compiled from data in Soil and fertilizer phosphorus in crop nutrition, *Agronomy*, IV: 418. Academic Press, New York, 1953. Used with permission.

times as much phosphorus added in fertilizer annually as is removed in crops, and in the East North Central states about twice as much. In the United States as a whole some 1,830,000 tons of it was removed from the soil in 1950 and 3,239,000 tons was applied. This leaves a net gain of 1,409,000 tons.

Phosphorus Content of Organic Soils. On a percentage basis organic soils are relatively high in phosphorus content compared to mineral soils. For example, Wilson and Stokes [5] found the average percentage of phosphorus in the surface foot of groups of soils from 5 muck areas in New York state to vary from 0.048 to 0.293. A more detailed summary of their results is given in Table 29. Harmer [6] reports the average

[4] Soil and fertilizer phosphorus in crop nutrition, *Agronomy,* IV: 408. Academic Press, New York, 1953.
[5] *Cornell University Agr. Exp. Sta. Bull.* 537, 1932.
[6] *Michigan Agr. Exp. Sta. Spec. Bull.* 314, 1941.

TABLE 29. LOWEST, HIGHEST, AND AVERAGE PERCENTAGES OF PHOSPHORUS
IN SOILS FROM THE PRINCIPAL CULTIVATED MUCK AREAS OF NEW YORK

	Area				
Range	Genesee-Orleans 13 Samples	Wayne 15 Samples	Oswego 12 Samples	Madison-Oneida 6 Samples	Orange 7 Samples
	0–12 In. Depth				
Highest	0.175	0.293	0.192	0.210	0.218
Lowest	0.070	0.052	0.048	0.105	0.052
Average	0.114	0.114	0.096	0.157	0.118
	12–24 In. Depth				
Highest	0.140	0.092	0.100	0.065	0.079
Lowest	0.035	0.009	0.035	0.035	0.031
Average	0.070	0.039	0.052	0.052	0.052

phosphorus content of 17 Michigan virgin mucks to be 0.12 per cent, with the percentage varying from 0.035 to 0.19. That fertilization has increased the phosphorus supply in cultivated mucks is shown by an average percentage of 0.22 in 12 cropped soils from Michigan.

The smaller amount of phosphorus in the second foot of soil than in the first foot is undoubtedly due to the greater degree of decomposition in the surface layer and to fertilizer application. Through decomposition a considerable decrease in volume of organic soils occurs with a resultant concentration of insoluble mineral matter. As a result the mineral material in much more than a foot of the original soil may be found in the surface foot of the decomposed soil. In this respect organic soils differ again from mineral soils in humid climates, as the B horizon of the latter frequently contains as much phosphorus as the A horizon or more.

If the phosphorus content of soils is expressed in terms of pounds per acre there is not a great deal of difference between the amounts in mineral and in organic soils; in fact mineral soils may average a little higher in phosphorus content. The variation, however, is not so great in organic as in mineral soils as none of them are reported as having only a trace of phosphorus.

Compounds of Phosphorus in Soils. Phosphorus occurs in soils in both organic and mineral combinations. The mineral fluorapatite, $[Ca_3(PO_4)_2]_3 \cdot CaF_2$, is the original source of much of the soil's supply of the element, and its occurrence in highly weathered soils indicates its resistance to decomposition. Hydroxyapatite, $[Ca_3(PO_4)_2]_3 \cdot Ca(OH)_2$, is also rather widely distributed in soils, and it was formerly thought that carbonate apatite $[Ca_3(PO_4)_2]_3 \cdot CaCO_3$ was not uncommon, especially in calcareous soils. More recent studies, however, have cast considerable doubt upon the existence of this mineral, although Fuller[7] in 1950 suggested that small quantities of applied phosphate may pass into this form. The evidence concerning the formation of this mineral is not conclusive according to Olsen.[8] Other compounds of calcium and phosphorus which are of more value from the standpoint of plant growth are dicalcium phosphate, $CaHPO_4$, and monocalcium phosphate, $Ca(H_2PO_4)_2$. Although the information concerning the presence of these salts in the soil is not too definite, it is quite generally agreed that the dicalcium phosphate is usually present, at least in small quantities, but that the mono compound occurs in only very low concentrations indeed. Applications of soluble phosphates will, of course, increase the amounts of both compounds temporarily. Proof of the occurrence of tricalcium phosphate, $Ca_3(PO_4)_2$, in the soil is yet lacking. Other complex compounds of calcium and phosphorus may be present under certain conditions.

The phosphate ion also combines readily with iron and aluminum. The combination may take the form of definite minerals such as dufrenite $[Fe_2(OH)_3PO_4]$, wavellite $[Al_3(OH)_3(PO_4)_2 \cdot 5H_2O]$, vivianite $[Fe_3(PO_4)_2 \cdot 8H_2O]$, or the phosphate may be held on the surface of hydrated iron and aluminum oxides. The combinations of phosphorus with iron and aluminum are more prevalent and stable in acid soils, and precise information as to their nature is not available.

Clay minerals containing hydroxyl groups, such as kaolinite, are able to adsorb the phosphate ion in greater or less quantities. It is assumed that the fixation occurs largely on the surface of the minerals although the ion may penetrate the crystal lattice to a small extent.

The quantity of phosphorus in the soil solution is always small, reports from different investigators indicating a concentration of from 0.1 p.p.m. to 0.5 p.p.m. of PO_4 in many soils. Some very fertile soils may contain 1.0 p.p.m. and many depleted acid soils less than 0.1 p.p.m.

Phosphorus in organic compounds makes up from 2.6 to 75.0 per cent of the total quantity of the element in soils according to Black,[9] although methods of determining the organic fraction are not entirely satisfactory. A study of seven Iowa soils by Pearson and Simonson[10] showed the quantity of organic phosphorus in the surface layer (0 to

[7] *Soil Sci.*, 70: 441, 1950.

[8] Personal letters, 1952.

[9] Soil and fertilizer phosphorus in crop nutrition, *Agronomy*, IV: 131. Academic Press, New York, 1953.

[10] *Soil Sci. Soc. Amer. Proc.*, 4: 162, 1939.

4 or 6 inches) to vary from 158 to 393 p.p.m. Also the percentage of the total phosphorus content in the organic form varied from 27.2 to 65.2. Fuller and McGeorge [11] found 31 per cent of the phosphorus in 19 Arizona soils to be present in organic compounds, and in 23 Colorado soils the percentage was 23 according to Greb.[12] Black [9] reports the quantity of organic phosphorus found in soils to vary from 18 p.p.m. to 1,679 p.p.m., the latter amount having been discovered in a peat from Finland. The quantity of phosphorus in organic combination decreases with depth below the A_1 horizon, a very small amount being present below 3 feet. The relationships between organic phosphorus, nitrogen, and carbon in mineral soils is also reported by Black [9] to average about 1:9:110, the ratio of N to P increasing with pH.

Phosphorus occurs in organic compounds in the bodies of both living and dead plants and animals of microscopic and larger size and in the products of partial decay of these organisms. Accordingly it is to be expected that the compounds are identical or similar to those found in the living organisms. Prominent among these is phytin and its derivatives. The calcium-magnesium salt of inosital phosphoric acid (phytin) is widely distributed in plants and constitutes the form in which much of the phosphorus in seeds is stored. In fact, 75 per cent or more of the phosphorus in seeds is in the form of phytin. Although cattle metabolize phytin, unfortunately some other animals do not. When a seed starts to grow the phytin content decreases and more inorganic phosphorus appears. The portion of the organic phosphorus in soils in the form of phytin varies considerably. Bower [13] found approximately 35 per cent of the organic phosphorus in the NaOH extract of Carrington and Webster soils to exist as phytin and 26.5 per cent of that in Fayette soil. Also phytin derivatives made up from 11.4 to 14.1 per cent. From a study of Canadian soils Wrenshall and Dyer [14] concluded that phytic acid forms two salts with ferric iron, $C_6H_6(PO_4)_6Fe_4$ and $[C_6H_{10}(PO_4)_6]_3Fe_8$, and also an aluminum salt. They consider it probable that these compounds exist in acid soils.

Other organic substances which contain phosphorus and are found in soils are the nucleoproteins. These are compounds of nucleic acids (polynucleotides) with proteins and are found in both plant and animal tissue. One of their activities appears to be concerned with the functions of the genes and chromosomes. Lecithin and other phospholipids

[11] *Soil Sci.*, 71: 45, 1951.
[12] Unpublished data (Master's thesis, Colorado A. & M. College).
[13] *Soil Sci.*, 59: 277, 1945.
[14] *Soil Sci.*, 51: 235, 1941.

are the third main group of organic compounds containing phosphorus which occur in soils. Bower [15] found that in a group of Iowa soils this form of phosphorus made up from one-third to one-half of the total organic phosphorus.

The Phosphorus Status of Tropical Soils. The great diversity in characteristics of soils in the tropics has been pointed out by Kellogg,[16] and also the marked variation in climatic conditions. In consequence any general statement of the phosphorus status of tropical soils would be inaccurate. Kellogg considers the phosphorus content of Latosols to be similar to that of the Red-Yellow Podzolic soils of the United States. The soils have a high phosphorus-fixing capacity, and tests for available phosphorus give very low results although the value of the methods used is not established for soils of this nature.

Mohr [17] presents a summary of the results of soil analyses made in the plantation region of Sumatra over a period of 25 years. The soils were divided into 7 groups, and the analyses were made by extraction with strong, hot acid. The average results for groups varied from 0.01 per cent to 0.06 per cent P_2O_5. In the groups the P_2O_5 content varied from 0 or a trace to 0.02, 0.03, 0.07, 0.14, 0.18, and 0.31 per cent, respectively. Evidently there is great variation in the phosphorus content of the soils, but experimental results indicate that except in young profiles a deficiency of available phosphorus is usually to be expected. Mohr points out that eroded soils in Sumatra are in need of all common nutrients and the addition of any one by itself is of little value. On the other hand, tobacco grows luxuriantly on recently cleared, tropical, high forest land because of the accumulation of nutrients in the humus.

On alluvial soil derived from marl and limestone ridges in East Central Java, an application of 87 kg. per hectare of superphosphate produced a yield of 20 quintals of paddy (rice) compared to 0.57 quintals on unfertilized soil and 0.69 quintals on soil fertilized with nitrogen. Results from eight experimental fields on "Bantam tuff loam" in West Java show marked but variable response to applications of superphosphate.

On the other hand, Sauchelli,[18] in reviewing an article by Ferrand,[19] suggests that the use of soluble phosphates be avoided except for crops

[15] *Iowa Agr. Exp. Sta. Res. Bull.* 362, 1949.

[16] An exploratory study of soil groups in the Belgian Congo. Institut national pour l'étude agronomique du Congo Belge, *Mémoir* 16, Brussels, 1950.

[17] *Soils of Equatorial Regions,* by E. C. Jul. Mohr. Translation by R. L. Pendleton. Edwards Brothers, Ann Arbor, Mich., 1944.

[18] *Phosphates in Agriculture,* p. 21. Davison Chemical Corp., Baltimore, 1951.

[19] *Le phosphore et son role en biologie.* Paris, 1949.

having a short growing season, because of the high fixing power of the soils for this nutrient. Rock phosphate is said to decompose fast enough to supply the phosphorus needs of many crops because of the rapid rate of mineral decay under the prevailing climatic and soil conditions. Also basic phosphates as well as rock are to be recommended because of the residue of calcium left.

The value of localized placement of phosphates in positions readily accessible to the roots of different crops is emphasized by several workers in order to reduce fixation of phosphorus and increase its effectiveness.

Phosphorus in Alkaline Calcareous Soils.[20]   Soils described as alkaline and calcareous contain calcium carbonate and have a pH above 7.0 but do not have a high percentage of exchangeable sodium, as do the "alkali" soils. Hibbard [21] considered the native phosphorus compounds in these soils to be mainly hydroxyapatite, fluorapatite, chlorapatite, wagnerite, wavellite, and organic substances, but probably other phosphates containing iron, aluminum, calcium, or manganese are present also. It is to be expected that calcium phosphates predominate, and attention will be centered on these compounds. Arizona and Colorado soils have been shown to contain rather large quantities of organic phosphorus even though their organic content is low. In fact, Fuller and McGeorge [22] state that the soils in Arizona contain only slightly less organic phosphorus than those in Iowa. An appreciable portion of the water-soluble phosphorus in these soils is considered to be organic.

In an extensive study of calcium phosphates Eisenberger et al.[23] found hydroxyapatite to be the most stable of these compounds in water. Olsen considers hydroxyapatite to be the final stable compound into which applied phosphorus passes. Studies have led to the conclusion that in calcareous soils phosphate is precipitated on the surface of calcium carbonate particles and that the carbonate may be precipitated on the surface of phosphate particles. In either event a decrease in solubility of phosphorus results. Phosphate is also precipitated on the surface of clay, the amount increasing as the quantity of calcium held by the clay increases. The amount of phosphorus occurring on the particle surfaces becomes highly important from the standpoint of plant utilization, as is pointed out on pages 149–150. In considering the

---

[20] A comprehensive discussion of the chemistry of phosphorus in calcareous soils is presented by Olsen in Soil and fertilizer phosphorus in crop nutrition. *Agronomy*, IV. Academic Press, New York, 1953.

[21] *Soil Sci.*, 31: 437, 1931.   [23] *Chem. Revs.*, 26: 257, 1940.

[22] *Soil Sci.*, 71: 45, 1951.

solubility of phosphates which have been applied and become "fixed" in the soil, it should be remembered that particle size has an influence on solubility. Some other factors bearing on phosphorus solubility will now be considered.

Soluble salts can be expected to have a marked though complicated effect on phosphate solubility in calcareous alkaline soils. The increase in solubility to be anticipated from the "salt effect" may be modified or nullified by an increased concentration of calcium ion because of the formation of more soluble calcium salts through the reaction of soluble salts with calcium carbonate. This increased concentration of a common ion (Ca) reduces hydrolysis of the calcium phosphates. As a result the effect of salts on phosphorus solubility will vary in different soils. Also the influence of salts on the absorption of phosphorus by roots is determined not alone by the effect on solubility but also by the nature of the salts and their influence on root membranes and on pH of the soil solution.

Several investigators have studied the relationship between soil pH and phosphorus solubility. McGeorge [24] placed the range of minimum solubility between pH 7.6 and 8.5, with an increase in solubility both above and below these values. On the other hand, Burd [25] placed minimum solubility near pH 7.0 and Gardner and Kelly [26] between pH 7.0 and 8.0. An average of results shows minimum solubility to occur between pH 7.0 and 7.5, according to Olsen.[27] In general the value of residual phosphorus is considered greatest in neutral soils, somewhat less in alkaline calcareous soils, and least in acid soils, especially those high in sesquioxides and kaolinite.

Correlations between the lime content of soils and phosphorus absorption by plants have been investigated by several workers. In soils containing between 1 and 4 per cent of lime, phosphorus absorption was found to be inversely proportional to the lime content, but when the amount of lime exceeded 4 per cent correlations were poor. Furthermore, additions of nitrogen fertilizers, such as $(NH_4)_2SO_4$ and NH_4NO_3, which produce acid reactions in the soil, increased the absorption of phosphorus when small amounts of calcium carbonate were present.

A higher proportion of the phosphorus in alkaline calcareous soils is soluble in weak acids and neutral salt solutions than in acid soils.

[24] *Arizona Agr. Exp. Sta. Tech. Bull.* 82, 1939.

[25] *Soil Sci.,* 65: 227, 1948.

[26] *Soil Sci.,* 50: 91, 1940.

[27] Soil and fertilizer phosphorus in crop nutrition, *Agronomy,* IV: 102. Academic Press, New York, 1953.

McGeorge [28] found 80 or more per cent of the phosphorus in Arizona soils to be extracted by 1 N HCl followed by 0.5 N NH$_4$OH. Attempts to measure phosphorus availability by methods used for fertilizers and non-calcareous soils have not been successful. For example, Lewis et al.[29] found that soils treated with citrate-soluble phosphorus gave only slightly greater yields than did unfertilized soil. On the contrary from 24.6 to 44.3 per cent of the water-soluble phosphorus added was recovered by three crops of lettuce. When water-soluble phosphates are added rapid fixation occurs with the establishment of a given level of availability, which varies little with time. In consequence the time of phosphate application is not so important as on non-calcareous soils. Ensminger and Lawson [30] studied the relationship between the lime content of a large number of irrigated soils in Idaho and the response of alfalfa, sugar beets, and potatoes to applications of treble super-phosphate. Their results showed the lowest response on soils containing 0.5 to 1.0 per cent of lime and a significantly greater response on soils with 1.0 to 2.0 per cent lime and on those having less than 0.5 per cent. No appreciable change in response to phosphate fertilizer was obtained in soils with higher lime contents than 1.0 to 2.0 per cent. It is suggested that a rather high response to phosphate fertilizer may be expected in soils containing approximately 1.0 per cent or more of lime.

A number of workers found a reasonably close correlation between phosphorus solubility in water charged with carbon dioxide and absorption of phosphorus by plants. McGeorge [31] reported a good correlation between phosphorus availability according to Neubauer tests and extraction with $CO_2 \cdot HO_2$. Also phosphorus absorption by plants increased as soil pH and quantities of Ca and CaCO$_3$ soluble in $CO_2 \cdot H_2O$ decreased.

In a comparison of methods for measuring available phosphorus, Olsen found that extraction with $CO_2 \cdot H_2O$ gave good results in soils with similar characteristics but a low correlation when soils of variable nature were tested. He proposed a method [32] involving the measurement of phosphorus on the surface of the particles in the soil. This value correlated closely with the A values found for 25 Western soils,

---

[28] *Ariz. Agr. Exp. Sta. Tech. Bull.* 82, 1939.

[29] *Soil Sci.,* 69: 55, 1950.

[30] *Soil Sci.,* 58: 253, 1944.

[31] *Arizona Agr. Exp. Sta. Tech. Bull.* 94, 1942.

[32] "The Use of Isotopes in Plant and Animal Research," proceedings of a conference at Kansas State College, 1952.

as shown in Table 30.   A further study of this method making use of a large number of soils is desirable.

TABLE 30.   CORRELATION OF A * VALUES ON 25 † WESTERN SOILS WITH SOLUBLE PHOSPHORUS BY VARIOUS METHODS AND WITH SURFACE PHOSPHORUS ‡

Method of Phosphorus Determination	Correlation	
	r	r^2
CO_2	0.128	0.016
H_2O	0.411	0.169
Bray	0.786	0.618
$NaHCO_3$	0.860	0.740
Surface phosphorus	0.952	0.905

* A is derived from the equation $A = B \dfrac{(1 - y)}{y}$ proposed by Fried and Dean (*Soil Sci.*, 73: 263, 1952) for measuring the available phosphorus in soils.

A = amount of phosphorus as available as the applied phosphorus.
B = rate of phosphorus application.
y = proportion of phosphorus in plants derived from the fertilizer.

† Seven of these soils had *p*H values below 6, seven contained $CaCO_3$ and had *p*H values above 7, and the *p*H values of the remainder were intermediate.
‡ Inorganic phosphorus in alkaline and calcareous soils. *Agronomy*, Vol. IV, Academic Press, New York, 1953, and also the original manuscript.   Used with permission.

Availability of Soil Phosphorus.   Because of the insolubility of iron and aluminum phosphates and of the very low solubility of the calcium phosphates, with the exception of monocalcium phosphate, plants in the majority of cultivated soils are forced to absorb their phosphorus from a very dilute solution of the element.   Sodium, potassium, and ammonium phosphates are quite soluble, but these salts occur in very few soils indeed, and when they are present other characteristics render the soil a poor medium for plant growth.   Magnesium phosphates are also more soluble than the calcium salts, but again few soils contain appreciable quantities of them.   The solubility of the calcium phosphates should be increased by addition of soluble salts if no interfering factors are present.   In the soil, however, the reverse action usually takes place because of the liberation of adsorbed calcium.

The age and degree of crystallization of the iron and aluminum phosphates have an effect on their availability to plants, according to Kurtz.[33]   Furthermore some workers believe that phosphorus adsorbed

[33] Soil and fertilizer phosphorus in crop nutrition, *Agronomy*, IV.   Academic Press, New York, 1953.

y the sesquioxides is used fairly readily by plants if the adsorption
apacity is saturated but that otherwise the utilization is low.   Additions
f lime to acid soils containing iron and aluminum compounds of
hosphorus tend to convert them into more readily available calcium
alts.   Results of Ohio experiments comparing the effect of lime appli-
ations with those of superphosphate on yields in a 5-year rotation are
hown in Table 31.   These data have been accepted by some workers

TABLE 31. COMPARATIVE EFFECT OF LIME AND SUPERPHOSPHATE ON THE
YIELD OF SEVERAL CROPS *

Average Yields for the
Period 1900–1933, bu. or lb. per acre

Soil Treatment	Corn	Oats	Wheat	Clover	Timothy
N, K, lime	45.3	43.0	18.6	2,393	2,795
N, K, superphosphate	41.9	49.6	28.5	2,221	2,346

* *Ohio Agr. Exp. Sta. Bull.* 553, 1935.

as evidence that phosphorus was liberated by the applied lime.   Other
investigators, however, have suggested that this conclusion is not entirely justified.

There are insufficient data to warrant a general statement concerning
the value of lime in the liberation of phosphorus for plant use, and undoubtedly the effect would vary greatly in different soils.   It is rather
generally assumed, however, that liming is a valuable practice in the
liberation of fixed phosphorus and in prolonging the availability of
applied phosphates in acid soils.

Not a great deal is known of the availability of organic phosphorus
to plants.   Black [34] pointed out that mineralization of organic phosphorus increases with a rise in temperature, especially above 25° or
30° C.

Rogers [35] and associates, in a study of the availability of phytin,
lecithin, nucleic acid, nucleotides, and calcium glycerophosphate in solution cultures to corn and tomatoes, found a ready utilization of phytin
and a moderate uptake of lecithin by both plants.   The other three
materials used were mineralized by enzymes on the roots of the two
crops to such an extent that a determination of their direct availability
was not possible.   On the other hand the organic phosphorus in a
water extract from a Webster silt loam was not absorbed by the crops

[34] Soil and fertilizer phosphorus in crop nutrition, *Agronomy*, IV: 139.   Academic Press, New York, 1953.
[35] *Soil Sci. Soc. Amer. Proc.*, 5: 285, 1940.

tested. Although most of the experimental data indicate that organic phosphorus is utilized to only a small extent, if at all, by plants there is not sufficient evidence to warrant a definite conclusion on the question.

In general there has been a gradual but slow decrease in the supply of available phosphorus in the plow soil, as a result of long-continued cultivation, unless heavy fertilization has been practiced. This trend is probably more pronounced in cleared forest soils than in prairie soils because of the smaller amount of organic matter they contained and its rapid decay. Also the increased loss of calcium resulting from cropping and leaching has permitted a larger share of the phosphorus to be converted into iron and aluminum phosphates.

There is a large supply of phosphorus in the subsoil which is accessible if the characteristics of the soil permit of ample root development, but which varies in availability.[36] The phosphorus in the B horizon of most soils is usually less available than that in the A horizon. The reaction of the C horizon also exerts a marked influence on the availability of the phosphorus content, although this is not true always, as was shown by Stanford and Pierre.[37] Also the availability varies with the plant species.

Utilization and Fixation of Applied Phosphates. Over 80 per cent of the phosphorus applied to American soils in fertilizers is in forms designated as available, and yet only a small part of it, usually from 5 to 15 per cent, is recovered in the first crop harvested after the application.

The problem of fertilizer phosphorus utilization is receiving renewed attention, and use of radioactive phosphorus permits the collection of more reliable data than formerly. The results show a great variation in the amount of the phosphorus in different crops obtained from fertilizer and also that the quantity varies in different locations. Undoubtedly soil characteristics, climatic conditions, rates of fertilizer application, fertilizer placement, and various other factors influence the quantity of phosphorus that crops will obtain from fertilizer. The results presented below[38] illustrate some of the points mentioned. In these tests ordinary superphosphate was applied, unless otherwise stated. Also the data are for the last sampling date of the season, and it is

[36] Winters and Simonson discuss in detail the relationship between subsoil characteristics and plant growth in *Advances in Agron.*, III: 1, 1951.

[37] Soil and fertilizer phosphorus in crop nutrition, *Agronomy*, IV: 265. Academic Press, New York, 1953.

[38] Mimeographed report of the North Central Regional Phosphate Conference, December 1951. Used with permission.

noteworthy that results for earlier samplings show different percentages of phosphorus utilization.

In Minnesota alfalfa obtained 15.8 per cent of its phosphorus content from fertilizer when 40 pounds of P_2O_5 were applied per acre and 45.9 per cent when the application was 120 pounds. On the other hand, results from two soils with 3 rates of application in Michigan showed that an average of only 2.6 per cent of the phosphorus in an alfalfa-bromegrass mixture came from the fertilizer. Oats, however, obtained 17.2 per cent of their phosphorus from fertilizer in Michigan. In North Dakota [39] 25.0 per cent of the phosphorus in sugar-beet roots was taken from fertilizer in one location and 46.5 per cent in another part of the state, and in Nebraska the percentage was 38.9. On the other hand 28.3 per cent of the phosphorus in potato tubers came from fertilizer in Nebraska and only 8.1 per cent in North Dakota.[39] Studies in Iowa showed the first cutting of red clover, alsike, and timothy to have obtained 18.8, 28.2, and 16.4 per cent of their phosphorus, respectively, from treble superphosphate. Many more examples of the variation in the percentage of plant phosphorus absorbed from fertilizer could well be given but it is unnecessary.

The percentage of the phosphorus in applied fertilizer that is used by crops can also be expected to vary with many conditions, including age of the plants, rate of fertilizer application, and soil characteristics. Studies involving radioactive phosphorus have confirmed this. The

TABLE 32. RECOVERY OF PHOSPHORUS BY OATS FROM SUPERPHOSPHATE APPLIED AT THREE RATES TO TWO MICHIGAN SOILS *

Per Cent of Fertilizer Phosphorus
Recovered by Plants at Indicated Dates

Lb. P_2O_5 per Acre	Hillsdale Sandy Loam			Miami Clay Loam		
	May 14	May 26	June 20	May 14	May 29	June 20
40	2.5	5.0	10.9	3.3	8.4	14.1
80	2.4	4.4	7.9	2.6	5.6	10.3
120	1.9	4.2	7.4	2.3	7.7	11.3

* Mimeographed report of the North Central Regional Phosphate Conference, December 1951. Used with permission.

data obtained by Lawton with oats on two Michigan soils are representative. They are presented in Table 32. It will be noted that a

[39] Data obtained through correspondence with Dr. D. L. Grunes. Also contained in mimeographed report of the North Central Regional Phosphate Conference, December 1951. Used with permission.

higher percentage of the phosphorus in the smaller applications has
been utilized and that total utilization is greater on the more fertile soil

The utilization of highly soluble phosphates is greater in the early
stages of plant growth than is the utilization of citrate-soluble phosphates
or of those containing a smaller percentage of water-soluble phosphorus
For example, Lawton found 5.3 per cent of the phosphorus in ammonium phosphate had been used by the oats at the first sampling date,
2.1 per cent of that in superphosphate, and only 1.0 of that in calcium
metaphosphate.

It is unfortunate that the loss of activity of P_{32} does not permit of
the measurement of the percentage of fertilizer phosphorus used by
crops during several years following its application. Some data from
field experiments bearing on this point are of interest.

As an average of 543 experiments in Alabama 60 pounds of applied
phosphate increased the yield of seed cotton by 241 pounds, which
contained 2.4 pounds or only 4 per cent of the applied phosphate.
Workers at the Ohio experiment station reported a recovery in crops
of 12.3 per cent of the applied phosphorus the first year, 8.9 per cent
the second year, and 7.1 per cent the third year. This makes a total
recovery in three years of 28.3 per cent of the phosphorus in the fertilizer. English experiments [40] show a recovery of from 24 to 34 per
cent of applied phosphorus in the course of 4 to 5 years. Pasture and
hay crops are more effective than grains or root crops in recovering
fertilizer phosphorus. Crops grown later use a portion of the remaining phosphorus but not a high percentage, although some workers believe the residual or fixed portion of the element is used to a greater extent than was formerly believed (Kurtz [41]). The extent of the utilization
is affected by the phosphorus status of the soil, being higher in soils relatively well supplied with the element. Experiments with fertilizer
containing P_{32} have shown that in the early stages of growth plants
draw a high percentage of their phosphorus from the fertilizer, but as
the root system is extended the soil supplies an ever-increasing proportion of the absorbed phosphorus.

The chemical compounds into which the residual phosphorus passes
and the possibility of making it available for crop use are pertinent
considerations for those interested in crop production. In soils well
supplied with lime the first process is the formation of insoluble or

[40] *Phosphates in Agriculture,* by Sauchelli. Davison Chemical Corp., Baltimore, 1951.
[41] Soil and fertilizer phosphorus in crop nutrition, *Agronomy,* IV. Academic
Press, New York, 1953.

difficultly soluble calcium phosphates. Hydroxyapatite and ultimately fluorapatite may be formed. It is Olsen's [42] opinion that in the presence of excess calcium carbonate a monolayer of phosphate ions is adsorbed on the surface of the carbonate particles. If the concentration of phosphorus in solution exceeds about 2×10^{-4} molar, dicalcium phosphate precipitates. Portions of the precipitate may remain in the soil for a considerable period (a year or more) in a metastable state, gradually becoming richer in calcium. Hydroxyapatite is the stable end-product, but it would be expected that some of the phosphorus would be present in various forms as monolayer or surface phosphate, dicalcium phosphate, transition forms, and hydroxyapatite.

In soils deficient in lime the phosphorus may be adsorbed on the surface of hydrated iron and aluminum oxides, or it may combine with soluble iron, aluminum, or manganese to form insoluble precipitates. The phosphate ion may also replace hydroxyl ions on the surface of certain clay minerals and hence become fixed by anion exchange. Considerable quantities of phosphorus may also become immobilized in the bodies of soil microorganisms especially when applications of readily decayable plant material are made.

There is considerable variability in the availability of phosphorus applied in manure and plant material because it is the portion of the element that is in inorganic form which is readily used by plants. Black [43] states that as an average the organic materials added to soils contain about equal amounts of organic and inorganic phosphorus. In average farm manure from 16 to 17 per cent of the phosphorus is considered to be readily available, but in well-rotted manure the percentage is higher. McAuliffe and associates [44] found the phosphorus in superphosphate to be somewhat more available to the first cutting of rye grass than that in manure, but cuttings taken near the end of the experiment had obtained about as much phosphorus from manure as they had from the superphosphate. Protein-bound phosphorus in sheep manure, from which the inorganic phosphorus had been removed, was only from 20 to 30 per cent as available as the phosphorus in superphosphate. Applied manure containing an unusually large amount of readily decayable organic matter may result in a biological tie-up of available phosphorus through a stimulation of the growth of microorganisms, in place of adding to the available supply of the element.

[42] Personal letter.

[43] Soil and fertilizer phosphorus in crop nutrition, *Agronomy,* IV: 141. Academic Press, New York, 1953.

[44] *Soil Sci.,* 68: 185, 1949.

A higher percentage of the phosphorus in young plant tissue is available than of that in mature plants. Fuller and Dean [45] reported that from 38 to 47 per cent of the phosphorus in the tops of wheat plants grown in solution cultures for 53 days was in mineral forms and 74 per cent of that in the roots. In soybean tops 55 per cent of the phosphorus was inorganic in form. The percentage of the total phosphorus in inorganic forms was reported by Pons and Guthrie [46] to be in wheat 3.8 to 4.8, in milo 5.9, in wheat straw 71, in cotton fiber 54, and in sweet potatoes 58. The percentage of total phosphorus and that in an inorganic form in several feedstuffs are shown in Table 33.

TABLE 33. PERCENTAGES OF TOTAL AND INORGANIC PHOSPHORUS IN SEVERAL FEEDSTUFFS *

Material	Per Cent Phosphorus		Material	Per Cent Phosphorus	
	Total	Inorganic		Total	Inorganic
Wheat straw	0.038	0.015	Potatoes	0.270	0.130
Mangels	0.069	0.006	Corn (grain)	0.303	0.028
Clover hay	0.183	0.080	Wheat (grain)	0.425	0.038
Meadow hay	0.210	0.120	Peanut cake	0.399	0.049
Alfalfa hay	0.238	0.122	Cottonseed		
Kale	0.261	0.135	meal	1.479	0.078

* Calculated from data in *Phosphates in Agriculture*, by Sauchelli.

Fuller and Dean [47] found young green plant tissue to supply 70 per cent as much phosphorus as did superphosphate to rye grass when equivalent quantities of the element were applied. Black [48] has arrived at the conclusion that the percentage of organic phosphorus in organic matters applied to soils is an index to whether phosphorus will be mineralized or immobilized by partial decay of the material. If the percentage falls between 0.15 and 0.78 mineralization will occur, but in the range of 0.0 to 0.21 per cent immobilization takes place. Just why the two ranges overlap is not known.

REMOVAL OF PHOSPHORUS FROM THE SOIL

The much smaller quantity of phosphorus than of potassium in soils is paralleled by the considerably lower amount contained in plants.

[45] *Soil Sci.*, 68: 197, 1949.
[46] *Ind. Eng. Chem., Anal. Ed.*, 18: 184, 1946.
[47] *Soil Sci.*, 68: 185, 1949.
[48] Soil and fertilizer phosphorus in crop nutrition, *Agronomy*, IV: 140. Academic Press, New York, 1953.

This advantage is offset to some extent by the concentration of the element in the portion of most crops that is harvested. Also, extremely small quantities are lost in drainage water, the amount seldom exceeding 0.9 pound per acre annually. On the other hand, heavy losses of phosphorus occur through erosion because it is contained largely in the organic matter and smaller-sized soil particles. Information concerning the removal of phosphorus from soils by crops and its functions in plant growth will be discussed in the following paragraphs.

Phosphorus Content of Crops. All classes of crops remove much smaller quantities of phosphorus from the soil than they do of nitrogen or potassium, as is shown by the data in Table 34.[49] The relatively

TABLE 34. QUANTITIES OF NITROGEN, PHOSPHORUS, AND POTASSIUM IN DIFFERENT CLASSES OF CROPS

Lb. in Average Yields

	7 Grain * Crops	10 Fruits †	10 Vegetables †	6 Legume Hays
Nitrogen	57.0	11.6	40.4	41.0
Phosphorus	8.3	2.3	7.7	11.9
Potassium	34.6	16.3	53.6	65.8

* Both grain and straw or stalks.   † Harvested portion only.

large amount of phosphorus in legumes is noteworthy, as is the small amount in fruits. The total amount of phosphorus removed from American soils by crops in a year has been estimated by Mehring and Parks as 792,465 tons.[50] Also the average amount of the element per acre per year removed by 100 principal crops in groups of states runs from 3.06 pounds for the West South Central states to 6.55 pounds for the Pacific group. The average for the United States is 4.37 pounds.

During the growing season phosphorus is found in largest quantity in the parts of the plant where cell division is taking place rapidly, but as maturity approaches it is stored largely in the seed or reproductive portion.

The addition of small increments of available phosphorus to soils deficient in this nutrient result in an increased growth of plants but a decreased percentage of phosphorus in them, according to Dean.[51] If

[49] The quantities of nitrogen, phosphorus, and potassium in commonly obtained yields of a number of crops are given in Table 21.

[50] Does not include phosphorus in plant residues usually returned to the soil, *Agricultural Chemicals*, October–November 1944.

[51] Soil and fertilizer phosphorus in crop nutrition, *Agronomy*, IV: 49. Academic Press, New York, 1953.

the additions are continued the percentage of the element in the plants will increase. In other words a curve depicting the phosphorus content of plants in percentage will be U-shaped if additions of phosphorus are used as abscissa and phosphorus percentage as ordinate. In general additions of considerable quantities of available phosphorus have resulted in increased percentages of the element in the leaves and stems of plants under most conditions. It has been found much more difficult, however, to increase the phosphorus content of the seeds. Results of experiments designed to determine the effect of phosphorus applications on the percentage of the element in the grain of crops have been decidedly variable.

Absorption of Phosphorus by Plants. Little is definitely known of the process by which phosphate ions enter plant roots although some progress has been made toward solving the problem. There is considerable evidence that plants absorb phosphorus in the mineral form primarily as the H_2PO_4 ion, and some workers believe that the extremely low concentration of this ion at high pH values accounts for the difficulty plants experience in obtaining phosphorus in alkaline soils. Pratt and Thorne,[52] however, maintain that in the pH range of 7 to 9 insolubility of phosphates is more important than physiological availability in determining intake of the element. Absorption of the HPO_4 and PO_4 ions is doubtless very slow compared to that of the H_2PO_4 ion. Arnon,[53] studying the nutrient intake of tomato, lettuce, and Bermuda grass in nutrient solutions, found that phosphorus might be lost rather than absorbed at a pH of 3 and that absorption was very small at pH 9, although other nutrients were taken up at the higher reaction. Phosphorus intake was greatest at pH values of 6 to 7. It has also been reported that a high intake of molybdenum is associated with a high phosphorus absorption.

Plant roots can absorb phytin and other inosital phosphates, but it is questionable whether they do so when growing in the soil. It is probable that the phosphorus of these compounds is converted into mineral forms by the soil organisms before it is absorbed. It has already been pointed out on page 151 that root enzymes can mineralize the phosphorus of nucleic acid.

Dean [53] points out that phosphorus intake by plants is slow at first, increases rapidly during the period of rapid growth, and then decreases. A graph showing the phosphorus intake of an annual takes the form

52 *Soil Sci. Soc. Amer. Proc.,* 13: 213, 1948.
53 Soil and fertilizer phosphorus in crop nutrition, *Agronomy,* IV. Academic Press, New York, 1953.

of a sigmoid curve. There is no "luxury consumption" of phosphorus as there is of potassium when supplies are large. It has been shown that plants do not absorb phosphorus from dry soil although they do absorb cations. Excretions from the plant root cells can affect absorption of phosphorus in soils. There is a considerable, but as yet unexplained, difference in the ability of plants to absorb phosphorus from different chemical forms and from different soils.

Studies by various investigators of the concentration of phosphate in solution necessary for optimum growth of different plants have led to results varying from 0.2 p.p.m. to 0.7 p.p.m. Some plants can absorb phosphate from solutions containing as little as 0.025 p.p.m. It is to be expected that several factors will influence the ability of plants to absorb phosphorus at a given concentration, including the concentration of other anions. A high concentration of NO_3 depresses the absorption of phosphate. In studying some 159 California soils Martin and Bingham[54] found grain crops responded to phosphate fertilization on 95 per cent of the soils that contained less than 0.3 p.p.m. of phosphate in the 1–10 water extract. There was no response to phosphorus fertilization, however, in 95 per cent of the cases in which the water extract contained more than 0.4 p.p.m. of PO_4. It has been shown that the rate of absorption of phosphorus by plants is considerably influenced by the concentration of the ion in the soil solution.

Activities of Phosphorus within the Plant. Phosphorus is intimately connected with the utilization of starch and sugar. Starch may be formed without phosphorus, but it is not readily changed to sugar. Phosphorus is also involved in photosynthesis.[55] Arnon[56] points out that photosynthesis involves phosphorus as well as carbon fixation. The element is a constituent of the cell nucleus, is essential for cell division, the formation of fat and albumen, and the development of meristematic tissue.

The straw of cereals is strengthened when sufficient phosphorus is present and the ratio of grain to straw is broadened. The element stimulates the development of roots and particularly of fibrous roots. It is also essential for blossom formation and fruit production. The quality of crops is improved by phosphorus, particularly that of grain crops. Leaf area in root crops is increased by the element, according

[54] *Calif. Agr.* 4: 7 and 12, 1950.

[55] H. G. Albaum, Metabolism of phosphorylated compounds in plants, *Ann. Rev. Plant Physiol.*, 3: 48, 1952.

[56] Soil and fertilizer phosphorus in crop nutrition, *Agronomy*, IV. Academic Press, New York, 1953.

to Russell,[57] without a decrease in the transportation of carbohydrates to the roots such as may result from nitrogen applications.

Crops insufficiently supplied with phosphorus are stunted and late in maturing. A discussion of plant symptoms indicating phosphorus deficiency is given on page 262.

Additions of sufficient amounts of available phosphorus to unbalance the nutrient relationships in the soil may cause premature ripening of crops with a corresponding decrease in yield. The result is most likely to occur on organic and quite sandy soils which are low in available potassium or nitrogen or both.

RETURN AND ADDITION OF PHOSPHORUS TO THE SOIL

Because of the tendency for phosphorus to be stored in the seed or fruit of plants, not so much of that taken from the soil during the growth period is returned in the stalks or straw of grain crops, when these are left in the field, as is true of potassium. Livestock also retain a larger proportion of the phosphorus than of the potassium that is contained in their feed. Under all types of farming therefore there is a rather large loss of phosphorus from the soil, and as a result most soils become deficient in this nutrient early in their cropping history. Some data concerning the amounts and means of phosphorus additions to soils will be presented in the following pages.

Return of Phosphorus in Plant Residues. The straw or stalks from commonly obtained yields of eight crops widely grown for grain contain only 2.49 pounds of phosphorus. The stalks and leaves of cotton plants producing a 500-pound yield of lint contain 3.49 pounds of phosphorus, and 2.49 pounds of the element are found in the stalks of tobacco plants yielding 1500 pounds of leaves. From these figures it is evident that the parts of crops frequently left on or returned to the field contain only comparatively small amounts of phosphorus. Other sources of this element must be found if the available supply in the soil is to be maintained.

The necessity of maintaining a high phosphorus content in the feed consumed by livestock is evidenced by the rapid appearance of symptoms of malnutrition in animals fed a phosphorus-deficient ration, as is shown in Fig. 21.

Manure as a Source of Phosphorus. The percentage of phosphorus in the food consumed by livestock that is excreted in the manure

[57] *Soil Conditions and Plant Growth*, p. 37. Longmans, Green & Co., London, 1950.

varies greatly. Fattening animals may excrete as much as 87 per cent,[58] but young growing animals fed a ration containing little concentrated feed may excrete only 50 per cent of the phosphorus they consume.

Fig. 21. A phosphorus deficiency in the feed is quickly reflected in the condition of the animals. The upper figure shows a cow fed on phosphorus-deficient straw, hay, a little grain, and later pasture. The lower figure shows the same animal 4 weeks after bone meal was fed while on pasture. From *Pennsylvania Agr. Exp. Sta. Bull.* 371, 1939. Used with permission.

Dairy cows receiving a good ration may excrete 63 per cent[59] of the phosphorus in their feed. Animals fed rations containing much grain excrete more of the phosphorus consumed than animals fed largely on roughage. It is estimated that the phosphorus in manure, applied to

[58] *Illinois Agr. Exp. Sta. Bull.* 209, 1918.
[59] *New Jersey Agr. Exp. Sta. Bull.* 730, 1946.

the acre of harvested crop land in 1947, ranged from an average of 0.087 pound in the West South Central states to 6.99 pounds in the New England states. For the United States as a whole the average is given as 1.96 pounds.[59a]

Unfortunately the quantity of phosphorus in manure as excreted is not a correct measure of the amount of the element applied to the soil. Losses in storing manure can be small, because virtually all the phosphorus is in the solid portion and little of it is water-soluble. With better methods of storage, such use of the pen-type barn and with the animals spending little time in open lots, a high percentage of the excreted phosphorus may be returned to the soil. With less efficient methods of storage, however, from 20 to 40 per cent of the phosphorus in the manure may easily be lost. If large quantities of concentrated feeds are purchased and the manure is well cared for, a relatively large amount of phosphorus may be applied to the soil in livestock farming. It should be remembered, however, that most of the phosphorus in manure is contained in organic compounds many of which decay comparatively slowly. As a result not over 16 to 17 per cent of the phosphorus content of manure can be considered readily available.

Fertilizers, the Main Source of Phosphorus. With the exception of intensive livestock enterprises in which large quantities of concentrated feeds are purchased, farmers must depend on fertilizers as a means of supplying phosphorus to their soil. Even on farms where all the crops grown are fed there is a constant loss of phosphorus through sale of animal products and in the handling of manure. These losses may not seem large when expressed in pounds per acre on an annual basis, but when considered in connection with the relatively small amount of phosphorus in most soils, and especially the very small quantity of the element in forms that will become available in a few years, they assume significant proportions.

There has been a rapid increase in the use of phosphate fertilizers in recent years. In fact, the use of phosphoric acid (P_2O_5) in fertilizer including rock phosphate increased approximately 47.4 per cent in the world during the period 1946–1947 to 1950–1951.[60] Table 35 gives the pounds of phosphorus applied to each acre in harvested crops in 1950 in the various groups of states. There has also been a considerable increase in phosphate use in other countries since the close of World War II.[60]

[59a] *Agricultural Chemicals*, October–November 1944.

[60] Soil and fertilizer phosphorus in crop nutrition, *Agronomy*, IV: 453, 454. Academic Press, New York, 1953.

Phosphorus

TABLE 35. ESTIMATED POUNDS OF PHOSPHORIC ACID (P_2O_5) APPLIED IN FERTILIZER TO EACH ACRE OF CROP LAND 1950 *

Group of States	Lb.	Group of States	Lb.
New England	25.0	East South Central	19.2
Middle Atlantic	29.8	West South Central	5.9
South Atlantic	29.4	Mountain	2.8
East North Central	16.8	Pacific	7.2
West North Central	3.5	U. S. average	10.8

* Soil and fertilizer phosphorus in crop nutrition, *Agronomy*, IV: 423. Academic Press, New York, 1953. Used with permission.

In the less intensively cropped areas of the United States more phosphorus is being removed annually from farm land than is being applied to it. Under intensive cropping, however, especially if special crops are grown, the reverse is true. Mehring and Parks give the relationship between removed and returned phosphorus for different regions, as is shown in Table 36.

TABLE 36. PERCENTAGE OF PHOSPHORUS REMOVED IN CROPS WHICH IS RETURNED IN FERTILIZERS AND MANURES *

Region	Per Cent	Region	Per Cent
New England	335	East South Central	218
Middle Atlantic	322	West South Central	53
South Atlantic	498	Mountain	74
East North Central	211	Pacific	83
West North Central	50	United States	142

* *Agr. Chemicals*, October and November 1949.

PHOSPHORUS FERTILIZERS [61]

Bones were the first materials high in phosphorus content to be used as fertilizers. English farmers were using bones as early as the seventeenth century, and by the middle of the nineteenth century bones were a common article of commerce. Around 1840 Liebig showed that treating bones with sulfuric acid resulted in a great increase in the solubility of their phosphorus content. It was Lawes, however, in 1842, who established the commercial practice of treating phosphates with sulfuric acid to make superphosphate. In the meantime Peruvian guano, which contains considerable phosphorus, came into use, being shipped

[61] A full discussion of phosphorus resources and processes of manufacturing phosphate fertilizers is contained in Fertilizer technology and resources, *Agronomy*, III: 117. Academic Press, New York, 1953.

into the United States in 1824 and into England in 1838. From these early beginnings the use of phosphate fertilizers developed rapidly and a number of different compounds of the elements are now used to enrich the soil.

Rock Phosphate. Phosphate rock is the source of a very high percentage of the phosphorus applied in fertilizers. Discoveries of the mineral in the United States date from 1867 when the South Carolina deposits were located. The Florida beds, which now furnish a high percentage of the phosphate used in the manufacture of superphosphates, were discovered in 1887. The demands of the Middle West for rock phosphate to be applied directly to the soil are supplied largely from Tennessee. The Arkansas and South Carolina deposits are mined very little at present, and utilization of phosphate from the mines in Idaho, Utah, and Wyoming is not large because of their distance from areas of heavy fertilizer use. It is estimated that the United States deposits contain some 13,291,543,000 long tons of rock phosphate. In 1949 some 8,877,474 long tons were mined, so that at the present rate of utilization our supply should last approximately 1,500 years, provided all the phosphate could be mined economically. Of the total production in 1949, 6,815,989 tons came from Florida and 1,344,470 tons from Tennessee and Virginia. The Western deposits supplied 826,474 tons.

The phosphates [62] in the Eastern deposits were precipitated from sea water or from water percolating through beds of limestone and are known as "phosphorites." They are forms of apatite, $Ca_{10}P_6O_{24}X_2$; in the formula X may represent fluorine, chlorine, or hydroxide. Some apatites, also occasionally designated as rock phosphate, have crystallized in large crystals from molten rocks and are of too low availability to be used for direct application to the soil.

Rock phosphate may be ground very finely and applied directly to the soil, or it may be used in the manufacture of superphosphates. Some 1,039,624 tons of rock were employed for direct application in the United States in 1951, and this made up 16 per cent of the total phosphorus applied as fertilizer. The East North Central states used 680,244 tons of rock phosphate for direct application. Illinois far exceeds any other state in the utilization of raw phosphate rock.

Many experiments have been conducted to determine the relative efficiency of rock phosphate and other phosphate fertilizers, primarily superphosphate. Results have varied widely with soil characteristics,

[62] *Phosphates in Agriculture,* by Sauchelli. Davison Chemical Corp., Baltimore, 1951.

climatic conditions, and cropping systems. Some crops such as the clovers, alfalfa, and buckwheat feed much more readily on rock phosphate than do wheat, barley, and root crops. Cook [63] showed a relationship between calcium utilization of a number of crops and their ability to obtain phosphorus from rock. The principle does not always hold, however. Summing up the results of experiments Rogers [64] states that in general from two to three times as much phosphorus must be supplied in rock phosphate as in superphosphate to obtain equal results in crop yields. However, many experiments have shown that rock phosphate and other basic phosphates have an appreciably higher availability in acid than in neutral or alkaline soils. For example, Russell [65] found a high availability of rock in acid soils located in cool moist climates. Rock and other basic phosphates are also recommended for use on tropical soils. McGeorge,[66] on the other hand, reported that rock and fused phosphates had very little value on the calcareous soils of Arizona. Applications of lime are also known to decrease the immediate effectiveness of rock phosphate. It has been suggested that this result comes about through the reversion of soluble phosphates as rapidly as they are formed in the soil. On the other hand, the efficiency of soluble phosphates has been shown to be increased by applications of lime to acid soils. The formation of calcium phosphates in place of iron or aluminum phosphates is one explanation of this result. Workers at the Illinois experiment station have recommended that rock phosphate be used to build up a reserve supply of phosphorus in the soil, but for wheat and other crops which absorb phosphorus only from readily soluble sources some superphosphate may also be used advantageously. In addition, if corn suffers root damage from insects or disease during the early stages of growth, some superphosphate applied in the hill or row is often desirable.

Basic Slag. Because of its high calcium and magnesium content, which often runs from 50 to 60 per cent in terms of the oxides, basic slag has given good results on acid soils, particularly for legumes. On account of the small quantity of the fertilizer produced in this country, around 40,000 tons, little attention is given to it.

Calcium Metaphosphate. By treating phosphate rock with gaseous P_2O_5 at high temperatures a salt of metaphosphoric acid is formed having the formula $Ca(PO_3)_2$ and commonly called "metaphos." Phos-

[63] *J. Amer. Soc. Agron.*, 27: 297, 1935.
[64] Soil and fertilizer phosphorus in crop nutrition. *Agronomy*, IV, 1953.
[65] *Minn. Agr., Bull.* 28, third edition, 1939.
[66] *Ariz. Agr. Exp. Sta. Tech. Bull.* 82, 1939.

phorus is first prepared by heating rock phosphate with silica (pebble) and coke in an electric furnace. The phosphorus is then burned to produce the gaseous P_2O_5. The fluid calcium metaphosphate formed in the process is drawn off as a slag, cooled, and then ground. The product contains 62 per cent or more of available P_2O_5, and both field and greenhouse trials have shown it to be a satisfactory source of phosphorus for commonly grown crops.

Superphosphate. Liebig, in his book published in 1840,[67] called attention to the preparation of soluble phosphate from bones by treatment with sulfuric acid. This discovery has had a great influence on the fertilizer industry, and the method, with refinements, is the basis of the preparation of a large part of the phosphate fertilizer used today. Liebig's announcement was followed in 1842 by the granting of a patent in England to Sir John Lawes for the manufacture of what he called superphosphate from mineral phosphates through treatment with sulfuric acid. The chemical reactions [68] involved in the acidulation of rock phosphate are numerous and involved, and there is no point in giving them in detail here. It is sufficient to say that the sulfuric acid acts on the phosphorites producing H_3PO_4 and HF. The H_3PO_4 then reacts with additional phosphorite forming $Ca(H_2PO_4)_2$ and HF. The final solid products are largely $Ca(H_2PO_4)_2 \cdot H_2O$ and $CaSO_4 \cdot \frac{1}{2}H_2O$ with some $Ca_2H_2(PO_4)_2$. The $CaSO_4 \cdot \frac{1}{2}H_2O$ will set in a short time producing a hard mass which must be ground before use. The reaction of H_2SO_4 with the phosphate rock is rapid, probably being completed within ten minutes. The decomposition of the remaining phosphorite by the H_3PO_4 is also rapid, being largely completed within an hour but continuing to a small extent for many weeks. This continued action and the setting of the calcium sulfate make it necessary to store superphosphate for a long period before it is ground for application to the soil or mixing with other fertilizer materials.

Ordinary superphosphate contains from 16 to 20 per cent of P_2O_5 (6.99–8.74 per cent P) and is used primarily to supply this nutrient. However, it contains in addition a large amount of calcium sulfate (40 to 50 per cent) and fractions of a per cent of eight or more other elements essential for plant growth. The beneficial effect of superphosphate on plant growth is sometimes undoubtedly due in part or largely to the nutrients other than phosphorus that it contains. The compo-

[67] *Organic Chemistry in Its Relation to Agriculture and Physiology.* Edited by Lyon Playfair, from last London edition. T. B. Peterson, Philadelphia, 1852.

[68] *Phosphates in Agriculture,* by Sauchelli. Davison Chemical Corp., Baltimore, 1951.

sition of a representative sample of superphosphate, as given by Sau-chelli,[69] is shown in Table 37.

TABLE 37. COMPOSITION OF A REPRESENTATIVE SAMPLE OF SUPERPHOSPHATE MADE FROM FLORIDA PEBBLE-ROCK PHOSPHATE AND OF AN AVERAGE TREBLE SUPERPHOSPHATE

Constituent	Per Cent in		Constituent	Per Cent in	
	Super-phosphate	Treble Super-phosphate		Super-phos-phate	Treble Super-phosphate
Potassium oxide	0.20	0.35	Iron oxide	1.00	1.36
Sulfur trioxide	31.00	3.40	Calcium oxide	24.00	19.99
Copper oxide	0.001–0.0064	0.015	Magnesium oxide	0.20	0.38
Zinc oxide	0.0005–0.02	0.005	Manganese oxide	0.02	0.019
Molybdenum oxide	0.002	. . .	Sodium oxide	0.20	0.97
Boron oxide	0.01	0.036	Phosphoric acid	20.00	46.29

Superphosphate is considered the most available of the commonly used phosphate fertilizers. Production of ordinary grade superphosphate in the United States reached 9,571,381 short tons in the year 1951–1952. This is an increase of 112 per cent over the 4,494,000 tons produced in 1941. Although most of the superphosphate is used in the preparation of mixed fertilizers an appreciable amount of it, as well as of other phosphates, is applied as such to the soil. For example, in the year 1949–1950 there were 1,855,000 tons of normal superphosphate applied directly, 265,000 tons of treble superphosphate, 2,000 tons of ammoniated superphosphate, 749,000 tons of rock phosphate, 287,000 tons of basic slag, and 10,000 tons of calcium metaphosphate.

Concentrated Superphosphate. Concentrated superphosphate is made by treating rock phosphate with H_3PO_4. This acid is obtained by treating phosphate rock with sufficient H_2SO_4 to liberate the H_3PO_4 and then filtering out the insoluble residues, or by oxidizing elemental phosphorus from an electric furnace to P_2O_5 and letting it combine in a gaseous state with H_2O. The first process is used much more extensively than the second. The concentrated phosphate is sold under the names "double" and "treble" or "triple" superphosphate. Because of their distance from heavy fertilizer-consuming areas much of the phosphate rock mined in the Western states is converted into concentrated superphosphate. This product can be economically shipped to the Central West whereas ordinary superphosphate cannot. Appreciable quantities of the concentrated product are, however, also produced in the Central West and South. Commercial production of treble super-

[69] *Phosphates in Agriculture,* by Sauchelli. Davison Chemical Corp., Baltimore, 1951.

phosphate in the year 1951–1952 amounted to 766,864 tons. In addition some 132,200 tons were produced by the T.V.A.

This product contains from 40 to 50 per cent P_2O_5, and its availability to crops is considered to be the same as that of ordinary superphosphate. In field trials, however, equal increases in crop growth are not always obtained from application of equivalent quantities of phosphorus in the two fertilizers. The result is frequently ascribed to the much smaller amount of sulfur contained in the concentrated product.

The composition of an average sample of treble superphosphate is given in Table 37. In addition to the constituents listed, small quantities of other elements are present, such as barium, strontium, arsenic, titanium, lead, iodine, bromine.

Ammoniated Superphosphate. Superphosphate is frequently treated with anhydrous ammonia or with aqueous ammonia. Up to 6 per cent of ammonia will be absorbed by ordinary superphosphate, but it is not considered advisable to add more than 3 to 4 per cent because of the formation of unavailable phosphates. Treble superphosphate will take up about 9 per cent ammonia without undesirable compounds being formed. The products formed in the ammoniation process are primarily monoammonium phosphate, diammonium phosphate, and dicalcium phosphate. Only a part of the monocalcium phosphate is changed to the dicalcium salt. In the event that more than 2.5 to 3.0 per cent of ammonia is added an appreciable quantity of tricalcium phosphate is formed, which is undesirable. Solutions of ammonia containing urea, nitrate of soda, or ammonium nitrate are also used to ammoniate superphosphate.

Ammoniated superphosphate is commonly used in the preparation of mixed fertilizers and a small amount is applied directly to the soil. The material is considered to be a satisfactory source of phosphorus although some experiments indicate that the availability of the phosphorus is somewhat less than that in the unammoniated phosphate.

Liquid Phosphoric Acid. The practice of putting liquid phosphoric acid in the irrigation water has developed in the Southwestern states, largely in California. The acid used contains about 55 per cent P_2O_5 and hence is a concentrated fertilizer. It can be shipped in iron drums or iron tank cars if it remains in the containers for only a short period. When diluted by the irrigation water the acid has not proved corrosive to crops, and the phosphorus is well disseminated through the soil and to probably a greater depth than with solid phosphate fertilizers. It may also be applied to crops after they have grown to an extent which makes application of solid fertilizer impractical. The phosphorus is quickly fixed in the soil by combination with calcium. Sometimes the acid is applied in furrows by means of a special drill attachment.

Nitrogen Phosphates. The economy of fertilizers containing both nitrogen and phosphorus and prepared by treating phosphate rock with nitric acid has long been recognized. However, technical difficulties have delayed the general utilization of the process. They include the corrosive action of nitric acid and of the slurries produced, and the tendency of the calcium nitrate formed to absorb moisture. Two types of processes employing nitric acid have been followed in Europe.[70] In one an excess of nitric acid is used, and then a part of the calcium nitrate is separated out and sold as such. The remaining solution is neutralized with ammonia before reduction to a dry form. In the second process sufficient sulfuric acid is added, after the initial reaction between nitric acid and rock phosphate, to convert the calcium nitrate into calcium sulfate. The slurry is then neutralized with ammonia, and usually potassium salts are added to make compounds such as 8-16-17, 11-9-20, and 13-11-12.

The shortage of sulfur and sulfuric acid have led to renewed efforts in the United States to perfect a practical method of preparing nitrogen phosphates by treating rock phosphate with nitric acid. One of the limitations in utilization of the process has been the expense of nitric acid manufacture. A new process devised by Daniels and Cottrell [71] gives promise of solving this problem, and the method is under test in pilot plants.

The treatment of phosphate rock with nitric acid is now being practiced in a limited way, and grades of fertilizer have been made which vary in nitrogen content from 8 to 17 per cent and in content of phosphoric acid from 11 to 35 per cent. Sometimes potassium salts have been added, with the formation of compounds such as 14-14-14, 11-11-11, and 12-11-11. A plant to make the latter grade was put into operation at South Point, Ohio, in 1953. Use is made of a mixture of H_2SO_4 and HNO_3, and the product is ammoniated with anhydrous ammonia. Potash salts are added. The final product is said to be in a granular and free-flowing condition.

The essential compounds in the final product are largely dicalcium phosphate, ammonium nitrate, and ammonium phosphate. One of the difficulties to be overcome in the process has been the loss of considerable nitrogen on drying and the decrease in availability of the phosphorus.

[70] *Fertilizer Resources and Requirements of the United States.* Prepared for the President's Materials Policy Commission, 1952.
[71] *Ind. Eng. Chem., 40,* 9: 17, 1948.

Bone Meal. Fresh bones contain approximately 23 per cent ash, of which some 87 per cent is calcium phosphate. Although bone is usually steamed to remove the fat and gelatin, the product has an availability considerably below that of superphosphate and is more effective on acid than on neutral soils. A large percentage of the bone meal manufactured is now used in animal feeds. The phosphoric acid content varies from 20 to 30 per cent and the nitrogen percentage between 1 and 2.

Tankage containing much bone is sometimes treated with sulfuric acid. Also bone black, used as a clarifying agent in sugar manufacture, is frequently acidified. Treatment with sulfuric acid transforms the phosphate in bones into monocalcium phosphate just as it does in rock phosphate. Accordingly the product is similar in availability to superphosphate.

Availability of Fertilizer Phosphorus. It is generally agreed that a soluble inorganic phosphate may be utilized by plants. Also it has been demonstrated that under many conditions plants can utilize quite freely some phosphates which are not water-soluble. Accordingly much study has been devoted to the development of a chemical method which will more accurately determine the availability of phosphates than does water solubility. The chemical methods devised vary somewhat in Europe and America, but all make use of weak organic acids or their salts. In this country solubility in an ammonium citrate solution is accepted as a measure of availability. This solution will dissolve dicalcium phosphate and possibly a certain amount of other phosphates which are not soluble in water. In testing rock phosphate and basic slag a citric acid solution is used, but the phosphate so dissolved is not designated as available. In fact there is a recognized difference in the absorption by various plants of citric acid-soluble phosphorus from different carriers.

Also, there is a variation in the availability of phosphorus soluble in ammonium citrate under different soil conditions. For example, studies in Idaho, Montana, and Arizona have shown that water-soluble phosphates are used by crops growing in alkaline calcareous soils much more efficiently than are phosphates which are soluble in ammonium citrate but not in water. Furthermore, there is a variation in the availability of ammonium citrate-soluble phosphorus from different carriers. Olsen [72] and his associates, in a study involving the response of sugar beets, wheat, barley, and potatoes to several sources of phosphorus in Colorado and of alfalfa in Arizona, Idaho, and Colorado, found consid-

[72] *Colorado Agr. Exp. Sta. Tech. Bull.* 42, 1950.

erable variation in the ability of crops to utilize phosphorus from different carriers. In addition the same crop varied in the amount of phosphorus it obtained from a given carrier during early and later

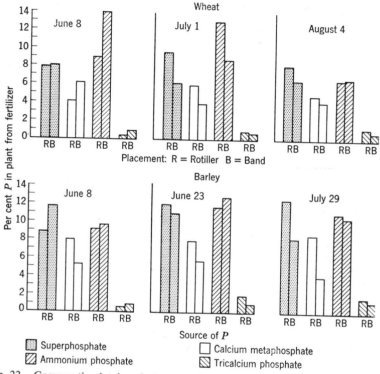

Fig. 22. Comparative intake of phosphorus from different carriers by wheat and barley at different stages of growth on Fort Collins loam. Note the much greater absorption of phosphorus by wheat in the early growth period from ammonium phosphate than from superphosphate. But when the plant approached maturity it contained more phosphorus obtained from superphosphate than from the ammonium salt. On the other hand, young barley absorbed phosphorus from superphosphate about as readily as it did from ammonium phosphate. Calcium metaphosphate and tricalcium phosphate were inferior sources of phosphorus in this soil. From *Colorado Agr. Exp. Sta. Tech. Bull.* 42, 1950.

periods of its growth. Figure 22 illustrates these points. The fertilizers tested contain P_{32} and included 20 and 43 per cent superphosphate, calcium metaphosphate, dicalcium phosphate, alpha tricalcium phosphate, ammonium phosphate (11-48-0), and liquid phosphoric acid. The alpha tricalcium phosphate furnished less phosphorus to the crops than did the other carriers. The great variation in the proportion of the phosphorus used by the same crop from a given fertilizer in different locations and by the same crop from different carriers is shown by the data in Table 38.

TABLE 38. TOTAL PHOSPHORUS IN ALFALFA, THE AMOUNT OBTAINED FROM DIFFERENT FERTILIZERS IN DIFFERENT STATES, AND THE PERCENTAGE OF FERTILIZER PHOSPHORUS USED (2 CUTTINGS IN ARIZONA AND COLORADO, 1 CUTTING IN IDAHO)

Fertilizer	State	P_2O_5 in Crop, lb. per acre	P_2O_5 from Fertilizer, lb. per acre	Percentage Fertilizer P_2O_5 Used
Superphosphate	Arizona	20.4	0.58	1.45
	Colorado	24.8	0.95	2.38
	Idaho	34.0	2.45	6.12
Ammonium phosphate	Arizona	19.2	0.30	0.75
	Idaho	34.2	2.00	5.00
Calcium meta-phosphate	Arizona	17.4	0.55	1.38
	Colorado	27.6	1.15	2.87
	Idaho	32.6	1.48	3.70
Alpha tricalcium phosphate	Arizona	17.8	0.16	0.41
	Colorado	24.5	0.25	0.62
	Idaho	33.9	0.58	1.45
Superphosphate	Colorado	27.9	1.57	1.96
Phosphoric acid	Colorado	27.6	1.98	2.48
None	Arizona	18.6	. . .	. . .
	Colorado	23.7	. . .	. . .
	Idaho	32.0	. . .	. . .

Many tests of the availability of different phosphates have been conducted upon the soils of humid regions. Results have varied with soil conditions, primarily with the reaction and phosphorus supply of the soil. Although crops vary in their feeding power on the phosphates tested, in general there has not been any great difference in the availability of superphosphate, calcium metaphosphate, and dicalcium phosphate on acid soils. There is evidence that water-soluble phosphates are used somewhat more readily by plants in the early stages of growth.

Movement of Phosphorus in Soils and Fertilizer Placement. Few phosphates are soluble, and hence when a completely water-soluble fertilizer is desired use is commonly made of ammonium, potassium, or occasionally sodium phosphate. The insolubility of most phosphates presents problems in obtaining a desirable distribution of phosphate fertilizers in the root zone of crops and of maintaining the applied phosphorus in an available condition. When soluble phosphates are applied the phosphorus is rendered insoluble approximately as soon as it comes in contact with the soil. Thus, a very limited distribution in the soil is obtained. Furthermore, the movement of phosphorus in the soil is inappreciable, and consequently phosphate fertilizers must be placed in the soil where it is desirable to have them, as far as is practical. Implements that are designed to place fertilizer more than a few inches

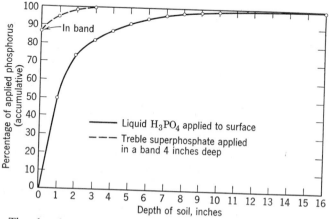

Fig. 23. The phosphorus in fertilizer remains largely in the soil area to which it is applied. Liquid phosphoric acid penetrates the soil to a greater depth than does the phosphorus in superphosphate, as is shown by the curve. This calcareous soil retained 85 per cent or more of the applied phosphorus in the surface 4 inches. From *Colorado Agr. Exp. Sta. Tech. Bull.* 42, 1950.

deep require additional power to operate, and increased crop response has not yet indicated that their use is justified. Tillage after phosphate application results in some further distribution of the nutrient through the soil. Efforts to prepare organic phosphates which will move through the soil with little fixation have not yet proved feasible. The movement of liquid phosphoric acid and of treble superphosphate applied to an alkaline soil was studied by Olsen et al.[73] Although 0.11 per cent of the phosphoric acid was found at a depth of 15 to 16 inches, 82.3 per cent of it remained in the surface 3 inches of soil. The treble superphosphate did not penetrate so deeply, and from 98 to 99 per cent of it was detected in the soil within 2 inches of the zone of application, and from 86.7 to 95.7 per cent did not move out of the band in which it was applied. The movements of the two sources of phosphorus are

[73] *Colorado Agr. Exp. Sta. Tech. Bull.* 42, 1950.

shown in Fig. 23. Ulrich [74] and associates also found that liquid phosphoric acid applied at the rate of 2,300 pounds P_2O_5 per acre to a loam of high phosphorus-fixing capacity penetrated to a depth of 11 inches in 43 days, although 86 per cent of the amount applied remained in the top 6 inches of soil.

Another aspect of the rapid fixation of phosphorus in soils is the greatly reduced availability of the nutrient. In consequence although thorough distribution of phosphate in the soil is desirable from the viewpoint of root contact with it, the reduced effectiveness of the fertilizer makes its dissemination inexpedient. To overcome the disadvantages of phosphorus fixation it is customary to place phosphate fertilizer in bands near the seed or to drop it in the hill for crops so planted. This practice has led to a greater efficiency in the use of fertilizer high in phosphate content. Another effort to reduce fixation consists of forming the fertilizer into pellets or compact granules. Fertilizer so prepared exposes less surface to the soil, thus reducing fixation, is more easily applied, and does not cake so readily during storage. The question of whether pelleted fertilizer is more effective in crop production is not fully answered.

REFERENCES

Bower, C. A. Studies on the forms and availability of soil organic phosphorus. *Iowa Agr. Exp. Sta. Res. Bull.* 362, 1949.

Dean, L. A. Fixation of soil phosphorus. *Advances in Agron.,* I: 391, 1949.

Haseman, J. F., Brown, E. H., and Whitt, C. D. Some reactions of phosphate with clays and hydrous oxides of iron and aluminum. *Soil Sci.,* 70: 257, 1950.

Lockett, J. L. Nitrogen and phosphorus changes in the decomposition of rye and clover at different stages of growth. *Ibid.,* 45: 13, 1938.

McAuliffe, C., Peech, M., and Bradfield, R. Utilization by plants of phosphorus in farm manure: II. Availability to plants of organic and inorganic forms of phosphorus in sheep manure. *Ibid.,* 68: 185, 1949.

Midgley, A. R. Phosphate fixation in soils, a critical review. *Soil Sci. Soc. Amer. Proc.,* 5: 24, 1940.

Midgley, A. R., and Deinklee, D. E. The availability to plants of phosphates applied with cattle manure. *Vermont Agr. Exp. Sta. Bull.* 525, 1945.

Olsen, S. R., Schmehl, W. R., Watanabe, F. S., Scott, C. O., Fuller, W. H., Jordan, J. V., and Kunkel, R. Utilization of phosphorus by various crops as affected by source of material and placement. *Colorado Agr. Exp. Sta. Tech. Bull.* 42, 1950.

Parker, F. W. "Phosphorus Status and Requirements of Soils in the United States," in Soil and fertilizer phosphorus in crop nutrition, *Agronomy,* IV. Academic Press, New York, 1953.

Pierre, W. H. The phosphorus cycle and soil fertility. *J. Amer. Soc. Agron.,* 40: 1, 1948.

[74] *Soil Sci.,* 64: 17, 1947.

Proceedings of the First Commonwealth Conference on Tropical and Subtropical Soils, 1948. *Tech. Communication, Commonwealth Bur. Soil Sci.,* 46, 1949.

Rogers, H. T., Pearson, R. W., and Pierre, W. H. Absorption of organic phosphorus by corn and tomato plants and the mineralizing action of exoenzyme systems of growing roots. *Soil Sci. Soc. Amer. Proc.,* 5: 285, 1940.

Salter, R. M., and Barnes, E. E. The efficiency of soil and fertilizer phosphorus as affected by soil reaction. *Ohio Agr. Exp. Sta. Bull.* 553, 1935.

Sauchelli, V. *Phosphates in Agriculture.* The Davison Chemical Corp., Baltimore, 1951.

Soil and fertilizer phosphorus in crop nutrition, *Agronomy,* IV. Academic Press, New York, 1953. Edited by W. H. Pierre and A. G. Norman.

Toth, S. J., and Bear, F. E. Phosphorus adsorbing capacities of some New Jersey soils. *Soil Sci.,* 64: 199, 1947.

9

Potassium

The essentiality of potassium in plant growth was known for many years before its use in fertilizers became common. Liebig's discussions in 1860 called attention to the value of potassium compounds as fertilizers and stimulated their use. The functions of potassium in plant growth have been and are the subject of many investigations, and the combinations or forms in which it exists in the soil have been intensively studied. Although potassium is lost in drainage water in considerable quantities it is nevertheless adsorbed by the soil colloids rapidly and in appreciable quantities when applied in soluble forms. Potassium will be discussed as a soil constituent and a plant nutrient under several headings.

Discussion Topics

Potassium content of soils.
Removal of potassium from the soil.
Addition and return of potassium to the soil.
Potassium fertilizers.

POTASSIUM CONTENT OF SOILS

During the earlier years of study of soils much attention was given to the total potassium content. It soon became evident, however, that the forms or physicochemical combinations in which the element existed in the soil were of much more importance to plant growth than was the total quantity present. Much study has been devoted to this subject.

Quantity of Potassium in Soils. The amount of potassium in soils varies greatly and on the average is considerably larger than the amounts of phosphorus or nitrogen present. The wide variation in the potassium content of soils of similar texture is brought out by the data in Table 39, as is the larger potassium supply in silt loams and clay loams than in sandy loams. Because soils are derived from parent materials which vary greatly in their content of potassium-bearing minerals it is to be

TABLE 39. Percentage Potassium Content of Soils of Different Texture and from Dry and Humid Climates *

Climatic Zone	Humid				Arid and Semi-arid
Number and Soil Class	30 Sandy Loams	25 Silt Loams	9 Clay Loams	53 Organic Soils	16 Silt Loams
Surface or A horizon					
Highest	2.09	2.29	2.41	0.47	2.45
Lowest	Trace	0.77	0.51	0.08	1.53
Average	0.51	1.39	1.47	0.16	2.05
Subsoil or B horizon					
Highest	2.22	2.26	2.49	0.22	2.39
Lowest	0.09	0.69	0.40	0.06	1.14
Average	0.60	1.53	1.57	0.11	1.94

* Data for mineral soils compiled from those in *Atlas of American Agriculture*, Part III, by C. F. Marbut.

expected that the percentages of this element in soils, even in those of similar texture, will be quite different. Also, because potassium-carrying minerals weather into clay fairly readily, soils containing appreciable quantities of clay may be expected to have above average potassium contents if other factors involved are similar. Furthermore the weathering of potassium minerals to clay-sized particles and also the strong fixation of the potassium ion by colloidal material lead to an enrichment in this element of the B horizon of many soils of humid climates. This situation is not always true, however. For example, Marbut [1] reports 0.20 per cent potassium in the B horizon of Greenville fine sandy loam from Butler County, Alabama, compared to 0.30 per cent in the A horizon. Likewise fine-textured soils are not always richer in potassium than are those of coarser texture.

Soils developed in arid and semiarid regions generally contain more potassium than those of similar texture developed in humid areas both because of insufficient water to leach soluble material down into the soil profile and because the colloids do not become unsaturated and move downward as they do in the podzolization process. Also the potassium content of the surface horizon is equal to, if not slightly greater than, that of the subsurface or subsoil.

The quantity of potassium in mucks and peats is small compared to the amount in average mineral soils. The solubility of the potassium

[1] *Atlas of American Agriculture*, III, "Soils of the United States."

contained in plant tissue probably accounts for this situation. Also the quantity in the second foot is appreciably lower than that in the first foot, according to the data from New York.[2] The limited supply of potassium in organic soils as well as in those of sandy texture has long been recognized, as evidenced by the recommendation of fertilizers rich in this nutrient for use on these lands. A survey of data from other states and countries shows the potassium content of New York peats and mucks to be quite representative for this group of soils, although the average may be slightly high.

Potassium Compounds in Soils. Although the total quantity of potassium in soils is of interest and of some value in anticipating the needs of various soils for potassium fertilizers, the quantities of this element in different chemical combinations are of more significance from the viewpoint of plant growth. The potassium supply of mineral soils has come primarily from orthoclase, microcline, muscovite, and biotite although other feldspars and micas have augmented the supply and in limited areas leucite has been a contributor. A large percentage of the potassium, possibly 90 to 98 per cent, still exists in these minerals. An appreciable quantity of this element, 1 to 10 per cent [3] according to some investigators, exists in a "fixed" or difficultly exchangeable form in the soil colloids. Exactly how these potassium ions are held is not known, but Russell [4] points out the possibility of their fitting into the hexagonal spaces in the surface oxygen sheets of the clay minerals. In this position they would touch 6 oxygen atoms and lie close to an hydroxyl group. It is also possible that in certain minerals similar to muscovite the sheets are so arranged that the hexagonal spaces lie opposite each other with 1 potassium ion occupying both spaces. It would thus be in contact with 12 oxygens and near 2 hydroxyl groups. Potassium ions held in either position described would be very difficult to replace. Potassium applied in soluble forms may first be adsorbed and then pass into the fixed or non-replaceable condition, or it is conceivable that potassium may pass directly from solution into the fixed form. A third fraction of the potassium, possibly not more than 1 to 2 per cent in most soils, may exist in an easily exchangeable position in the colloids and in the soil solution. Also a small quantity of potassium may be held as a constituent of organic matter, particularly if an appreciable quantity of fresh plant residues is present. The proportion

[2] *Cornell University Agr. Exp. Sta. Bull.* 537, 1932.
[3] Some workers report as much as 11 to 18 per cent. *Soil Sci. Soc. Amer. Proc.,* 5: 152, 1940.
[4] *Soil Conditions and Plant Growth,* p. 110. Longmans, Green & Co., London, 1950.

of the exchange capacity of soils in humid climates that is satisfied by potassium is small, but in some soils in arid regions it is comparatively high.

Availability of Soil Potassium. The ease with which plants may utilize the potassium held in the different forms described in the preceding section is pertinent to soil productivity. It is generally assumed that easily exchangeable ions are readily available for plant use. In fact the quantity of replaceable potassium is generally taken as a measure of the available supply of this element, although, as was pointed out by Reitemeier,[5] various factors prevent the assumption from being universally correct. For example, Volk [6] concluded that a measurement of exchangeable potassium as an indication of the need for further additions of the element was inaccurate for 35 per cent of the Alabama soils studied. On the other hand, Bray [7] considers exchangeable potassium as the only important available source of the element during a given season in cornbelt soils, notwithstanding the fact that these soils release non-exchangeable potassium at a relatively rapid rate. DeTurk et al.[8] observed a decrease of 40 per cent in the replaceable potassium in some Illinois soils during the growing season, but the supply was restored by the following spring. Also Lilleland [9] found a decrease in exchangeable potassium in samples taken at 1-foot intervals to a depth of 4 feet in 21 prune orchards. The reduction in potassium content was ascribed to extraction of the nutrient by the tree roots and its return to the surface soil in fallen leaves. Furthermore, DeTurk and associates presented evidence of a definite equilibrium between the replaceable and the non-replaceable potassium in a number of soils. Also it has been shown by several investigators that plants cannot use all the replaceable potassium, and plants vary considerably in their ability to utilize both exchangeable and non-exchangeable forms of the element.

Potassium in the soil solution and that in organic matter, because it is water-soluble, can be absorbed readily by plant roots unless some factor, such as the concentration of other ions, interferes. On the other hand fixed potassium ions are considered to pass into an available state at a relatively slow rate. But again this change takes place at different rates in soils with different characteristics. The change is thought to be accelerated by a low level of exchangeable potassium. Although most of the fixed potassium passes into the exchangeable form before being released to the soil solution, a small part may pass directly into solution. The dynamic nature of the different forms of potassium in the

[5] *Advances in Agron.*, III: 117. Academic Press, New York, 1951.
[6] *J. Amer. Soc. Agron.*, 34: 188, 1942.　[8] *Ibid.*, 53: 1, 1943.
[7] *Soil Sci.*, 66: 83, 1948.　[9] *Ibid.*, 34: 11, 1932.

soil and the speed with which one form passes into another, whether it be into a more or a less available state, are of great significance in plant nutrition. Bray [10] suggested that in investigating the potassium status of a soil one should be more interested in whether the non-replaceable potassium can maintain a high level of replaceable potassium for a

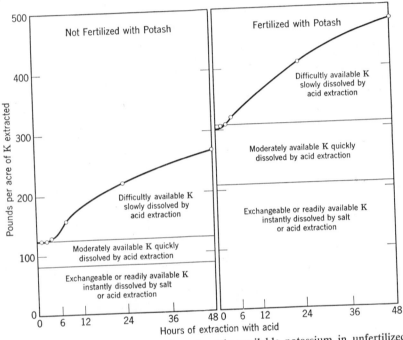

Fig. 24. Amounts of readily and moderately available potassium in unfertilized and potassium-fertilized Antigo silt loam and slow solution of difficultly available forms. Extractant used was 0.5N HCl. Much of the applied potassium has passed into the exchangeable form, and a considerable amount has become moderately available. A small portion also has passed into a difficultly available state. From *Soil Sci. Soc. Amer. Proc.*, 10: 82, 1945. Courtesy of Attoe and Truog.

considerable time than in the quantity of the element actually in a replaceable state. The relative quantities of difficultly available, moderately available, and readily available potassium, as measured by acid extraction, in a silt loam and the effects of potassium fertilization on the quantities of the element in these forms, as determined by Truog, are shown in Fig. 24.

Plants may remove appreciably more potassium from a soil than is contained in the readily available forms, as the data by Bear [11] and

[10] *Soil Sci. Soc. Amer. Proc.*, 3: 101, 1939.
[11] *Soil Sci.*, 58: 139, 1944.

associates show (Table 40). It will be noted that in 8 cases out of the 16 reported the crops removed more potassium than was contained in

TABLE 40. QUANTITIES OF EXCHANGEABLE POTASSIUM IN SOILS BEFORE GROWING SEVEN CROPS OF ALFALFA AND QUANTITIES REMOVED IN THE CROPS *

Soil Series	Potassium Content †		Soil Series	Potassium Content †	
	Soil	Crop		Soil	Crop
Washington	467	655	Merrimac	385	330
Hoasic	418	499	Fox	512	333
Lakewood	19	96	Gloucester	329	238
Dover	627	473	Hagerstown	567	210
Bermudiar	460	548	Whippany	373	156
Colts Neck	369	447	Sassafras	157	160
Lansdale	967	519	Sassafras	0	137
Chester	488	800	Papakating	937	132

* *Soil Sci.*, 58: 145, 1944. Williams & Wilkins Co., Baltimore. Used with permission.

† In milligrams per pot of soil or the crops grown thereon.

an exchangeable state. The kind of crop grown influences to some extent the use made of non-exchangeable potassium, and it would also be assumed that the supply of exchangeable potassium would be a contributing factor. However, it has been shown that plants may draw heavily on the non-exchangeable potassium even when a considerable quantity of the element is present in an exchangeable form. For example, Chandler [12] and associates cropped 11 soils intensively to ladino clover, with the following average results in pounds per 2,000,000 pounds of soil: exchangeable potassium before cropping, 175; after cropping, 70; potassium contained in crop, 218; non-exchangeable potassium used, 113. It is of interest that one soil contained as much exchangeable potassium after cropping as it did before, thus indicating that all the element used came from the non-exchangeable supply. It is evident that a knowledge of the rate at which non-exchangeable potassium will be converted into a usable form would be helpful in determining the need of a given soil for potassium fertilization.

There has been much divergence in the results reported by different investigators concerning the relative fixation of potassium by calcareous and non-calcareous soils, and also of the effect of lime on the movement of potassium from the exchangeable to the non-exchangeable state. After a careful study of the published reports Peech and Bradfield [13]

[12] *J. Amer. Soc. Agron.*, 37: 709, 1945.
[13] *Soil Sci.*, 55: 37, 1943.

arrived at the conclusion that certain calcareous soils can fix considerable quantities of potassium in non-exchangeable forms and that sometimes lime may increase this fixation. Nevertheless they question whether moderate applications of lime, even when long-continued, will significantly increase the movement of potassium into the non-exchangeable state, and even if this occurred whether it would affect the intake of the nutrient by crops.

The same investigators reviewed studies of the effect of the degree of calcium saturation of the colloids and of addition of lime on the equilibrium between exchangeable potassium and that in solution. The conclusion was reached that in the presence of salts of strong acids lime will increase the adsorption of potassium by acid soils because the quantity of exchangeable calcium would be increased. However, if the colloids were already saturated, lime additions would increase the amount of potassium in solution. Furthermore, on slightly acid soils liming will not affect the quantity of potassium in solution because the tendency for the calcium ions on the complex to be replaced by the potassium ions would be offset by the replacing effect of the increase in calcium ions in the soil solution. Also, regardless of the degree of base saturation of the colloids, addition of $CaSO_4$ will increase the supply of potassium in solution.

The above conclusions based on studies of soils containing soluble salts of strong acids differ from those based on studies of soils not containing such salts. Under this condition adsorbed potassium passes into the soil solution by hydrolysis, and Peech's investigations showed an increase in the process when Ca-clay was added to K-clay. Likewise the addition of lime to K-clay caused an increase in the potassium in solution. It appears established then that an increase in the hydrolysis of adsorbed potassium will result in an increase in the degree of calcium saturation of the colloid, and in consequence liming will result in more soluble potassium.

MacIntyre [14] does not agree with the above conclusion and bases his opinion on the following experimental results. Workers at the Tennessee experiment station studied for a period of 20 years the effect of applications of various kinds of lime on the loss of potassium in drainage water from a clay loam having a pH of 6.4. The uncropped soil was contained in lysimeters 12 inches deep. The results showed an average loss of 328 pounds of potassium from the unlimed soil and only 292 pounds from the one receiving a fairly heavy lime application.

[14] *Tennessee Agr. Exp. Sta. Bull.* 212, 1949.

Heavy liming reduced the loss to 250 pounds. Studies with a Virginia soil gave similar results.

Little is known of the availability of the potassium in soil minerals. Dennison [15] and associates found the potassium in finely ground muscovite and biotite to be fairly available. On the other hand orthoclase gives up its potassium very slowly because of its resistance to weathering processes, and microcline is yet more slowly decomposed. It has been shown, however, by Graham [16] and associates that mineral particles of the size of silt yield appreciable quantities of calcium and sometimes of potassium to acid clay when the two are intimately mixed. It should not be forgotten, also, that the soil is bathed continuously during the growing season with water containing carbon dioxide and that this solution is not only a good solvent, but the hydrogen ions present may replace some of the potassium from the crystal structure of the minerals. Although these processes may be slow or limited in their activity they undoubtedly result in the liberation of appreciable quantities of potassium during the course of a year.

REMOVAL OF POTASSIUM FROM THE SOIL

In view of the relatively large quantities of potassium in most soils it was long considered that removal of the nutrient in crops and by drainage waters was of little significance to soil productivity. These losses, however, are deductions from the readily available potassium supply, which is usually small, and so are worthy of consideration.

Loss of Potassium by Leaching. Considerable potassium is lost from the soil in drainage water, especially if additions of manures or fertilizers containing relatively high percentages of the element are made. Losses from unfertilized soils of fine texture are usually greater than from sandy soils because of the larger quantities present in soluble and exchangeable forms. For example, Shaw [17] and associates report a 20-year average loss of 324 pounds per acre of potassium from Cumberland clay loam contained in a lysimeter 12 inches deep, compared to a 237-pound loss from an Onslow fine sandy loam. It should be noted, however, that the Cumberland soil was studied at Knoxville under a precipitation of 48.23 inches and the Onslow soil was at Blacksburg where the precipitation is 36.38 inches.

[15] *U.S.D.A. Tech. Bull.* 128, 1929.
[16] *Soil Sci. Soc. Amer. Proc.,* 12: 332, 1947. Also *Soil Sci.,* 49: 277, 1940.
[17] *Tennessee Agr. Exp. Sta. Bull.* 212, 1949.

Losses of potassium in drainage water from sandy soil are appreciable when heavy fertilization is practiced. For example the application of 2,000 pounds of a 5-7-5 fertilizer was followed by a loss of 3.30 pounds of potassium per acre during a 3-month period from an uncropped Norfolk loamy fine sand in Florida,[18] when the fertilizer was applied broadcast. When the fertilizer was placed in bands the loss increased to 8.85 pounds per acre. In this connection it is significant that the growing of a turnip crop reduced the loss of potassium to 0.82 pound from the broadcast application and to 0.62 pound when the band method of applying was used. The same station reports an increase in the potassium concentration of drainage water from 6.4 p.p.m. to 12.6 p.p.m. as a result of the additions of Crotalaria striata as cover-crop material to uncropped soil. With lemon seedlings growing in the soil the losses were reduced to 0.6 p.p.m. without cover-crop material and 1.2 p.p.m. with addition of the Crotalaria.

That additions of potassium-bearing fertilizer increase the loss of the element in drainage is shown by data from Broadbalk field in which each plot is underlain by a tile line. Drainage water from the plot receiving nitrogen and phosphorus fertilizer contained only 0.83 p.p.m. of potassium and that from the plot receiving potassium in addition to nitrogen and phosphorus contained 2.74 p.p.m. It is also of interest that the substitution of sodium in the fertilizer for potassium resulted in a drainage-water content of 2.24 p.p.m. of potassium.

Intake of Potassium by Plants. Just as there has existed a difference in experimental results concerning the effect of lime on potassium fixation and the supply of the element in the soil solution, so there has not been agreement in regard to the effect of the concentration of the calcium ion on the absorption of potassium by plants. Peech and Bradfield [19] explain this divergence of results by pointing out that addition of lime to acid soils containing neutral salts will decrease the potassium concentration and increase the calcium concentration of the soil solution and hence result in a lower absorption of potassium by plants. Applying the same reasoning to calcareous soils containing a good supply of exchangeable potassium, it would be expected that they would respond to application of potassium fertilizer because of the high Ca to K ratio and the low concentration of potassium in solution. With slightly acid soils, however, as pointed out on page 182, the application of lime would not affect appreciably the Ca/K ratio in the soil solution or the intake of potassium.

[18] *Florida Agr. Exp. Sta. Bull.* 416, 1945.
[19] *Soil Sci.*, 55: 37, 1943.

Considering the effect of liming soils containing no neutral salts, the following point was brought out. Although light applications will not replace all the exchangeable hydrogen they will increase the soluble potassium but will not materially affect the Ca/K ratio or the absorption of potassium by plants.

Results of studies concerning the effect of other cations and of the pH of the nutrient solution on the absorption of potassium by plants have been reviewed by Pierre and Bower.[20] They concluded that the following six factors have a definite bearing on the influence other cations may exert on potassium absorption: (1) concentration of K ions; (2) relative concentration of the other cation and K ion; (3) the kind of cation; (4) other cations present; (5) kind of plant; and (6) pH of the solution.

The reviewers did not think that there was sufficient data to determine whether suppression of potassium intake was more likely to occur at high or low levels of concentration, and in fact available data differ on this point.

As might be surmised the greater the concentration of the opposing cation the greater was found to be the depression of potassium absorption. In fact a low concentration of certain ions, such as calcium, in respect to potassium may increase uptake of the latter.

There is considerable variation in the effectiveness of different cations in reducing potassium absorption. In general calcium is less effective than sodium or magnesium. The tendency of a plant to take in sodium influences its activity in the suppression of potassium absorption. Apparently, for plants which use little sodium, magnesium restricts the intake of potassium more than does sodium. The depressing effect of ammonium is also variable, and the conclusion reached by some investigators that monovalent cations are more effective in replacement than are divalent cations is not always true.

The presence of other cations and their nature unquestionably influence the effect of a given cation on potassium absorption. Also the quantity and nature of the anions present are probably influencing factors. It has been shown that in the presence of high concentrations of certain ions, such as calcium and magnesium, sodium may increase potassium intake, and vice versa. This whole problem is complicated. It is noteworthy that potassium exerts a greater influence on the intake of other cations than they do on potassium absorption.

Of all the factors concerned with the effect of various ions on the absorption of others the plant itself is most influential. As yet there is

[20] *Soil Sci.*, 55: 23, 1943.

no satisfactory explanation of the variation in the effect of given ions on the uptake of potassium by different plants. The idea that a cation which is taken up by a given plant in large quantities will depress the intake of another cation is not always true.

The pH value of the solution does not appear to influence the intake of potassium by several plants as much as it does the absorption of some other cations. The solution reaction, however, may play a part in the depressing effect of other cations on potassium utilization. For example there is evidence that at high pH values calcium and ammonium depress potassium intake more than at lower values.

Potassium Content of Crops. Crops remove more potassium from the soil than they do other mineral elements, as is shown by the average composition of eight of the most commonly grown crops of England, as reported by Russell.[21] The harvested portions of these crops, including the leaves of root crops, contain on an acre basis 83.2 pounds of potassium, 15.9 pounds of sodium, 26.1 pounds of calcium, and 9.5 pounds of magnesium. Also the potassium content of these crops about equals the 82.6 pounds of nitrogen and far exceeds the 9.7 pounds of sulfur and 11.7 pounds of phosphorus contained in them. The average nitrogen content of six grain crops,[22] considering both grain and straw, is 53.1 pounds compared to 32.4 pounds of potassium. In contrast seven root and tuber crops [22] contain only 43.9 pounds of nitrogen compared to 75.3 pounds of potassium, based on the analysis of the root or tuber only. That legumes usually contain more potassium than non-legumes is shown by an average of 1.75 per cent for 12 legume hays compared to 1.51 per cent in 11 non-legume hays, as reported by Morrison.[23] It is noteworthy, however, that the percentages of potassium in the legume hays varied from 0.82 to 2.79 and in the non-legume hays from 0.83 to 2.35. Furthermore when legumes and non-legumes are grown on identical soils, which are low in potassium content, the non-legumes have usually been found to contain more of the element than the legumes. The reported higher potassium content of legumes, therefore, may be due to their growth on more productive soils than the non-legumes.

As is well known, the vegetative portion of any crop contains more potassium than does the seed, with the exception of soybeans, in which the reverse is true. The contrast between the potassium contents of the

[21] *Soil Conditions and Plant Growth,* p. 483. Longmans, Green & Co., London, 1950.
[22] Calculated from data in *Fundamentals of Soil Science,* second edition, p. 314. John Wiley & Sons, New York, 1952.
[23] Calculated from data in *Feeds and Feeding.*

seed and straw or stover of common crops is illustrated by an average of 7.6 pounds in the seeds from seven crops [23] and 26.7 pounds in the stems and leaves. The amounts of potassium, nitrogen, and phosphorus contained in average yields of several crops are given in Table 21.

The amount of potassium in plants varies with several factors among which are: quantity of available potassium in the soil, amount and nature of other cations present, and the age and nature of the plants. It is recognized that most plants will take up much larger amounts of potassium than are needed for maximum growth if large quantities of the element are present in an available state and unless some other factor interferes. This excessive absorption of potassium is designated as "luxury consumption," and the phenomenon is frequently taken into consideration in determining the quantity and time of application of potash fertilizer to certain crops. Also it is well known that certain plants have the capacity to absorb and store large quantities of potassium even when the growth medium contains limited supplies.

The effect of the presence of other cations in the soil or growth medium on the intake of potassium has been discussed on page 185. It has long been recognized that the potassium content of plants changes with age. The changes in the potassium content of cereals with age are well illustrated by the data obtained by Knowles and Watkin [24] in a study of the wheat plant. Samples were taken at nine different periods, beginning on April 30 and continuing until August 6. Only the above-ground portion of the plant was sampled. Some of the data obtained are reproduced in Table 41. It will be noted that the percentage of potassium

TABLE 41. POTASSIUM CONTENT OF WHEAT PLANTS AT DIFFERENT STAGES OF GROWTH *

	Potassium Content of Dry Matter, per cent								
Sampling	1	2	3	4	5	6	7	8	9
Part of plant									
Whole	3.40	2.66	2.26	1.57	0.99	0.72	0.63	0.58	0.52
Straw				1.62	1.04	0.76	0.71	0.67	0.63
Heads				1.12	0.77	0.63	0.52	0.46	0.40

* J. Agr. Sci., 21:613, 1931. Used with permission.

was high in the early stages of growth but decreased quite rapidly as the plant gained size and more slowly as maturity was approached. On the other hand the total quantity of the element in the plant increased rather rapidly until a maximum was reached and then also decreased

[24] J. Agr. Sci., 21: 613, 1931.

appreciably as the plant matured. The same pattern was followed by
the potassium content of the straw. The quantity of potassium in the
heads, however, decreased to a much less extent with maturity although
the percentage decreased markedly. This decrease in the potassium
content of the heads was not due to a loss from the grain but from the
other portions of the head. How much of the loss of potassium from
the plants as they matured was due to leaching by rain and how much
to accumulation in older leaves which dropped off is not known. There
is also evidence that in some plants at least a certain amount of potassium may be excreted into the soil by the roots.

Role of Potassium in Plant Growth. Although not a constituent
of the plant tissues potassium is nonetheless essential for growth in all
plants. The effects of this element on growth begin with its influence on the intake of other nutrients. The interrelationship of potassium and other cations in the absorption process has already been
discussed. It is also known that readily absorbed cations such as
potassium and calcium are concerned in the intake of nitrate and other
anions. For example, Nightingale [25] has observed that when the potassium supply is low pineapple plants do not absorb nitrate readily.

It has long been recognized that potassium plays some part in the
formation of proteins. This may come about through the element having some function in the reduction of nitrates, as has been shown by
several investigators, and also by its assistance in the utilization of ammonium ions in amino acid and/or protein synthesis. Some workers
believe potassium is instrumental in the formation of amino acids, but
others consider the element of importance in the formation of proteins
from amino acids. As an agent in protein formation potassium also
stimulates the utilization of carbohydrates. On the other hand there is
abundant evidence that this element plays an important role in photosynthesis and hence in the building up of carbohydrate supplies in the
plant. The increase in production of carbohydrates caused by potassium
accounts for its function in offsetting the detrimental effects of a high
nitrogen content in plants and thus inducing fruitfulness when otherwise
an excessive vegetative growth might result with limited fruit development. Potassium evidently plays an important part in the nitrogen-
carbohydrate ratio in many plants. Figure 25 shows the effect of different amounts of potassium on the development of tomatoes grown on
a potash-deficient soil.

Enzymatic action in plant cells appears to be markedly influenced
by potassium. The movement of iron in the plant is facilitated

[25] *Soil Sci.,* 55: 73, 1943.

by potassium, and hence it has an indirect effect on the formation of chlorophyll. The tendency of phosphorus to hasten maturity is modified by ample supplies of potassium and resistance to disease is increased. The latter effect is undoubtedly due in part to the prevention of an excessive accumulation of nitrogen in the leaves. Thickening of cell walls, changes in reaction and composition of cell sap, and increased

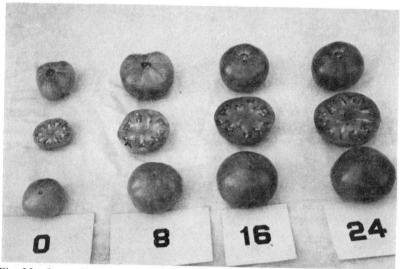

Fig. 25. Increasing the quantities of potash has a marked effect on the development of tomatoes well supplied with phosphoric acid. The plumpness, color, and amount of seed cavity of the fruit are greatly influenced. From left to right, the percentages of potash in the fertilizer were 0, 8, 16, and 24. *Michigan Agr. Exp. Sta. Spec. Bull.* 314. Courtesy of Paul M. Harmer.

vigor of the plant probably contribute to disease resistance also. Potassium also regulates to some extent the absorption and retention of water by plants and so has a part in resistance to damage by frost and drought.

Transpiration is regulated to a degree by potassium and root development is encouraged. The weight per bushel of seeds is raised through an increase in plumpness, and plant stems are strengthened by adequate supplies of the element.[26] Potassium plays a part in cell division, and accordingly when the supply is limited the element moves to the growing tips. This action results in a greater longitudinal than lateral growth, and hence beets, carrots, sweet potatoes, radishes, and similar crops are long and small in diameter when potassium is in in-

[26] *Soil Sci. Soc. Amer. Proc.*, 17: 369, 1953.

sufficient supply. Likewise cucumbers will be constricted at the stem end. Plant symptoms of potassium deficiency are discussed more fully on page 263.

ADDITION AND RETURN OF POTASSIUM TO THE SOIL

In most parts of the United States more potassium is removed from the soil than is applied. In some intensively farmed areas, however, removal and additions of potassium are about equal, and in a few locations more of the element is applied to the soil than is removed. For example, Mehring and Parks [27] estimate that return of potassium in manure and fertilizers exceeds removal of the element in crops by 10 per cent in New England, 15 per cent in the Middle Atlantic states, 75 per cent in the South Atlantic states, and 6 per cent in the East North Central states. In other regions of the United States removal of the element in crops exceeds additions by the following percentages: West North Central 68, East South Central 41, West South Central 85, Mountain 67, and Pacific 76. For the United States as a whole additions amount to 63 per cent of crop removal.

Potassium is returned to the soil in crop residues and manure. Additions to the soil on a given farm can be made through applications of manure produced from feed, primarily hay, which has been grown on other farms, and through use of potassium-carrying fertilizers. The quantities of this element supplied to the soil through the sources mentioned will be discussed briefly.

Manure as a Source of Potassium. As is pointed out in Chapter 16, all types of livestock excrete a high percentage of the potassium they consume in feed and water. As a result, if a farmer feeds most of the crops he grows and takes precautions to conserve the manure, particularly the liquid excrement, his soils will receive a regular supply of readily available potassium. Under such a system little potash fertilizer need be used unless the soil was deficient in this nutrient when the system of farming was undertaken. Ultimately, however, it would become necessary to use potassium fertilizer in humid climates because of the loss of the element in drainage water.

Unfortunately a large proportion of the potassium excreted is in the liquid manure and virtually all that contained in the feces is water-soluble. Accordingly the loss of this element is very high under the average methods of caring for manure, and the use of fertilizers containing potassium is increasing on livestock farms. Farms for which large

[27] *Agr. Chem.*, October and November 1949.

quantities of feed are purchased, particularly hay, receive considerable quantities of available potassium derived from other farms. The need for potassium fertilizers in such cases should be small.

Return of Potassium in Crop Residues. Because the seeds of most crops contain only a small amount of potassium a large part of the element absorbed by plants remains in the leaves, stems, and roots. Accordingly under a cash crop-farming system most of the potassium taken up by crops is left on the soil. Under these conditions the use of potassium-carrying fertilizers would not be needed were it not for the losses of the element by leaching and for the fact that many soils were depleted of their supply of available potassium before the use of modern harvesting methods became common. Also when hay or straw is sold large quantities of potassium leave the farm. The solubility of potassium in plant residues makes them a source of the element in readily available form.

POTASSIUM FERTILIZERS [28]

The use of potassium fertilizers on a small scale dates from about the time of the beginning of the Rothamsted field experiments. Although wood ashes were applied for soil improvement before that time they were not recognized as a source of potassium for plants. The German potash deposits near Stassfurt were the first ones discovered (1839), but they were not developed as a source of fertilizer potassium for many years. Those in Alsace-Lorraine were located in 1904. Potassium salts are now produced in Germany, France, United States, Russia, Poland, Spain, Palestine, and to a small extent in Ethiopia, Brazil, Chile, Canada, India, Australia, Peru, Norway, and Sweden.

Some efforts had been made to locate deposits of soluble potassium salts in the United States before World War I but with indifferent success. The high price of potassium fertilizers during that war, amounting to $500 per ton for 80 per cent muriate, stimulated the search. During the war many minor sources of fertilizer potassium were developed, but with the resumption of imports from Europe virtually all of them, except the plant on Searles Lake, California, were discontinued. The deposits near Carlsbad, New Mexico, were discovered in 1925, and then began the development of a potassium fertilizer industry which ultimately supplied the needs of the United States. At present the principal sources of domestic potassium are the mines near Carlsbad, the brines in Searles

[28] A full discussion of potash resources and methods of preparing potash fertilizers is given in Fertilizer technology and resources, *Agronomy,* III: 257. Academic Press, New York, 1953.

Lake, and a small plant near Wendover, Utah. Smaller quantities are
recovered as by-products from the tobacco, sugar, and several other
industries.

Potassium Chloride as a Fertilizer. The potassium salt most
commonly used as a fertilizer is the chloride which is usually designated
as muriate of potash. It contains from 48 to 62 per cent of K_2O, the
purer grades being the most common. Approximately 80 per cent of
the potassium applied to soils is derived from the muriate containing
60 per cent or more of K_2O. This salt is used extensively in mixed
fertilizers and is employed in large quantities in some areas for direct
application to the soil.

Use of Potassium Sulfate. Under the name of sulfate of potash,
potassium sulfate is the second most commonly used potassium fertilizer.
It contains from 48 to 52 per cent of K_2O and like the chloride it is
highly soluble. It is more expensive to prepare than the chloride and
in consequence is employed primarily for crops which are believed
to be injured in quality by the chloride. Tobacco appears to be more
easily damaged than other crops, a reduction in burning qualities resulting from too high a concentration of chlorine (over 20 to 25 pounds
per acre), although small amounts are reported to improve the texture
of the leaf and increase yields somewhat [29] without impairing the burning quality. Sugar and starch formation is said to be affected in potatoes
and beets by the presence of an excess of chlorine. Also a reduction in
the amount of sugar that can be crystallized from sugar beets (and a
waxy condition of the starch in potatoes) has been reported when chlorides are present in excess. Probably the quantity of chlorine contained
in customary applications of fertilizer is too small to have much effect
on crop quality, and most potato and beet growers do not object to the
use of muriate of potash in the preparation of their fertilizers. In
some areas, however, farmers are willing to pay higher prices for
fertilizer which does not contain chlorides.

Kainite and Manure Salts. Crude potash salts containing mainly
the chlorides of potassium, sodium, and magnesium are sometimes marketed under the name of manure salts. The potash content varies from
around 19 to 32 per cent. Another product consisting primarily of a raw
salt from the potash mines, and similar to 20 per cent manure salt, is sold
as kainite. Little if any of the mineral kainite ($KCl \cdot MgSO_4 \cdot 3H_2O$) is
found on the market. Occasionally manure salts or kainite are in demand because of the impurities they contain, but on the whole the use
of them is small in the United States.

[29] *J. Amer. Soc. Agron.*, 21: 140, 1929.

Sulfate of Potash-Magnesia. This double sulfate is now being produced in appreciable quantities in the United States. It contains about 22 per cent of K_2O and 18 per cent of MgO. This product contains more magnesium and somewhat less potash than a similar material prepared in Germany and sold on the American market before World War II. The German product contained approximately 26 per cent K_2O and 12 per cent MgO.

REFERENCES

Bear, F. E., Prince, A. L., and Malcolm, J. L. The potassium-supplying powers of 20 New Jersey soils. *Soil Sci.*, 58: 139, 1944.

Bowling, J. D., and Brown, D. E. Role of potash in growth and nutrition of Maryland tobacco. *U.S.D.A. Tech. Bull.* 993, 1947.

Collings, G. N. *Commercial Fertilizers.* Blakiston Co., Philadelphia, fourth edition, 1950.

DeTurk, E. E., Wood, C. K., and Bray, R. H. Potash fixation in cornbelt soils. *Soil Sci.*, 55: 1, 1943.

Graham, E. R., and Turley, H. C. Soil development and plant nutrition III. The transfer of potassium from the non-available to the available form as reflected by the growth and composition of soybeans. *Soil Sci. Soc. Amer. Proc.* 12: 332, 1947.

Knowles, F., and Watkin, J. E. The assimilation and translocation of plant nutrients in wheat during growth. *J. Agr. Sci.*, 21: 612, 1931.

Nightingale, G. T. Physiological-chemical functions of potassium in crop growth. *Soil Sci.*, 55: 73, 1943.

Peech, M., and Bradfield, R. The effect of lime and magnesium on the soil potassium and on the absorption of potassium by plants. *Ibid.*, 55: 37, 1943.

Pierre, W. H., and Bower, C. A. Potassium absorption by plants as affected by cationic relationships. *Ibid.*, 55: 23, 1943.

Reitemeier, R. F. Soil potassium. *Advances in Agron.*, III: 113, 1951.

Russell, E. J., revised by Russell, E. W. *Soil Conditions and Plant Growth.* Longmans, Green & Co., London, 1950.

Wall, M. E. The role of potassium in plants, III. Nitrogen and carbohydrate metabolism in potassium-deficient plants supplied with either nitrate or ammonium nitrogen. *Soil Sci.*, 49: 393, 1940.

10

Calcium and Magnesium

The fact that calcium and magnesium are essential in the growth of plants has long been known. Much effort has been expended in determining the roles of these elements in the growth process, and some of their functions are well established, but how and why certain other results are dependent on their presence in available form is not understood. Aside from potassium and hydrogen, no other cations have received so much attention from a fertility standpoint as have magnesium and calcium.

Calcium salts are applied primarily to change conditions in the soil which are related to its reaction, although in special cases, such as the application of gypsum to peanuts, the need for a high concentration of calcium ions is recognized. On the other hand, magnesium is applied primarily to correct a deficiency of the element as a plant nutrient. The supply in soils of the two elements, additions and losses of them, and their functions in plant growth will be discussed under four headings.

Discussion Topics

Calcium and the soil.
Relationship of calcium to plant growth.
Quantities and reactions of magnesium in soils.
Magnesium and the growth of plants.

CALCIUM AND THE SOIL [1]

The calcium content of soils varies more than does that of any other mineral element. Likewise, with the possible exception of sodium, no mineral element has greater effects on the properties of a soil than does calcium. Salts of calcium are added in considerable quantities to virtually all crop land in the humid areas of the United States, and relatively large amounts of the element are lost in drainage water.

[1] Kelley presents an excellent discussion of the effects of calcium on soil properties and plant growth in *Soil Sci.,* 40: 103, 1939.

194

Calcium Content of Soils. The great variation in calcium content of American soils is shown by the analyses of some 23 representative soil types by Robinson,[2] as reported by Bear.[3] The lowest percentage found was 0.086 for a fine sandy loam in Alabama and the highest was 1.76 for a silt loam in Idaho. Had the soils studied included some of those from the Southwest desert region, the calcium content would have been much higher. For example, Breazeale and Smith[4] reported a calcium percentage of 6.56 for the surface 6 inches and 24.4 for the $6\frac{3}{4}$- to $9\frac{3}{4}$-inch layer of an Arizona soil containing a caliche accumulation. In humid regions light-textured soils are usually lower in content of calcium than those of higher clay content unless their topographical position has reduced leaching or led to an actual accumulation of calcium. For example, 12 New Jersey[5] sands and sandy loams were found to have a calcium percentage of 0.207 compared to a percentage of 0.451 for 25 loams and silt loams. Age is also a factor in the calcium content of soils, and some young sandy types contain much more of the element than many more mature heavy soils.

Extreme variations in calcium content are also found in organic soils. Some of those developed in soft-water swamps may have a calcium percentage of 0.22 or less (*p*H 3.8), and other deposits developed in association with marl may contain very large amounts of calcium.

Forms of Calcium in the Soil. Calcium is a constituent of a number of primary rocks and minerals among which anorthite, gabbros, and basalts are the most common. In the carbonate form calcium occurs both alone and with magnesium in many arid soils and in younger types in humid regions. In highly weathered soils the carbonate of calcium has disappeared from the surface horizons and often to a considerable depth in the profile. Small quantities of calcium phosphate, as apatite, are found in most soils with relatively large quantities near rock phosphate deposits.

Concentrations of calcium sulfate are found in some arid soils and beds of gypsum occur in numerous locations. Traces of calcium bicarbonate and nitrate are common constituents of the soil solution. One of the most insoluble salts of calcium commonly formed in the soil is the phosphate, which is produced at slightly acid to alkaline reactions. The most important form of calcium in soils as a whole is that associated with the colloids. Replaceable calcium is considered readily avail-

[2] *U.S.D.A. Bull.* 551, 1917.
[3] *Soils and Fertilizers,* fourth edition. John Wiley & Sons, New York, 1953.
[4] *Ariz. Agr. Exp. Sta. Bull.* 131, 1930.
[5] *N. J. Agr. Exp. Sta. Bulls.* 362 and 366, 1922.

able, although its availability to different crops may vary with the crop grown and the type of clay mineral present, as is shown on page 200.

Calcium and Soil Formation. Minerals containing high percentages of calcium are relatively easily weathered, and soil formation is, therefore, comparatively rapid in material containing considerable quantities of such minerals. A marked reduction of the calcium content is one of the first steps in the development of most soils in humid regions, and accompanying this loss various important changes take place.

So long as there is an abundant supply of calcium in the soil the colloidal material will contain a high percentage of the element and hence will be in a stable and flocculated state. However, as the calcium is removed by leaching in humid climates it is replaced on the complex by H ions, with the result that the colloids become dispersed and are carried downward. A concentration of colloidal material will therefore occur in a lower depth. This process is exemplified by the development of a B horizon high in clay content in podzolized soils and in true podzols of a B horizon containing much organic matter. The development of an A_2 horizon is concomitant with the formation of the B horizon. In some soil material very high in clay content a dense claypan may develop.

Furthermore, the H-clays formed by replacement of the Ca and Mg ions on the clay minerals are unstable, and SiO_2 splits off from them leaving minerals of lower silica-alumina ratio. Under climatic conditions which induce laterization this splitting off and removal of SiO_2 is accelerated, with a resultant accumulation of the sesquioxides. The significance of calcium in soil development processes is indicated by the designation of two great soil groups as Pedalfers and Pedocals.

Effect of Calcium on Soil Structure. It is commonly recognized that the characteristics of soil colloids are greatly influenced by the nature of the cations adsorbed on them. For example, Kelley and Brown [6] showed that sodium-saturated colloids cause soils to be sticky when wet and very hard when dry. On the other hand, Baver [7] demonstrated that a high percentage of calcium ions on the complex resulted in flocculation. As a result soils in which the colloids contain much calcium are usually in a high state of aggregation and so are porous and are said to be in good tilth. This condition facilitates good aeration, rapid absorption of water, and an increased capacity to hold capillary water. A good state of tilth also encourages root development, rapid emergence of seedlings, and the activity of aerobic microorganisms.

[6] *Soil Sci.*, 20: 477, 1925.
[7] *J. Amer. Soc. Agron.*, 20: 921, 1928.

In humid climates removal of Ca ions from the colloidal complex is accompanied by a substitution for them of H ions. In arid climates, however, Na ions frequently replace Ca ions on the colloids. The resultant poor physical condition of the soil is one of the major problems in the management of alkali soils. Just as additions of lime are used to replace the H ions with Ca ions in acid soils, so soluble calcium is needed to replace the Na ions in alkali soils. This calcium may be supplied by addition of soluble calcium salts or, if $CaCO_3$ is present, by increasing its solubility with CO_2 produced through the decay of organic matter, or with sulfuric acid which may be applied directly or developed in the soil from added sulfur.

Calcium and Cation-Exchange Capacity. The cation-exchange capacity of a soil is determined both by its content of colloidal material and by the kind of clay minerals present when clay minerals are the source of an appreciable part of the exchange capacity. Both Gieseking [8] and Kelley [9] have called attention to the fact that clay minerals with relatively high cation-exchange capacities are developed in material comparatively rich in bases, primarily calcium and magnesium. A high organic-matter content also seems to contribute to the development of montmorillonite, and when moisture supplies permit high-lime soils are usually well supplied with organic matter. Clay minerals with low cation-exchange capacities such as kaolinite, on the other hand, are thought to develop in highly weathered material. Moreover, as pointed out on page 196, a splitting off of SiO_2 from clay minerals results when Ca ions are largely replaced by H ions on the complex. This results in the formation of minerals resembling kaolinite or halloysite which have low cation-exchange capacities. It appears then that calcium supply is a pertinent factor in the cation-exchange capacity of the clay minerals formed in many soils.

RELATIONSHIP OF CALCIUM TO PLANT GROWTH

Not only does calcium affect various soil properties which have an influence on plant growth, but the element serves as a nutrient itself. In addition, calcium has much to do with the availability and absorption by the plant of several other nutrient elements.

Calcium Content of Plants. Next to potassium calcium is the most abundant basic element in plants. However, compared to the potassium

[8] *Advances in Agron.*, 1: 177. Academic Press, New York, 1949.
[9] *Soil Sci.*, 40: 107, 1935.

content the calcium content of most crop plants is quite low. For example, the average potassium content of an acre yield of six grain crops (aerial portion) is 27.8 pounds [10] compared to 6.6 pounds of calcium, and 14 non-leguminous dry roughages have an average calcium content of 0.34 per cent compared to a potassium content of 1.49 per cent.[11] On the other hand, the ratio of potassium to calcium is much narrower in legumes, as is shown by an average potassium content of 1.68 per cent in 12 leguminous hays compared to a calcium percentage of 1.25.[11] That legumes contain much more calcium than non-legumes is shown by the data of Daniel.[12] Analyses of a large number of samples of 25 grasses gave an average calcium content of 0.351 per cent of the dry tissue compared to 1.373 per cent for many samples of 12 legumes.

The calcium in plants is present mainly in the leaves and stems rather than in the seed. For instance, the average calcium content of eight grains was found to be 0.09 per cent compared to 0.59 per cent in the straw. In discussing the average calcium content of plants it should be borne in mind that the percentage of calcium in different specimens of a given plant species is by no means uniform. In fact, it will vary widely with the quantity of available calcium in the soil. For example, Smith and Hester [13] showed the calcium content of cabbage to increase from 4.42 per cent to 7.40 per cent as the result of applications of lime. Other factors than liming may influence the calcium content of plants. Daniel and Harper [14] found the calcium content of several species of grasses and of alfalfa to increase under low moisture conditions and to decrease when effective moisture supply increased. The concentration of other cations in the soil solution is also known to affect the amount of calcium taken up by plants. Many investigations have shown that when calcium supplies are low, or the supply of some other cation is excessive, the calcium content of plants is reduced. This situation may have an effect on the nutrition of animals, including man, when produce from calcium-deficient soils alone is consumed unless the deficiency is offset by foods containing much available calcium, such as milk in the human diet. Figure 26 presents the rate of gain of lambs fed hay grown on untreated soil and that treated with phosphate, and with lime and phosphate.

[10] *Fundamentals of Soil Science*, by C. E. Millar and L. M. Turk. John Wiley & Sons, New York, second edition, 1952.

[11] Prepared from data in *Feeds and Feeding*, by Morrison.

[12] *J. Amer. Soc. Agron.*, 26: 496, 1934.

[13] *Soil Sci.*, 65: 117, 1948.

[14] *J. Amer. Soc. Agron.*, 27: 644, 1935.

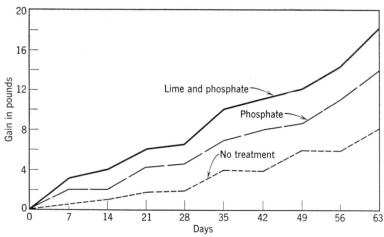

Fig. 26. Rate of gain of lambs fed constant amounts of soybeans and lespedeza hay produced on a Missouri soil receiving different treatments. "Liming had little effect on the calcium or phosphorus content of the forages. The protein was higher, however, and lignin and silica were lower where lime was applied." *Soil Sci.,* 65: 122, 1948. Williams & Wilkins Co., Baltimore. Used with permission. Courtesy of G. E. Smith and J. B. Hester.

Functions of Calcium in Plant Growth. Although the presence of calcium is essential for the normal development of plants, the quantity of the element required by different plants varies considerably. An adequate supply of calcium appears to stimulate the development of root hairs and, in fact, of the entire root system. The element is necessary for normal leaf development and tends to accumulate in the leaves as well as in the older parts of plants such as the bark. The abundance of calcium in leaves may be due to the presence of calcium pectate in the middle lamellae. The element may also protect the plant against accumulations of oxalic acid by neutralizing it, and when a deficiency of calcium exists various substances such as aluminum and manganese may accumulate in plants in harmful concentrations. The translocation of carbohydrates and proteins and their storage during seed formation are influenced by calcium.

Adequacy and Utilization of Soil Calcium. There has been considerable discussion of the possibility of a deficiency of calcium as a nutrient element in acid soils and particularly for crops requiring large amounts of the element. Some investigators [15] have reported marked growth increases in several crops as a result of the addition of non-alkaline calcium salts, such as the sulfate, to acid soils. Other workers have

[15] *Soil Sci.,* 28: 261, 1929.

not obtained such distinct results. It may be concluded that on acid soils of low exchange capacity additions of calcium salts may be beneficial to certain crops, especially peanuts and tobacco. However, on strongly acid soils with high cation-exchange capacities salts of calcium with strong acids are of little value compared to applications of lime. An insufficient supply of available calcium to meet the needs of some crops has also been reported when a high percentage of exchangeable sodium was present. In non-calcareous soil a sodium-saturation percentage of 40 appears to be sufficient to cause a calcium deficiency. In alkali soils containing calcium carbonate and having a pH above 9.0 or 9.5 a calcium deficiency was also found.[16] This situation is ascribed to the suppression of calcium bicarbonate formation by the excess of calcium carbonate.

In correlating the supply of exchangeable calcium with the need of crops for the element, account must be taken of the type of clay mineral present. It has been shown that for certain crops, including peanuts, cotton, and soybeans, the availability of adsorbed calcium is higher from kaolinitic than from montmorillonitic types of clay. Furthermore, as the calcium saturation becomes lower, the decrease in availability is greater in the montmorillonite than in the kaolinite.[17] In fact, montmorillonite clays show a broad zone in which calcium is ionized only slightly, and according to Marshall [18] more than 70 per cent saturation with calcium is necessary before a great amount of this element becomes available for plant use. This phenomenon is explained by Marshall on the basis of the difference in the proportion of adsorbed calcium which is held internally by the two types of minerals. Very little, if any, of the adsorbed calcium is so held by kaolinitic minerals; therefore, the ions are readily replaced and are available for plant use. On the other hand, a large share of the adsorbed Ca ions are held internally in montmorillonite, illite, and beidellite; thus a relatively small portion of them are ionized and hence available. Calcium ions adsorbed after a high percentage of calcium saturation has been reached are most readily available. For example, Marshall shows that with a montmorillonitic clay only a trace of the adsorbed calcium is active at 70–80 per cent calcium saturation, but at 80–90 per cent saturation the active calcium is three times as great. With kaolinite, however, a considerable part of the adsorbed calcium is active at a saturation of only 39–59

[16] *J. Amer. Soc. Agron.*, 38: 723, 1946; also *Arizona Agr. Exp. Sta. Tech. Bull.* 60, 1936.

[17] *Soil Sci.*, 61: 369, 1945; also *Soil Sci. Soc. Amer. Proc.*, 8: 179, 1943.

[18] *Soil Sci.*, 65: 57, 1948.

per cent. Several investigators have shown that little increase in plant growth occurs with additions of calcium above that needed to give 40 per cent saturation. From these considerations it is evident that in soils containing clay of the montmorillonitic type a much higher level of calcium must be maintained than in those containing kaolinitic clays if an equal concentration of calcium ions is to exist in the rhizophere. This situation probably explains why satisfactory stands of legumes are obtained on some soils with small local applications of lime and not on others.

Influence of Calcium on Availability and Absorption of Other Nutrients. Calcium ions exert an influence on the absorption by the plant of some other ions, and the concentration of calcium ions may modify appreciably the quantity of potassium, magnesium, sodium, and other cations taken up by plants. This topic is discussed on pages 41–42. Also, applications to acid soils of calcium salts capable of changing the reaction have a marked effect on the solubility of manganese and aluminum and otherwise alter conditions in a way to distinctly affect the growth of many plants. In addition, an excess of calcium in such forms may cause decreased plant growth because of a depressed availability of iron, manganese, or boron. These effects are discussed in other sections of this book.

An adequate supply of active calcium is also essential for the optimum activity of microorganisms that produce nitrates as well as for aerobic forms that fix nitrogen in association with many legumes, primarily red, white, and sweet clover and alfalfa. The nodulation of soybeans has been shown to vary with calcium supply even in acid soils. According to Albrecht,[19] the supply of calcium in soils with a pH of 5.5 or higher has a marked effect on nodule formation even though the reaction is not altered.

The effect of active calcium on the supply of available phosphorus in the soil is of especial significance. It is a common observation that in soils containing sufficient calcium to give them a slightly acid to slightly alkaline reaction phosphorus has a relatively high availability. Also, phosphorus applied to such soils is largely changed to calcium salts which, although of low solubility, are fairly available to most plants. In addition, it has been found that application of lime to acid soils increases the amount of readily soluble phosphorus.[20] On the other hand, phosphorus availability is low in the presence of an appreciable excess of calcium in the carbonate form.

[19] *J. Amer. Soc. Agron.*, 25: 512, 1933.
[20] *J. Amer. Soc. Agron.*, 29: 526, 1937.

Losses of Calcium from the Soil. As has been mentioned, rocks and minerals containing considerable quantities of calcium weather quite rapidly in humid climates. Also, most compounds of calcium formed in the soil have appreciable solubilities or permit the ready hydrolysis of the calcium contained. Furthermore, the usually abundant production of carbon dioxide leads to the formation of calcium bicarbonate. All these factors result in a large loss of calcium in drainage water when rainfall permits. The great variation in composition of soils and of the different horizons of the profiles, and in management practices and climatic conditions, makes impracticable any generalization concerning the amount of calcium lost in drainage waters. That the loss in general is great, however, is evidenced by the extent of limestone deposits and marl beds and by the prevalence of hard water. Likewise, over a period of years the quantity of calcium sold from farms in crops, in the skeletons of livestock, and in livestock products is considerable. For example, the body of a 1,000-pound steer contains 9.1 pounds of calcium, the grain, cobs, and stover of a 50-bushel crop of corn contain 11.9 pounds of the element, and there are 40.7 pounds in 1,500 pounds of tobacco leaves.

Return of Calcium to Soils. Because a high percentage of the calcium content of crops is in the vegetative portion, any system of farming which includes the addition of crop residues to the soil results in the return of a large share of the calcium removed in crops. Manure applications also supply considerable calcium although dairy cows and young stock remove appreciable quantities of the element from their feed. Forbes [21] found that, of the 82.7 pounds of calcium (as CaO) contained in the feed required to produce 10,000 pounds of milk, 82 per cent was excreted in the manure.

The liming of acid land results in large additions of calcium, and any soil which is maintained at a pH satisfactory for the growth of alfalfa, sweet clover, and red clover will contain ample calcium to meet crop requirements. Also, fertilizers which contain phosphorus supply appreciable quantities of calcium with the exception of the water-soluble ammonium, sodium, and potassium phosphates. Complete fertilizers containing 12 to 20 per cent of the three major plant nutrients have an average calcium content of 10.5 per cent, according to Mehring.[22] Grades of fertilizer containing 21 to 40 per cent of plant nutrients carry 8.4 per cent calcium, and those having more than 40 per cent of nitrogen, phosphoric acid, and potash contain only 3.3

[21] *Ohio Agr. Exp. Sta. Bull.* 363, 1922.
[22] *Amer. Fertilizer*, Jan. 22, 1938.

per cent calcium. Although fertilizers as a whole are slightly acid in reaction the quantity of calcium supplied in repeated, heavy applications is considerable and may be of importance in plant nutrition in slightly buffered acid soils.

QUANTITIES AND REACTIONS OF MAGNESIUM IN SOILS

Magnesium does not occur in such large quantities in soils as calcium and sodium usually do. Likewise magnesium does not exert so marked an influence as calcium on the physical and chemical conditions of soils and on biological activities.

Magnesium Content of Soils. The average magnesium content of 23 representative soil types of the United States is 0.36 per cent, according to the data of Robinson as given by Bear.[23] One was reported to contain no magnesium, and the highest percentage found was 1.1 per cent. That soils in different climatic zones vary in their magnesium content is shown by the data in Table 42. It is evident that the amount

TABLE 42. MAGNESIUM CONTENT OF SEVERAL SOILS FROM THE GREAT SOIL GROUPS *

Soil Group and Number of Samples	Magnesium Content, per cent	Soil Group and Number of Samples	Magnesium Content, per cent
15 Gray-brown Podzolic	0.30	7 Chernozems	0.80
21 Red-yellow Podzolic	0.05	9 Brown	0.71
10 Prairie (Brunigra)	0.40	6 Desert	1.34

* Prepared from data in *Atlas of American Agriculture*, Part III, by Marbut.

of magnesium increases as leaching decreases. Also, under the same climatic conditions fine-textured soils have been found to contain more magnesium than do sandy ones. In general, the magnesium content of the subsoil or B horizon is higher than that of the surface.[24] For example, the average percentage of magnesium in the B horizon of 15 Gray-brown Podzolic soils was shown to be 0.63 compared to 0.30 in the A horizon, and in the B horizon of 21 Red-yellow soils 0.065 compared to 0.05 in the A horizon. Likewise, the B horizon of 10 Prairie soils (Brunizem) was found to contain 0.63 per cent magnesium and the A horizon 0.40 per cent.

The New York agricultural experiment station[25] reports the average magnesium content of 53 mucks to be 0.30 per cent, with the high-

[23] *Soils and Fertilizers,* fourth edition. John Wiley & Sons, New York, 1953.
[24] Shown by data in *Atlas of American Agriculture,* Part III, by Marbut.
[25] *Cornell University Agr. Exp. Sta. Bull.* 537, 1932.

est percentage being 0.57 and the lowest 0.07.   With few exceptions the subsoil (12- to 24-inch layer) contained somewhat more magnesium than the surface foot.

Magnesium-Deficient Soils.   An insufficient supply of magnesium for satisfactory crop production has been reported in the sandy soils of the Atlantic coastal area from Florida to Maine.   Not only is it necessary to supply magnesium for the intensive production of vegetables, but also general field crops such as cotton, corn, and tobacco often show symptoms indicating an insufficient supply of the element.   Also, acid sands in the midwestern states are sometimes deficient in magnesium for maximum crop production, and some organic soils require additions of the element.   In some alkali soils containing no calcium carbonate a magnesium deficiency has been reported when the percentage of sodium saturation reached 40 or more.[26]   In the presence of calcium carbonate a pH of 9.0 or 9.5 was required in addition to a high sodium saturation to produce a deficiency of magnesium.

Forms of Magnesium in the Soil.   The most common soil minerals containing magnesium are dolomite and the silicates, hornblende, augite, olivine, talc, and serpentine.   Magnesium also occurs as an adsorbed ion on the colloidal fraction, and it appears in solution as the bicarbonate and to a slight extent as the nitrate.   In acid soils of the humid region magnesium ranks third in order of adsorbed cations, being exceeded by hydrogen and calcium ions.   In soils of semiarid and arid regions it ranks second to calcium, except in some alkali soils in which it may be exceeded in amount by sodium.

Magnesium ions adsorbed on the soil colloids have much the same effect on their characteristics as do Ca ions, except that Mg ions tend to decrease the state of flocculation.[27]   Seldom, however, are there sufficient Mg ions present to affect the state of aggregation materially.   Mg ions are held with somewhat less energy by soil colloids than are Ca ions, and hence a somewhat lesser concentration is necessary for the nutrient to be readily available to plants.

Losses of Magnesium from Soils.   Magnesium-containing minerals weather more slowly than do calcium-rich minerals, and serpentine and talc are particularly resistant to decomposition.   Also, the quantities of the element lost in drainage waters are small compared to the loss of calcium, although the bicarbonate has an appreciable solubility and the nitrate and sulfate are highly soluble.   The small loss of magnesium is exemplified by the analyses of Mississippi river water at

[26] *J. Amer. Soc. Agron.*, 38: 723, 1946.
[27] *J. Amer. Soc. Agron.*, 20: 721, 1928.

various locations, as cited by Bear [28] and also by the data from lysimeter studies at Cornell University.[29]   Drainage water from Dunkirk clay loam, which contained about the same quantities of the two elements in the surface foot, carried approximately five times as much CaO as MgO.   Furthermore, the small amounts of magnesium in most limestones indicate a relatively small loss of the element in drainage water. The small removal of magnesium compared to the loss of calcium is undoubtedly associated with the much smaller quantity of magnesium in the soil.

Because of the accumulation of magnesium in the seeds of crops larger amounts of it are sold from the farm in grain farming than of calcium or potassium.   On the other hand, in livestock farming little magnesium is sold from the farm because of the small amounts in animal bodies and livestock products.

Magnesium Returned to the Soil. When crop residues are applied to the soil approximately one-half of the magnesium contained in the aerial portions of the plant is returned.   Also, manure contains appreciable quantities of magnesium because animals retain only a small part of the amount of the element contained in their feed.   Forbes [30] reported that the excretion in manure was 32.5 pounds of the 34.7 pounds of MgO contained in the feed consumed for the production of 10,000 pounds of milk.

Most limestones contain at least low percentages of magnesium carbonate and dolomitic stones may carry up to 45 per cent.   In consequence, liming the soil usually involves the application of considerable quantities of magnesium.   Fertilizers containing superphosphate also generally carry small quantities of magnesium because of the use of dolomitic limestone to neutralize the residual acidity from the acidulation process.   Mehring and Lundstrom [31] give the average MgO content of 16–20 per cent superphosphate as 0.47 per cent and of the 44 per cent grade as 0.38 per cent.   Complete fertilizers containing 12 to 20 per cent plant nutrients are reported to have 1.21 per cent MgO, and those containing 21 to 40 per cent total nutrients average 1.08 per cent MgO content.   In mixtures carrying more than 40 per cent plant food the MgO content drops to 0.64 per cent.   Although the quantities of magnesium contained in commonly used applications of fertilizer are not large they are appreciable in view of the relatively small quantity of the element contained in average yields of most crops.

[28] *Soils and Fertilizers,* fourth edition. John Wiley & Sons, New York, 1953.
[29] *Cornell University Memoir* 134, 1930.
[30] *Ohio Agr. Exp. Sta. Bull.* 363, 1922.
[31] *Amer. Fertilizer,* Jan. 22, 1938.

In preparing fertilizers for use on magnesium-deficient soils it is customary to add appreciable quantities of magnesium. If the addition is made before the fertilizer is cured, dolomite or other insoluble compounds may be used, because the magnesium will become soluble during the curing process. On the other hand, if the magnesium compound is mixed in shortly before application of the fertilizer it is more desirable to use a soluble salt.

Magnesium Content of Plants. Crops in general remove much less magnesium from the soil than they do calcium. For example, Russell [32] shows acre yields of eight crops, including grains, roots, tubers, and hay, to contain an average of 9.6 pounds of magnesium compared to 26.1 pounds of calcium. However, there is a vast difference in the relative amounts of the two elements contained in different crops. This is shown by the fact that a 30-bushel wheat crop requires 6.6 pounds of calcium and 4.3 pounds of magnesium, whereas 2 tons of red-clover hay contain 64.4 pounds of calcium to 17.0 pounds of magnesium, and 6 tons of potatoes remove from the soil 2.4 pounds of calcium compared to 3.8 pounds of magnesium. That legumes are particularly rich in magnesium is evident from the fact that 12 leguminous hays have an average content of 0.29 per cent compared to 0.19 per cent for 16 non-leguminous roughages. [33] It is also interesting to note that on the average the seed of grain crops contains somewhat more magnesium than does the straw, which is the opposite of the calcium content. There are some exceptions, such as oats, in which 50 bushels of grain contain 1.9 pounds of the element compared to 3.5 pounds in the 2,500 pounds of straw. Oily seeds are particularly rich in magnesium.

MAGNESIUM AND THE GROWTH OF PLANTS

As a constituent of chlorophyll magnesium enters into the composition of plant tissue. In this respect it differs from most of the other cations required for plant growth. Furthermore, the distribution of magnesium in plants and its functions in growth processes are quite different from those of calcium although the two elements have similar chemical properties.

The Role of Magnesium in Plant Growth. Magnesium is essential in the growth of all green plants. The chlorophyll molecule

[32] *Soil Conditions and Plant Growth,* eighth edition. Longmans, Green & Co., London, 1950.
[33] Calculated from data in *Feeds and Feeding,* by Morrison,

contains 2.7 per cent of magnesium, but this is only a small part of the total magnesium content of leaves. It has been shown that considerably more magnesium is necessary to bring about a maximum rate of photosynthesis than is needed to prevent the development of magnesium-deficiency symptoms. Accordingly, it can be assumed that plant growth has already been restricted before evidence of mag-

Fig. 27. Cotton leaves showing distinct symptoms of magnesium deficiency (*right*) and normal growth (*left*). South Carolina Agr. Exp. Sta. Courtesy of H. P. Cooper.

nesium deficiency is exhibited and that an application of the nutrient at that time cannot produce as large a crop as would have been obtained if the magnesium supply had been adequate throughout the growth period. Symptoms of magnesium deficiency in cotton are shown in Fig. 27.

The element is also connected with the transportation of phosphorus in the plant, and there are data to show that an ample supply of magnesium may increase the utilization of fertilizer phosphorus and the phosphorus content of the seed. Its function as a phosphorus carrier associates magnesium with the formation of lecithin and nucleoproteins, which accounts for its concentration in seeds. Magnesium is also related to the movement of carbohydrates from the leaves to the stems of plants. The low carbohydrate content of magnesium-deficient leaves which has been observed in some plants is doubtless due to the low rate of photosynthesis.

There is more magnesium in the leaves than in the stems of plants, and it accumulates in the growing tips of stems and roots. Apparently magnesium ions may be used over and over in growth processes, so that the total supply needed by a plant is not great.

REFERENCES

Allaway, W. H.   Availability of replaceable calcium from different types of colloids as affected by degree of calcium saturation.   *Soil Sci.*, 59: 207, 1945.

Beeson, K. C.   The mineral composition of crops with particular reference to the soil in which they were grown.   *U.S.D.A. Misc. Pub.* 369, 1941.

Bower, C. A., and Turk, L. M.   Calcium and magnesium deficiencies in alkali soils.   *J. Amer. Soc. Agron.*, 38: 723, 1946.

Camp, A. F.   Magnesium in citrus fertilization in Florida.   *Soil Sci.*, 63: 43, 1947.

Fried, M., and Peech, M.   The comparative effects of lime and gypsum upon plants grown on acid soil.   *J. Amer. Soc. Agron.*, 38: 614, 1946.

Kelley, W. P.   The agronomic importance of calcium.   *Soil Sci.*, 40: 103, 1940.

Reed, J. F., and Cummings, R. W.   Use of soluble sources of calcium in plant growth.   *Soil Sci.*, 65: 103, 1948.

Truog, E., Goates, R. J., Gerloff, G. C., and Berger, K. C.   Magnesium-phosphorus relationships in plant nutrition.   *Ibid.*, 63: 10, 1947.

Zimmerman, M.   Magnesium in plants.   *Ibid.*, 63: 1, 1947.

11

Sulfur

Sulfur has been recognized as an essential constituent of plants since the work of de Saussure in 1804. For centuries before this date sulfur compounds had been applied to soils because of their observed beneficial effect on plant growth, but these benefits were not ascribed to sulfur. During the period 1760–1850 large quantities of gypsum were applied to soils both in Europe and in the United States. Various theories were advanced to explain the beneficial effects on crop growth, among the most interesting being that of Liebig, who maintained that the $CaSO_4$ absorbed ammonia from the air. On the other hand Davy maintained that the amount of lime sulfate in plants was increased by gypsum applications. Both these theories were discredited by the investigations of Boussingault (1884), which showed no increase in the $CaSO_4$ in plant ash as a result of gypsum fertilization and no increase in crop yields except for a few plants such as lucerne, sainfoin, and clover in "artificial" meadows. The yield of "natural meadows" was not increased. Owing to the work of Boussingault and probably more to the wide use of superphosphate after the beginning of its manufacture by Lawes in 1843, little attention was paid to application of sulfur compounds until the beginning of the nineteenth century. The low sulfur requirement of plants, according to the ash analyses of Wolff, also contributed to the loss of interest in the element. Considerable attention has been given to the sulfur problem since the beginning of the twentieth century, as will be observed from the following discussion.

Discussion Topics

The sulfur content of soils.
Additions of sulfur to soils.
Removal of sulfur in crops and by leaching.
Changes which sulfur undergoes in soils and effect of sulfates on soil properties.
Forms and functions of sulfur in plants.
The need for sulfur applications in crop production.

THE SULFUR CONTENT OF SOILS

Because a considerable part of the sulfur in soils of humid climates is contained in the organic matter it undergoes comparatively rapid changes in form, as does the soil nitrogen. As a result of sulfate for-

TABLE 43. SULFUR AND PHOSPHORUS CONTENT OF SURFACE SOILS

Location of Soil Group	Lb. per Acre						Ratio P:S
	Sulfur			Phosphorus			
	Maxi-mum	Mini-mum	Aver-age	Maxi-mum	Mini-mum	Aver-age	
Illinois	Over 2,000	200	Below 800	2,030	710	1,070	1.34
Indiana	1,120	160	300–600				
Iowa	1,233	441	815	1,538 *	1,289 †	1,390	1.71
Kansas	1,240	320	730	1,260	460	809	1.11
Kentucky	1,420	180	563	12,100 ‡	300	1,727	3.06
Ohio	1,112	362	680				
Oregon	760	300	560	1,540	960	1,250	2.23
Texas	1,280 §	256 §	522 ‖	1,572 §	227 §	595 ‖	1.14
Wisconsin	1,120	256	667	2,707	349	1,397	2.09
26 soil types in the U. S.	31,220	240	1,008	2,096	349	1,187	1.18
Gray-brown pod-zolic soils ¶	1,840	320	728	3,210	87	1,062	1.46
Red-yellow soils **	2,080	80	488	2,960	Trace	596	1.22

* Average of 4 soils on Missouri loess.

† Average of 4 soils on Iowan drift.

‡ This figure is so high it appears the sample must not have been representative.

§ Average for soils of a county. One soil contained only 80 lb. of sulfur.

‖ Average for soils in 20 counties.

¶ Eighteen samples from eastern states only. Includes the following soil series: Sassafras, Collington, Colts Neck, Chester, Nason, Leonardtown, Hagerstown, Maury, Ontario, Gloucester, and Merrimac.

** Fifty-six samples. Includes the following series: Norfolk, Marlboro, Orangeburg, Tifton, Dade, Greenville, Grenada, Decatur, Hanceville, Nacogdocher, Cecil, Georgeville, Durham, Appling, Davidson, and Iredell.

mation there is an appreciable loss of sulfur in drainage water. In arid climates, on the other hand, quite a different situation pertains concerning the transformations and losses of sulfur.

Sulfur in Surface Soils. Among the first studies of the sulfur content of soils is that by Dymond [1] and associates, who determined the amount of the element in the soils of Essex County, England. During the first thirty years of the present century attention was given to the sulfur content of American soils by workers in a number of state experiment stations. The results of several of these studies are summarized in Table 43. Because reference is frequently made to the relative quantities of sulfur and phosphorus in soils, the table also shows the amount of phosphorus in the soils of several states and soil groups and the ratio of the average phosphorus content to the average sulfur content. It will be noted that on the average there is appreciably more phosphorus than sulfur. Frequently, however, the situation is reversed. This seems to be true quite often in the Red and Yellow soils, according to the data in *Atlas of American Agriculture,* Part III.

Sulfur in Subsoils. Subsoils have been found to contain less sulfur than surface soils usually, as would be expected from the fact that a considerable portion of the sulfur is contained in the organic matter. In some acid soils, however, an accumulation of sulfates is found at varying distances below the surface. Table 44 presents the relationship

TABLE 44. SULFUR CONTENT OF SURFACE AND SUBSOIL, LB. PER ACRE

State	Oregon	Kentucky	Iowa	Kansas	Texas	Ohio
Surface	558	667	815	730	522	1056
Subsoil	409	464	376	600	492	528
Difference	149	203	439	130	30	528
Difference, %	26.7	30.4	53.8	17.8	5.7	50.0

between the sulfur content of the surface or plow layer of soil and that of the subsoil, as found by various workers. It is evident that there is no consistent relationship between the amounts of sulfur in the plow layer and lower horizons. Probably in areas of lower rainfall, where the line of demarkation between the humus-rich and lower horizons is not so pronounced as it is in the timbered soils of the East Central states, so great a contrast in sulfur content of the surface and subsoil should not be expected.

Often the depth at which the subsoil samples were taken is not recorded. However, Ames and Boltz give the average sulfur content of

[1] *J. Agr. Sci.,* 1: 217, 1905.

a number of Ohio soils for the depth 0–6, 6–12, 12–18, and 18–24 inches as 1,056, 830, 686, and 528 pounds, respectively. The gradual decline in sulfur content with depth is evident from these data.

Forms of Sulfur in Soils. Because sulfates which might be expected to occur commonly in soils are appreciably soluble, the quantity of sulfur in the sulfate form in soils of humid areas is small. As rainfall diminishes the quantity of less soluble sulfates, especially calcium, can be expected to increase until heavy concentrations occur in the soil profile such as the caliche of some arid soils. Naturally the occurrence of such concentrations is dependent upon a source of sulfates, and all arid soils do not contain high concentrations of sulfates. The extreme of sulfate accumulation as a result of weathering is illustrated by the white dunes of the White Sands National Park in New Mexico, which are composed of relatively pure gypsum. Gypsum beds also occur in numerous places in humid regions as the result of the evaporation of ancient seas. Such accumulations, however, are not connected with soil development processes.

Sulfides, principally of iron, sometimes occur in considerable quantities, but seldom where chemical processes of weathering are dominant over the physical processes. The exception, of course, is where such sulfides are components of larger soil particles and hence have not been submitted to the processes of oxidation, hydration, and solution.

Frequently much of the sulfur occurs as a constituent of organic matter. Illinois workers [2] report a fairly constant ratio between organic carbon and sulfur of 50:1 in soils containing 40,000 pounds per

TABLE 45. QUANTITY AND FORM OF SULFUR IN MINNESOTA SOILS *

Soil Area of State	Total Sulfur, lb. per acre	Per Cent of Total Sulfur		
		In Organic Form	In Inorganic Form	In Sulfate Form
Chernozem soils	976	73.3	26.7	2.8
Black Prairie soils	880	71.0	29.3	4.9
Podzols of				
North East region	202	49.5	49.5	7.9
North Central region	176	45.4	55.6	6.8

* *Soil Sci.*, 59: 125, 1945. Williams & Wilkins Co., Baltimore. Used with permission.

acre of organic matter. As the organic content increases, the ratio becomes wider. On the other hand, studies in Minnesota brought

[2] *Illinois Agr. Exp. Sta. Ann. Rep.,* pp. 15 and 17, 1935–1936.

out much variation in the proportion of total sulfur occurring in the organic, inorganic, and sulfate form, as is shown in Table 45.

The proportion of the total sulfur in soils occurring in inorganic compounds could be expected to vary with mineralogic composition, texture, age, and climatic conditions.

Decrease in Sulfur Content with Cultivation. When soils are brought under cultivation the accelerated rate of decay of organic matter and erosion, and the increased leaching, as well as the removal of crops, should result in a decrease in sulfur content. That this has occurred is shown by the results of studies in several states. For example, in Wisconsin [3] the average sulfur content of a number of virgin soils was found to be 772 pounds per acre compared to 416 pounds in the corresponding cropped samples. These results represent a loss of 46.1 per cent. Likewise, in Kansas [4] the average sulfur content of several virgin and cropped soils was 920 pounds and 540 pounds, respectively. In other words 41.3 per cent of the sulfur was lost during the cropping period. In Kentucky,[5] however, only 27.1 per cent of the sulfur in virgin soils was lost by cropping.

Sulfur Content of Organic Soils. Accumulations of slightly decomposed plant material have been studied rather extensively, in the earlier days more as a possible source of fuel rather than as soil resources. In more recent years, however, much attention has been given these lands from the standpoint of their crop-production capabilities. The sulfur content of mucks and peats is highly variable, as shown by the following data [6] based on moisture-free material. The highest percentage of sulfur found in 69 organic soils in Wisconsin was 1.67, the lowest 0.16, and the average 0.56. In Minnesota 2.55 per cent was the highest sulfur content found in 214 samples, 0.13 per cent was the lowest, and 0.40 per cent was the average. In a study of 40 mucks from Florida the sulfur percentage was found to vary from 4.13 to 0.07 with an average of 1.09. Data from other states are similar and show a wide spread between the maximum and minimum sulfur percentages in organic soils within a given state and in deposits in different states. There appears to be no logical basis for these wide variations, but possibly the explanation of them lies in one or all of the following facts: (1) There is a great difference in the degree of decomposition of the material in different deposits. With drainage and cultivation the rate of decay is rapid. (2) Surface waters from surrounding land

[3] *Wisconsin Agr. Exp. Sta. Res. Bull.* 14, 1911.
[4] *Soil Sci.,* 14: 421, 1922.
[5] *Kentucky Agr. Exp. Sta. Bull.* 188, 1941.
[6] Compiled from data in *U.S.G.S. Bull.* 728, 1922.

frequently drain into organic soil areas. Should the adjoining upland be fertilized with sulfur-containing materials, appreciable quantities of sulfur might be carried into the muck and peat. (3) Springs are of frequent occurrence in many organic soils, and these waters may contain sulfur compounds which would be concentrated in the profile over a period of years. (4) There is a very wide difference in the percentage of mineral matter in organic soils. In some there is 10 per cent or less and in others there may be around 80 per cent.

ADDITIONS OF SULFUR TO SOILS

The more general use of combines and other types of mechanical harvesters, which has resulted in a greater return of crop residues, has reduced the loss of sulfur from soils. Likewise, the more general and increased use of commercial fertilizers has resulted in the addition of considerable quantities of the element to large acreages of intensively cropped land.

Sulfur in Manure and Crop Residues. Part of the sulfur removed from the soil in crops is returned to it in manure and crop residues. Even though all the crops grown on a farm are fed to livestock on the farm all the sulfur removed from the soil is not returned in the manure. Animals retain an appreciable portion of the sulfur in their feed, and some sulfur is lost during the handling of the manure. On the other hand, in some states the farmers purchase a large amount of feed from out-of-state sources, and under such conditions considerably more sulfur may be added to the soil in manure than was removed from it in the feed crops grown. For example, Kelly and Midgely [7] estimated that over 486 tons of sulfur are added annually to Vermont soils in manure produced from purchased feed.

The sulfur content of manure will vary with many factors, as does the content of any other plant nutrient. Brown and Kellogg [8] found horse and cow manure to contain 1.23 and 1.60 pounds of sulfur per ton, respectively. There appear to be few data showing loss of sulfur from manure under different methods of storage and handling.

Additions of Sulfur in Precipitation. Many studies have been made to determine the quantities of sulfur brought to the earth in rain and snow. The results from some of them are summarized in Table 46. It is evident that the quantities of sulfur contained in precipitation vary greatly from state to state and also at different points within a

---

[7] *Vermont Agr. Exp. Sta. Pamphlet* 23, 1950.

[8] *J. Amer. Soc. Agron.,* 7: 97, 1915.

TABLE 46. SULFUR IN PRECIPITATION, LB. PER ACRE

State	Maximum	Minimum	Average for Non-Industrial Areas
Indiana	127.1	20.0	27.0
Oklahoma	17.0	5.6	8.7
Texas	18.5	3.1	9.0
Minnesota	196.7	3.13	4.2
Tennessee	232.4	12.7	...
New York	77.5	38.2	...
Kentucky	41.2	17.1	24.1
Alabama	30.7	2.9	13.0

state. As would be expected the atmosphere near centers of high fuel consumption contains much more sulfur than the atmosphere far removed from centers of population or industry. In fact the quantity of sulfur brought to the earth from the air in some rural areas is of small significance in supplying the needs of crops for this element.

There is also considerable variation in quantities of sulfur contained in precipitation at different seasons of the year.[9] In general there is less in the warmer months when less fuel is consumed, but the difference is not so great as might be anticipated. Possibly snow is not so effective in collecting sulfur gases from the atmosphere as is rain. Another question of practical significance is whether much of the sulfur contained in snow falling when the ground is frozen is not carried away in runoff water and hence never enters the soil.

Some questions as to the actual quantities of sulfur received by the soil from precipitation arise also from the work of Alway, which shows containers made of common metals to be corroded by the SO_2 in the air. The sulfates so produced are added to the sulfur in the precipitation, making the amount abnormally large. For example, using gauges exposing 553, 70, and 0 square inches of galvanized iron, the quantities of sulfur in the collected precipitation were 170, 66, and 26 pounds per acre, respectively. These results render questionable the accuracy of the data reported concerning the sulfur added to the soil by precipitation in various localities. However, it seems justifiable to conclude that quantities of sulfur large enough to be of consequence in crop production are brought to the earth near centers of population or of industry. On the other hand the quantity of sulfur in precipitation in areas far removed from large fuel-consuming centers is quite small.

Sulfur Dioxide Content of Air. The quantity of SO_2 in the air near smelters emitting large amounts of the gas has been studied for

[9] *Oklahoma Academy of Science Proc.*, 23: 73, 1943.

many years because of the possible detrimental effect on vegetation in the neighborhood. Only recently, however, has atmospheric sulfur dioxide attracted attention as a source of sulfur for the soil and for plants.

Studies were made by Alway and associates,[10] using so-called "candles" which consist of cylinders exposing 100 sq. cm. of cloth coated with lead dioxide. At intervals the cloth was removed, and the sulfur absorbed by the dioxide was determined. Results showed much variation with differences in location of the candles which influenced air movement. Likewise, nearness to cities was a factor. For example, measurements at four locations in Minnesota, namely, in Minneapolis, at the University Farm, in the center of a town of 1,300 inhabitants, and in a rural district in the northwestern portion of the state, showed 345.1, 105.9, 40.5, and 2.23 pounds of sulfur per acre of exposed dioxide-coated fabric, respectively. Measurements covered the period from January to October. Kelly and Midgley [11] found the quantity to vary from 13.08 to 43.64 pounds per acre at five locations in Vermont. Evidently concentrations of SO_2 in the air vary greatly.

It has been quite generally agreed among research workers that concentrations of around 1 p.p.m. of SO_2 in the atmosphere will cause some damage to especially sensitive plants and higher concentrations may cause defoliation.

Absorption of Sulfur Gases by Soil. Experiments by Alway et al.[10] show that soil will absorb sulfur oxides from the atmosphere. The quantity so absorbed varies with the amount of the gases in the atmosphere and the movement of air over the soil surface. In areas far removed from cities it is doubtful whether the quantity of sulfur absorbed by soils covered with crops during much of the growing season is sufficient to supply a significant part of the crop's sulfur requirement.

Absorption of Sulfur Gases by Plants. It has been definitely established that some plants can absorb SO_2 from the atmosphere and utilize the sulfur so obtained in growth processes. It is yet to be established, however, that this source of sulfur is a significant one for commonly grown crops, especially in areas where the SO_2 content of the atmosphere is very low.

Sulfur Supplied in Fertilizers. Organic materials, the sulfates of ammonia and potash, and ordinary grades of superphosphate are the most commonly used fertilizers containing appreciable quantities of sulfur. In studying the composition of a large number of fertilizers,

[10] *Soil Sci. Soc. Amer. Proc.,* 11: 229, 1937.
[11] *Vermont Agr. Exp. Sta. Pamphlet* 23, 1950.

Mehring and Lundstrom [12] arrived at the following conclusions regarding the sulfur content of mixed goods.

1. Complete fertilizers containing 12–20 per cent of the nutrients, N, P_2O_5, and K_2O, carry an average of 8.09 per cent sulfur.
2. Complete fertilizers with 21–40 per cent of the three nutrients contain an average of 6.90 per cent sulfur.
3. Complete mixtures with more than 40 per cent of the three nutrients average 1.4 per cent sulfur.
4. Mixtures of nitrogen and potash contain only 0.14 per cent sulfur.
5. Mixtures of phosphorus and potash average 6.43 per cent in sulfur content.

It is evident that applications of medium to large quantities of fertilizers supply appreciable amounts of sulfur to the soil. In Table 47 is

TABLE 47. SULFUR APPLIED IN FERTILIZERS, LB. PER ACRE OF CROP LAND

States	Sulfur	States	Sulfur
New England	19.46	East South Central	15.20
Middle Atlantic	16.71	West South Central	3.49
South Atlantic	27.28	Mountain	1.14
East North Central	6.32	Pacific	6.48
West North Central	0.89		

shown the pounds of sulfur per acre of crop land in groups of states supplied in the quantity of fertilizer used by these states. In making these calculations the average sulfur contents shown above were applied to the tonnages of the fifteen principal fertilizers used in the groups of states for the year 1949–1950, as shown by Scholl and Wallace. The sulfur in the superphosphate and ammonium sulfate applied directly was also included. For the acreage of crop land the harvested acreage of fifty-two crops in 1949 was taken. Although not absolutely accurate these data indicate that in some groups of states the sulfur supplied in fertilizers alone is sufficient to meet the needs of the crops grown. On the other hand, in other states the sulfur in fertilizers used is only a small part of that needed by crops.

REMOVAL OF SULFUR IN CROPS AND BY LEACHING

As crop yields have increased through the use of improved varieties and cultural practices the quantities of sulfur, as well as of other nutri-

[12] *Amer. Fertilizer*, Jan. 22, 1938.

ents, removed in crops have increased. This loss has been compensated, at least in part, by a wider use of cover and green-manuring crops, which reduce losses of sulfur by leaching and erosion, and by a greater return of crop residues and heavier fertilization.

Sulfur Content of Crops. All crops contain appreciable quantities of sulfur, but the percentage present in the dry plant tissue is decidedly variable. Early reports of the sulfur content of plants were based on the analysis of the ash and were consequently entirely too low because much of the sulfur was volatilized during the ashing process.

Among commonly grown crops cereals are comparatively low in sulfur content, with legumes appreciably higher and cruciferae much richer in the element. For example, the dry tissue (grain and straw) of barley, oats, and wheat average 0.161 per cent sulfur, of alfalfa and several clovers (various stages of maturity) 0.253 per cent, and of the edible portions of rutabaga, turnip, cabbage, cauliflower, and kale 0.869 per cent. Cotton leaves and stalks are reported to be high in sulfur content, and Shedd found an average of 0.458 per cent of sulfur in the dry matter of 32 varieties of tobacco. A comparison of the quantities of four nutrients contained in several crops are presented in Table 48.

TABLE 48. NUTRIENTS CONTAINED IN SEVERAL CROPS,* LB. PER ACRE

Crop	Quantity	Sulfur	Nitrogen	Phosphorus	Potassium
Alfalfa	2 tons	11	91	22	118
Corn (grain, stalk, and cobs)	40 bu.	6	60	11	35
Cotton (seed and lint)	600 lb.	1	13	3	6
Cotton (stalks, burrs, and leaves)	2,400 lb.	12	50	4	17
Oats (grain and straw)	40 bu.	7	35	6	23
Potatoes (tubers)	200 bu.	4	40	9	60
Sweet potatoes (roots)	200 bu.	2	28	9	60
Rice (grain and straw)	1,900 lb. (grain)	3	37	7	35
Wheat (grain and straw)	25 bu.	5	42	8	19

* From *Texas Agr. Exp. Sta. Bull.* 414.

The sulfur removed by good yields of all crops is significant in view of the comparatively small amounts found in most soils.

Sulfur in Drainage Water. Lysimeter studies in several states show considerable but quite variable quantities of sulfur in drainage water. So many factors influence the amounts of this element lost from the soil by leaching that no general or average figure can be arrived at. Perhaps the data from the Illinois experiment station [13] are as representative as any. During a 10-year period the average number of pounds per acre of sulfur in the drainage water varied from 54.9 from cultivated but uncropped land to 35.4 from soil growing alfalfa continuously. Under various cropping systems the loss varied from 42.6 pounds to 53.3 pounds. All the soils received 200 pounds of superphosphate containing 21.5 pounds of sulfur annually.

As virtually all sulfates that are likely to occur in soils are appreciably soluble, it is to be expected that losses of sulfur in drainage water will be considerable in humid regions.

CHANGES WHICH SULFUR UNDERGOES IN SOILS AND EFFECT OF SULFATES ON SOIL PROPERTIES

The oxidation of sulfur in the soil with the formation of sulfurous and sulfuric acids is an important reaction from the standpoint of productivity because through it sulfur is converted into available forms. Also, the addition of sulfates to soils may influence biological activities; furthermore it results in readjustments between adsorbed cations and those in solution.

Oxidation and Reduction of Sulfur. The changes that sulfur, which exists in organic compounds, undergoes during decomposition of organic matter in the soil depend on the conditions pertaining during the process. If sufficient air is present the sulfur emerges in the sulfate (SO_4) form, having first been reduced to hydrogen sulfide and then oxidized. Some carbon disulfide may be produced also. Elemental sulfur may be produced during the oxidation process, which may be in part chemical but is largely carried on by autotrophic organisms. Sulfites are produced as an intermediate step in the oxidation but are changed into sulfates so rapidly that no great accumulation of them occurs. The process of oxidation to sulfites and sulfates is known as sulfofication. The sulfurous and sulfuric acids produced in the soil as a result of the addition of elemental sulfur, or of organic materials containing sulfur, exert a solvent action upon minerals. The addition of sulfur is one means employed to reduce the pH of soil for the growing of certain crops or decorative plants. This point is discussed more fully in the chapter dealing with soil reaction.

Under anaerobic conditions any hydrogen sulfide or carbon bisulfide produced during the decay of organic matter is not oxidized. Also various other reduction products are formed, such as mercaptans. In addition, sulfates which may have been present when the anaerobic condi-

[13] *Illinois Agr. Exp. Sta. Ann. Rep.*, Vols. 47 and 50, 1933–1934 and 1936–1937.

tions developed, or sulfates applied later, are reduced to sulfites and possibly to elemental sulfur, hydrogen sulfide, and other reduction products if the anaerobic conditions continue.

Action of Sulfates in Soils. The application of the sulfates of iron and aluminum results, through hydrolysis, in the formation of sulfuric acid and hydroxides of the cations. Accordingly these sulfates are sometimes added to soils to increase their acidity. Ammonium sulfate also is converted into sulfuric and nitric acids in the soil.

As previously mentioned, calcium sulfate was added to soils in considerable quantities in the form of gypsum until around 1850. Large quantities are now added in superphosphate and in mixed fertilizers containing this material. Although $CaSO_4$ is somewhat soluble the application of the salt to many soils increases their soluble salt content much more than can be accounted for by the solubility of the $CaSO_4$. This phenomenon can be accounted for largely by the replacement by calcium of cations, which form much more soluble sulfates, from the colloidal fraction.

Application of $CaSO_4$ to soils deficient in sulfur or calcium may also stimulate biological activities. Sometimes this accelerated biological action may increase the quantity of soluble materials. It is also possible that the cations replaced by the calcium may stimulate bacterial action.

The calcium supplied by $CaSO_4$ in fertilizers is of importance in crop production in areas where soils are subject to excessive leaching. This is true of considerable areas in the southeastern states. As previously pointed out, the sulfur is also needed in many of these soils and likewise in sections of several other states. Fortunately, high concentrations of $CaSO_4$ do not appear to be detrimental to the normal growth of many crops.

FORMS AND FUNCTIONS OF SULFUR IN PLANTS

As a constituent of volatile compounds in many plants sulfur has a striking influence on their flavor. Sulfur also is a constituent of some proteins and when a deficiency of the element occurs chlorophyll formation and root development are restricted.

Sulfur Compounds in Plants. Sulfur occurs in plants chiefly in the form of proteins, sulfates, and volatile compounds. In proteins it exists as the amino acids, cystine, methionine, and cysteine. Also vitaman B_1 and biotin are present in many, if not all, plants. It is possible that the food value of plants is improved by an increase in content of these amino acids and vitamins through the addition of sulfur to soils

deficient in the element. Other organic compounds containing sulfur
are synthesized by members of other plant families.

Among the most common volatile compounds are S-glucosides which,
when hydrolyzed, produce mustard oil, and vinyl and allyl sulfides and
mercaptans. Although volatile compounds are more plentiful in members of the mustard family they are also found in onion, garlic, and
representatives of other families of plants.

The quantity of sulfur in the inorganic form (sulfates) in plants varies
greatly. The amount of sulfate in the soil appears to have considerable
influence on the amount in plants, and there is some evidence to show
that an accumulation of sulfates represents sulfur in excess of the plant's
needs. Studies by Peterson [14] have shown the percentages of the total
sulfur in several crops which exists as soluble sulfates to be as follows:
rutabagas, 37; cabbage, 24; alfalfa hay, 50; and sugar beets, 34.

Sulfur is not concentrated in a particular part of plants but is fairly
evenly distributed. A mature corn plant was found to have its sulfur
content distributed as follows: leaves, 40 per cent; stem, 23 per cent;
grain, 26 per cent; and roots, 11 per cent.

Role of Sulfur in Plant Growth. Aside from serving as a constituent of protein and various other compounds in plants, sulfur has an
influence on chlorophyll development. Although not a constituent of
chlorophyll, plants deficient in sulfur exhibit a pale green or yellow
color.

The root systems of several plants have been observed to be greatly
enlarged by applications of sulfur, and the numbers of nodules on the
roots of legumes have been increased.

Plants deficient in sulfur are high in carbohydrate and nitrate content.
The rate of nitrate reduction is decreased, but starch digestion and translocation of sugars is not restricted.

THE NEED FOR SULFUR APPLICATIONS IN CROP PRODUCTION

Although a number of states have recognized the need for application of sulfur to at least some of their soils, others have found no increase in crop yields from sulfur additions. Further studies may reveal
additional need for the element in areas where fertilizers are not used
extensively.

The Need of Mineral Soils for Sulfur. A number of states have
reported considerable increases in crop yields from applications of sulfur-
containing materials. Usually there are certain areas in these states in

[14] *Amer. Chem. Soc. Proc.* 36:1290, 1914.

which a sulfur deficiency occurs rather than in all the soils of the state. For example, in some of the Western states soils that are irrigated with water from given sources receive sufficient sulfur in the water, and unirrigated areas receiving water from other sources are in need of sulfur additions. Also areas in north central and northwestern Minnesota are insufficiently supplied with sulfur although no response in plant growth has been observed in some of the other sections of the state.

As nearly as can be determined from information available at present, there are some 8 states in which applications of sulfur are considered unnecessary. These are Arizona, Iowa, Kansas, Nebraska, New Mexico, North Dakota, South Dakota, and Utah. On the other hand in the following 8 states it is considered desirable to apply sulfur, in addition to that supplied in precipitation and in present fertilizer applications, to some soil areas: California, Florida, Idaho, Minnesota, Montana, Oregon, Washington, and Wyoming.

In the remaining states considerable quantities of sulfur are added to the soil either in precipitation, or in fertilizer, or both. Under present conditions, applications of additional sulfur are not considered necessary for satisfactory crop production.

Use of Sulfur on Organic Soils. In general little response in crop yield to applications of sulfur compounds to organic soils has been observed. In other words, sulfur as a plant nutrient does not appear to be deficient in mucks and peats. In this connection, however, it should be recalled that these lands are usually fertilized heavily, and the fertilizer generally contains appreciable quantities of sulfur. On the other hand, many organic soils have too high a pH value for the best growth of a number of crops, especially onions, spinach, beans, potatoes, and other crops sensitive to a deficiency of manganese. As a result sulfur is frequently applied to such soils in order to develop a desirable reaction. Applications range from a few hundred pounds of granulated sulfur to a ton or more per acre. When the high pH extends to considerable depth, 1 application of sulfur is disked in, followed by deep plowing, and then a second application is worked into the surface soil.

REFERENCES

Alway, F. J., Marsh, A. W., and Methley, W. J. A nutrient element slighted in agricultural research. *J. Amer. Soc. Agron.,* 32: 913, 1940.
Alway, F. J., Marsh, A. W., and Methley, W. J. Sufficiency of atmospheric sulfur for maximum crop yields. *Soil Sci. Soc. Amer. Proc.,* 11: 229, 1937.
Bertramson, B. R., Fried, M., and Tisdale, S. L. Sulfur studies of Indiana soils and crops. *Soil Sci.,* 70: 27, 1950.

Bogdanoff, S. M.   Amount of sulfur in plants.   *J. Russ. Phys. Chem. Soc.,* 31: 471, 1899.

Brown, P. E., and Kellogg, E. H.   Sulfur and permanent soil fertility in Iowa. *J. Amer. Soc. Agron.,* 7: 97, 1915.

Conrad, J. P.   Sulfur fertilization in California and some related factors.   *Soil Sci.,* 70: 43, 1950.

Crocker, W.   Sulfur deficiency in soils.   *Soil Sci.,* 60: 149, 1945.

Dymond, T. S., Hughes, F., and Jupe, C. W. C.   The influence of sulfur as manure upon the yield and feeding value of crops.   *J. Agr. Sci.,* 1: 217, 1905.

Evans, C. A., and Rost, C. O.   Total organic sulfur and humus sulfur of Minnesota soils.   *Soil Sci.,* 59: 125, 1945.

Fraps, G. S.   Possibilities of sulfur as a soil amendment.   *Texas Agr. Exp. Sta. Bull.* 414, 1930.

Fried, M.   The absorption of sulfur dioxide by plants as shown by the use of radioactive sulfur.   *Soil Sci. Soc. Amer. Proc.,* 13: 135, 1948.

Hart, E. B., and Peterson, W. H.   Sulfur requirements of farm crops in relation to the soil and air supply.   *Wis. Agr. Exp. Sta. Res. Bull.* 14, 1911.

Kelly, J. B., and Midgley, A. R.   Sulfur in Vermont agriculture.   *Vermont Agr. Exp. Sta. Pamphlet* 23, 1950.

McCool, M. M., and Johnson, A. N.   Nitrogen and sulfur content of leaves of plants within and at different distances from industrial centers.   Boyce Thompson Inst., *Contrib.* 9: 371, 1938.

Neller, J. R., Killinger, G. B., Jones, D. W., Bledsoe, R. W., and Lundy, H. W. Sulfur requirements of soils for clover-grass pastures in relation to fertilizer phosphate.   *Florida Agr. Exp. Sta. Bull.* 475, 1951.

Peterson, W. H.   Forms of sulfur in plant materials and their variation with the soil supply.   *Amer. Chem. Soc. Proc.,* 36: 1290, 1914.

Powers, W. L.   *The Use of Sulfur in Soils.*   Texas Gulf Sulfur Co., Houston, Texas.

Scholl, W., and Wallace, H. W.   Commercial fertilizers; consumption in the United States.   *U.S.D.A. Bur. Plant Ind. Soils, Agr. Eng.,* 1951.

Setterstrom, P. W., Zimmerman, P. W., and Crocker, W.   Effect of low concentrations of sulfur dioxide on yield of alfalfa and cruciferae.   Boyce Thompson Inst., *Contrib.* 9: 179, 1938.

Shedd, O. M.   The relation of sulfur to soil fertility.   *Kentucky Agr. Exp. Sta. Bull.* 188, 1941.

Thomas, M. D., Hendricks, R. H., and Hill, G. R.   Sulfur content of vegetation. *Soil Sci.,* 70: 9, 1950.

12

Micro and Some Non-Essential Nutrients

For many years 10 elements were all that were considered necessary for the normal growth of plants, and although several others are commonly found in plants in appreciable quantities their essentiality has never been established. Among these may be placed sodium, silicon, and chlorine. More accurate research methods, including the use of highly purified chemicals and water, have shown that several elements are necessary for the proper nutrition of plants even though occurring in most plants in very small quantities. Because of the minute amounts of these elements usually present in plant material they have been designated as micronutrients. It is interesting to note that all these elements are toxic to plants if they are available in the soil in more than very small quantities.

The economic importance of the minor elements is shown by the fact that thousands of acres in Western Australia have been made productive through the application of some of them. Likewise on many acres of organic soils in the Florida Everglades, in New York, Michigan, and Indiana the yields and quality of crops have been greatly improved by application of micronutrients. Considerable quantities of these elements are also used on mineral soils in several states.[1]

It is recognized that these elements may function in the metabolic processes of the plant or in antagonism to other elements, or both. The supply in the soil, availability, and function in plant growth of the micronutrients and of several elements commonly found in plants but not considered essential will be discussed under the following topical headings.

Discussion Topics

Manganese.	Molybdenum.
Copper.	Sodium.
Boron.	Silicon.
Zinc.	Other elements.

[1] The quantities of several micronutrients used in the United States and in various states are given in *Fertilizer Rev.*, October–December 1953.

MANGANESE

Few soils contain more than a small fraction of a percentage of manganese, and yet there are few soils which do not contain enough of the element to supply the needs of crops for many years if it passes into an available form at an appreciable rate. Robinson [2] reported an average Mn content of 0.059 per cent for 26 representative soils, with the percentage varying from 0.0031 to 0.395. Only one sample contained more than 0.139 per cent and the majority of them less than 0.077 per cent. If the soil containing 0.395 per cent be omitted from the list, the average Mn content would be 0.046 per cent.

In most soils producing manganese-deficient crops the problem is one of availability of the element rather than of total supply. Replaceable as well as easily reduced manganese is included in the "available" supply. Peech determined the quantities of replaceable manganese, zinc, and copper in surface and subsoil samples of representative soils from Florida citrus groves. His results are summarized in Table 49. Commenting on the very small quantities of the elements found in replaceable form Peech called attention to the fact that the supply was low in the virgin soils and that it has been greatly reduced by leaching due in part to the continued use of acid-forming fertilizer. Also much smaller quantities of the nutrients were found in the subsoil than in the surface because the exchange capacity resides largely in the organic content.

Manganese Requirement of Crops. Manganese was shown to be a constituent of plants by Scheele about 1775, but it was not until the early part of the present century that the element was proved to be essential for plant growth. Crops require extremely small quantities of manganese, probably because the element is not a constituent of the plant tissues and the supply is translocated to the points where it is most needed. McHargue [3] states that different plant species growing on the same soil type will vary considerably in their manganese content and that in general legumes contain the least amounts and the grasses the greatest amounts. Also soybeans grown in water cultures contained less iron when the manganese content of the plants was high, and vice versa.

Beeson [4] reports a variation of from 1 to 2,262 p.p.m. of manganese in some 172 plants or plant parts. The smaller amount was found in apples and the larger quantity in the leaves of cigar-wrapper type of tobacco. Very small amounts, 2 p.p.m., were also reported in dates, mandarin, peanut, pear, watermelon, and yam tuber. Some of the

[2] *U.S.D.A. Bull.* 122, 1914.
[3] *Soil Sci.,* 60: 115, 1945.
[4] *U.S.D.A. Misc. Pub.* 369, 1941.

TABLE 49.　EXCHANGEABLE MANGANESE, ZINC, AND COPPER, IN SOILS FROM FLORIDA CITRUS GROVES

Pounds per Acre-6-In. of Soil

Soil Series	Manganese						Zinc						Copper					
	Surface Soil			Subsoil			Surface Soil			Subsoil			Surface Soil			Subsoil		
	Max.	Min.	Avg.	Max.	Min.	Avg.	Max.	Min.	Avg.	Max.	Min.	Avg.	Max.	Min.	Avg.	Max.	Min.	Avg.
Norfolk	17.0	0.2	3.2	5.3	0.0	0.8	5.6	0.8	0.91	0.96	0.08	0.36	4.2	0.06	0.55	3.0	0.04	0.26
Blanton	7.5	0.3	3.3	1.5	0.1	0.8	2.0	0.16	0.80	0.56	0.16	0.32	0.68	0.06	0.31	0.36	0.04	0.15
Eustis	8.5	1.7	3.9	4.7	1.0	2.6	1.4	0.24	0.54	0.48	0.16	0.24	0.80	0.04	0.34	0.12	0.04	0.08
Lakewood	1.2	0.7	0.9	0.1	0.1	0.1	0.16	0.08	0.12	0.08	0.40	0.24	0.22	0.12	0.17	0.10	0.06	0.08
Orlando	2.5	1.5	2.0	1.7	1.5	1.6	0.32	0.32	0.32	0.16	0.16	0.16	0.12	0.06	0.09	0.12	0.06	0.09
Gainesville	3.9	2.3	3.1	1.3	0.9	1.1	0.32	0.24	0.28	0.08	0.08	0.08	0.22	0.20	0.21	0.60	0.06	0.33
Portsmouth	5.1	1.1	2.6	1.7	0.5	0.9	1.4	0.16	0.50	0.96	0.16	0.52	0.24	0.12	0.16	0.12	0.06	0.09
Parkwood	9.3	0.3	3.2	11.5	0.3	2.4	2.2	0.08	0.45	0.96	0.08	0.31	1.20	0.08	0.30	0.20	0.06	0.12

variations found in the manganese content of plants of the same species are: spinach, 10 p.p.m. to 694 p.p.m.; timothy cut for hay, 11 p.p.m. to 165 p.p.m.; turnip roots, 5 p.p.m. to 65 p.p.m.; wheat grain, 5 p.p.m. to 260 p.p.m.; and wheat straw, 22 p.p.m. to 150 p.p.m. The great variation in the amount of manganese in plants is evident. High soil acidity is one of the factors which leads to a large intake of manganese by plants, but other factors may also be involved.

Availability of Manganese in Soils. It is quite generally agreed that manganese is absorbed by plants in the divalent form, and hence studies of availability revolve around factors which bring about reducing conditions in soils. Poor drainage may lead to a high availability of manganese, as may also a very compact layer in the upper subsoil which restricts aeration. In addition, acidity in soils is usually accompanied by a high manganese availability and sometimes by a sufficient intake of the element to prove toxic to certain plants.

Manganese deficiency in crops is seldom encountered except on soils with near neutral or alkaline reactions. Overliming may easily result in a deficiency of the element. A shortage of available manganese may usually be overcome by increasing the soil acidity through application of sulfur or of dilute sulfuric acid. The latter method is the more rapid in its effect. A yet more rapid but less lasting remedy for manganese deficiency is the application of a solution of manganese sulfate near the plants or the spraying of the foliage with a solution of the salt.

Functions of Manganese in Plants and Symptoms of Deficiency. Although the exact part manganese plays in the growth of plants is not known there is evidence that its chief value lies in its participation in oxidation-reduction reactions. For example, under conditions of poor aeration ammonium salts are used more efficiently when the supply of manganese is ample. With a limited supply of manganese, however, nitrate is a superior source of nitrogen presumably because the oxygen from the nitrate ion can assist in the respiration process. An excess of manganese may induce chlorosis due, probably, to inactivity of iron because of its oxidation by manganese.[5] On the other hand a deficiency of manganese results in a limited development of chlorophyll and hence chlorosis, although the element is not a constituent of chlorophyll. Also an excess of iron brings about symptoms of manganese deficiency. It has been suggested by Somers and Shive [6] that a ratio of iron to manganese of approximately 2.0 in the nutrient medium is optimum for plant growth.

[5] *Hawaii Agr. Exp. Sta. Bull.* 52, 1924.
[6] *Plant Physiol.,* 17: 582, 1942.

The above-normal concentration of nitrates and of several amino acids in manganese-deficient plants has led to the opinion that manganese is concerned with the synthesis of proteins or of some amino acid. Several crops have been found to be lower in reducing sugar and sucrose content when the supply of manganese was limited. Also the purity of sugar from sugar cane is higher where ample manganese is available. It would appear that the element plays some part in sugar formation.

Schreiner and Dawson were among the first workers to report the finding of plants showing manganese-deficiency symptoms. Their observations were made on tomatoes in Florida in 1927. Also gray speck of oats was identified as a manganese-deficiency disease in 1927 by Carne, although the disease was not reported in America until 1941 by Sherman and Harmer.[7] The most commonly observed symptom of insufficient manganese is chlorosis, primarily in the younger leaves. The veins remain green but the interveinal tissue becomes light green to white, is often mottled, and in some plants the necrotic areas may fall out. Some plants shed badly affected leaves. Other symptoms of manganese deficiency are retarded growth and failure to blossom.

Crops belonging to the grass family are quite sensitive to a deficiency of manganese. The symptoms exhibited by wheat and barley are different from the gray speck of oats in that streaks of yellow parallel to the midrib appear in the upper leaves. The tips of the leaves do not remain green as in oats, but neither does the yellowing start at the leaf tips as is true when nitrogen or potassium are in short supply. The leaves of all three grains droop or break over when the affected area covers the width of the leaf.

Alfalfa and clovers are far less sensitive to a deficiency of manganese than are many crops. Beans of various kinds are quite sensitive and so are sugar beets. Symptoms of deficiency have been reported in tomatoes, strawberries, peaches, potatoes, and sugar cane.

COPPER

During the latter part of the last century a stimulation of plant growth from the use of bordeaux was ascribed to the copper content of the mixture. Similar reports were made in the early years of the present century. Experiments involving the control of "dieback" in citrus and various other fruit trees by use of bordeaux spray and copper sulfate additions to the soil followed, but the thought that the treatments involved the supplying of an essential element was not expressed. Also

[7] *J. Amer. Soc. Agron.*, 33: 1080, 1941.

when in 1927 growth of several crops on organic soils in New York [8] and Florida [9] was greatly increased through the use of copper sulfate the phenomena were not considered as evidence of the essentiality of copper. In fact it was 1930 before Sommer [10] showed that copper is required for the normal growth of plants.

Copper Content of Soils. It has not been a common practice to determine the copper content of soils. In studying the composition of 26 representative American soils Robinson [11] reported copper present in 8 samples but did not test for it in 18 soils. Holmes [12] studied the copper and zinc contents of soils in many sections of the United States. Some of his results are presented in Table 50. Holmes also determined

TABLE 50. COPPER AND ZINC CONTENTS OF SEVERAL SOIL TYPES *

Soil Type and Location	pH	Copper, p.p.m.	Zinc, p.p.m.
Nacogdoches fine sandy loam, Texas	5.3	12	87
Clinton silt loam, Wisconsin	5.9	20	70
Kirvin fine sandy loam, Texas	6.2	28	34
Marshall silt loam, Iowa	5.5	30	70
Houston black clay, Texas	8.1	20	65
Colby silty clay loam, Kansas	8.3	57	81
Shelby silt loam, Missouri	5.4	40	69
Vernon fine sandy loam, Oklahoma	7.6	24	27
Muskingum silt loam, Ohio	4.7	45	120
Palouse silt loam, Washington	6.7	46	76
Cecil sandy clay loam, North Carolina	5.6	43	53

* *Soil Sci.*, 56: 359, 1943. Used with permission.

the copper content of 12 soils from the area drained by the western tributaries of the Mississippi River. The amount of copper found varied from 17 to 36 p.p.m., with an average of 26 p.p.m. Six soils from the watersheds of the eastern tributaries of the Mississippi varied in copper content from 19 to 28 p.p.m. and averaged 23 p.p.m. Also 11 samples of alluvium deposited by the river contained an average of 20 p.p.m., with the amount varying from 13 to 34 p.p.m. In all the surface soils studied the copper content varied from 8 to 57 p.p.m. In some soils there was considerable difference in the quantities of copper in the different horizons of the profile, but in many there was not. Holmes opined that the differences in copper content between soils and

[8] *Phytopath.* 17: 49, 1927.
[9] *Florida Agr. Exp. Sta. Bull.* 190, 1927.
[10] *Amer. Fertilizer,* 72, 6: 15, 1930, and *Plant Physiol.* 6: 339, 1931.
[11] *U.S.D.A. Bull.* 122, 1914.
[12] *Soil Sci.,* 56: 359, 1943.

in horizons of the same soil were associated with the amounts of clay and organic matter present. The extent of weathering, soil reaction, and nature of the parent material are also contributing factors in determining the retention of the copper originally present. In highly acid soils the copper content is usually low because of losses by leaching. This fact is illustrated by a study of 7 soils from an area within 15 miles of Kinston, North Carolina.[13] The copper content of 3 samples with pH values from 4.1 to 4.4 averaged 9.3 p.p.m. and that of 4 soils with pH values running from 4.9 to 6.0 averaged 20.8 p.p.m.

Few determinations have been made of the minor-element content of organic soils. Allison and Gaddum [14] determined spectrographically the quantities of 15 trace elements in the ash of an Everglade peat and an Okeechobee muck. Also Harmer [15] found the copper oxide (CuO) content of the plow layer of 23 Michigan mucks to average 0.0045 per cent, with the percentages varying from 0.009 to 0.0115. Some of the areas were under cultivation and had been heavily fertilized and others were in the virgin state.

Copper Requirement of Crops. Beeson's compilation [16] of the copper content of some 148 plants or plant parts shows a variation of from 1 p.p.m. to 560 p.p.m. The larger amount was found in celery and the smaller quantity in parts of several plants. A considerable number of the samples analyzed contained 5 or less p.p.m. of copper, and only 38 samples contained more than 20 p.p.m. The copper content of 30 celery samples ranged from 2 to 560 p.p.m. with the average being 238 p.p.m. The average copper content of a number of crops is given in Table 51.

Crops growing on neutral or alkaline soils seldom respond to applications of copper salts, although some calcareous sandy soils of south Australia are an exception. On acid soils, however, certain crops are frequently in need of additional copper. This is particularly true on organic soils, and Harmer [17] has divided the crops often grown on the muck soils in Michigan into groups on the basis of their response to copper application. Harmer also reports that the need for copper is greater in hot, dry seasons than in those that are cooler and more moist.

Functions of Copper in Plant Growth and Symptoms of Deficiency. Copper is considered to be active in the processes of respiration. There is evidence that copper in association with protein serves

[13] *Soil Sci.,* 56: 359, 1943.
[14] *Soil Sci. Soc. of Florida Proc.* II: 68, 1940.
[15] *Michigan Agr. Exp. Sta. Spec. Bull.* 314, 1941.
[16] *U.S.D.A. Misc. Pub.* 369, 1941.
[17] *Soil Sci. Soc. Amer. Proc.,* 10: 284, 1945.

TABLE 51. AVERAGE COPPER CONTENT OF SEVERAL CROPS *

Material	Number of Samples	Copper, p.p.m.	Material	Number of Samples	Copper, p.p.m.
Alfalfa, cut for hay	8	9	Tomato, fruit	51	14
Field bean, seed	12	11	Potato, tubers	143	8
Garden beans, edible			Barley, grain	12	16
pods and seeds	24	13	Oat, grain	29	11
Beet, roots	15	10	Oat, straw	26	11
Cabbage, heads	26	4	Wheat, grain	108	9
Carrot, roots	15	11	Wheat, straw	24	3
Lettuce, edible part	45	19	Corn, stover	16	5

* Compiled from data in *U.S.D.A. Misc. Pub.* 369.

as a catalyst in various oxidation processes in the plant. The element is also concerned with the chlorophyll content of plants. Several investigators have reported a higher chlorophyll content in plants as a result of copper applications. On the other hand a copper deficiency does not always result in chlorosis, and Bailey and McHargue [18] found more copper in the lower, necrotic parts of tomato plants than in younger parts of non-chlorotic plants. These and other studies have led to the suggestion that copper serves as a protective agent against the destruction of chlorophyll. Whether this end is accomplished by the union of copper with the chlorophyll or by some other process is not known.

It has also been suggested that copper may benefit some crops through the neutralization of some harmful substance in the soil.[19] Evidence of this function is deduced from the fact that greatly different quantities of the element are required to give maximum yields of crops on different copper-deficient soils.

The most frequently observed evidence of copper deficiency in plants is "dieback," that is, the death of the young growing tips. This symptom has been reported in a number of different kinds of fruit trees. Dieback is frequently followed by the development of axillary buds below the dead tips which results in a bushy growth known as rosetting.[20] Chlorosis of the older leaves sometimes occurs also.

Cereals frequently exhibit "reclamation disease" if the copper deficiency is severe. The name arises from the fact that the disease has frequently been observed in crops growing on newly reclaimed organic soils in Europe. Symptoms of the disease are a graying and withering

[18] *Amer. J. Botany,* 30: 559, 1943.
[19] *Soil Conditions and Plant Growth,* p. 52, eighth edition, 1950.
[20] *Soil Sci.,* 60: 72, 1945.

of the leaf tips followed by the leaves becoming flaccid and bending or turning backward.

Tomato plants deficient in copper are bluish green, do not produce blossoms, and have the growth of both tops and roots stunted.[21] Mc-Murtrey [22] reports a wilting of the upper leaves, bending of the seed-head, and breakdown of the older leaves of tobacco when the supply of copper is insufficient. Harmer [23] and other workers have observed a pale yellow coloration of the outer scales of yellow onion bulbs and a dieback of the leaf tips when the crop was grown on copper-deficient soil. He also reports a burning of the leaf edges of spinach similar to that caused by potassium deficiency. Additions of copper to soils having a low available supply have not only increased yields of many crops but have resulted in a darker green in spinach and lettuce, an orange yellow rather than pale yellow in carrots, and an increased sugar content in carrots, table beets, and sugar beets.

BORON

Boron was found to be a constituent of some plants by Wittstein and Apaiger in 1857. Little attention was given to the fact, however, until the work of Bertrand in 1912 and of Brenchley in 1914 gave rise to considerable research on the relation of the element to plant growth. Although Jay suggested, in 1895, that boron might be found in all plants it was not until 1923 that Warington proved the element was essential for the growth of plants. The functions of boron in plant nutrition and the effects on plants of an insufficient supply have been the subject of many studies.

Boron in Plants and Soils. The boron content of different plant species varies, and, moreover, the quantity taken up by any given plant is affected by the available supply in the growth medium. For example, Eaton [24] found considerable difference in the boron content of different kinds of plants grown in sand cultures and an abnormally high content in all of them because the cultures contained a higher concentration of boron than field soils. Robinson and Edgington [25] state that the amount of boron in plant leaves seldom exceeds 70 p.p.m. under natural conditions. As much as 3,875 p.p.m. in muskmelon leaves has been reported, however.

Cereals seem unable to absorb boron as readily as many plants, and the dry tissue seldom contains more than 0.1 to 0.3 p.p.m. Dicotyle-

[21] *Soil Sci.*, 60: 72, 1945.
[22] Unpublished manuscript.
[23] *Michigan Ext. Bull.* 123, 1936.
[24] *J. Agr. Res.*, 69: 237, 1944.
[25] *Soil Sci.*, 60: 20, 1945.

donous plants are better absorbers of the element than monocotyledon-
ous. Tomatoes, potatoes, pears, and tobacco sometimes contain as
much as 18 p.p.m. in the dry tissue.

The boron content of soils is not high except in some arid regions.
Under climatic conditions which lead to the development of strongly
acid soils it is often reduced to a low level by leaching. Whetstone [26]
and associates report three regions in which soils are likely to be deficient in boron for crops which require appreciable amounts, namely:
the Atlantic Coastal Plains extending westward to the Appalachian
mountains; a belt across northern Michigan, Wisconsin, and Minnesota;
and the Pacific Coastal region and Pacific Northwest. Some 300 soil
samples were tested and boron was found in all of them. Soils from
areas not receiving either excessive or very limited rainfall were found
to vary in boron content from 4 to 88 p.p.m. The content of available
boron varied from 0.4 to 64.8 p.p.m. Areas of unusual soils, especially mucks and peats, in other regions may also be insufficiently supplied with boron.

The availability of boron in soils is related to their reaction. Availability is relatively high in acid soils if the supply has not been reduced
through leaching, but in neutral and alkaline soils plants have difficulty
in absorbing boron. Overliming may result in boron deficiency.

Functions of Boron in Plants and Symptoms of Deficiency.
The exact functions of boron in plant growth are not known. The
element is concerned with the intake of calcium and its utilization by the
plant. If the plant contains too little calcium its tolerance for boron is
low. On the other hand a plant high in calcium content has a high
boron requirement. There is also a relationship between potassium and
boron within the plant. For example, if a plant contains a large supply
of potassium and there is a boron deficiency, the deficiency symptoms
are intensified. The activities of boron in the plant also appear to be
associated with those of the NO_3 and PO_4 ions. This fact leads to the
belief that boron may be concerned in the synthesis and breakdown of
protein and carbohydrates. The work of Beckenbach [27] indicates that
plants have a high boron requirement when well supplied with nitrates
or when they are obtaining insufficient phosphate. Boron appears to
be fixed in the plant tissue so that it cannot move to parts where it is
most needed. As a result a continuous supply is needed to meet plant
requirements.

More definite results have been obtained in the study of plant characteristics induced by an insufficient supply of boron. Boron deficiency

[26] *U.S.D.A. Bur. Plant Ind. Tech. Bull.* 797, 1942.
[27] *Florida Agr. Exp. Sta. Tech. Bull.* 395, 1944.

affects primarily the metabolically active tissues of the plant, but the symptoms produced in different plants vary because of a variation in the location of the most active tissue. Many of the disorders in crops resulting from a boron deficiency were recognized as "diseases" long

Fig. 28.   Lettuce transplants of the same age growing on boron-deficient soil in Vermont.   The plant on the right received borax, and the one on the left did not. A deficiency of boron caused death of the first growing tip, which resulted in multiple branching and rosette.   From *Better Crops with Plant Food,* American Potash Institute, Washington, D. C., 1948.   Courtesy of A. R. Midgley and D. E. Dunklee.

before their cause was known.   Some of the most commonly observed effects on plants are: dying of the growing tips (Fig. 28), inhibition of blossoming, disorders in the xylem which result in obstruction in conducting systems, poor development of the root system, and breakdown and discoloration of cell walls especially in the phloem.   Symptoms of boron deficiency develop more rapidly in the summer than in the spring or fall.   This phenomenon appears to be related to length of day rather than to temperature, and rate of growth, which is related to length of day, may be a factor. Some of the diseases which have attracted most attention are: cracked stem in celery, heart rot of sugar beets, top rot of tobacco, internal cork of apples, and girdle or canker in table beets. Tillering in wheat is stimulated by a lack of boron, but head development is restricted.

Toxicity of Boron in Plants. Growth in many plants is stimulated by very small amounts of boron although the response in different species is variable. On the other hand, boron is toxic to virtually all plants when present in more than very small quantities. But again there is great variability in the susceptibility of plant species to boron toxicity. Furthermore numerous investigations have shown that a variety of factors including climatic conditions, soil characteristics, and plant vigor influence the toxic effect of boron for a given plant. As a result of the susceptibility of crops to boron toxicity only small amounts of the element are recommended for application to correct a boron deficiency. The actual amounts vary with the crop to be grown and the method of application but seldom exceed from 30 to 50 pounds of borax per acre when broadcast or 10 pounds when applied in the row. In fact considerably smaller quantities should be applied on strongly acid soils for some crops such as corn and tobacco.

ZINC

Some attention was given to the effect of zinc on plant growth in studies of *Aspergillus* spp. about 1900. However, it was not until Javillier in France, between 1907 and 1912, showed an increased growth of wheat, corn, lupines, and peas from application of $ZnSO_4$ that attention was attracted to the effect of the element on the growth of higher plants. Although Maze (1914) reported zinc to be necessary for the growth of corn, it was not until 1926 that the work of Sommer and Lipman [28] was accepted as proof of the essentiality of the element. Since that date it has been shown that previously noted diseases of several crops are the result of a zinc deficiency.

Supply of Zinc in Soils. Although zinc is "common and rather widely diffused," according to Clarke,[29] he does not give the quantities present in igneous or sedimentary rocks or in the lithosphere. Also the zinc content of soils has seldom been determined. Holmes [30] found an average of 24 p.p.m. of zinc in 7 soils near Kinston, North Carolina, with the quantity varying only between 21 and 31 p.p.m. Twelve soils

[28] *Plant Physiol.,* 1: 231, 1926.
[29] Data of Geochemistry, *U.S.G.S. Bull.* 695, 1920.
[30] *Soil Sci.,* 56: 359, 1943.

from the area drained by the western tributaries of the Mississippi River varied in zinc content between 34 and 105 p.p.m. with an average of 79 p.p.m. Six soils from the watersheds of eastern rivers flowing into the Mississippi contained an average of 75 p.p.m. of zinc with the quantity varying from 59 to 97 p.p.m. The alluvium deposited by the Mississippi was also sampled at 11 locations and was found to contain from 50 to 120 p.p.m. of zinc with an average of 94 p.p.m. The zinc contents of some 11 representative soil types from 9 different states, as determined by Holmes, are given in Table 50. In his studies he found no soil containing less than 16 p.p.m. of zinc and none containing more than 147 p.p.m. It should be noted, however, that Holmes did not include organic soils in his studies. Numerous reports have appeared of soils so low in zinc content or in supply of available zinc that crop growth was restricted.

Hibbard [31] made a survey of the zinc content of soils and rocks in central California. The result of tests on some 140 samples led to the conclusion that in general the zinc content varied from 1 to 5 p.p.m. although some samples contained much more. There was a tendency for zinc to be accumulated in the surface because of its return in plant residues and its fixation by the soil. One sample taken to the depth of 2 inches under an old redwood contained 94 p.p.m. of zinc. Other samples high in organic content also contained above-average quantities of the element. The quantities of replaceable zinc in a number of Florida soils are given in Table 49. A few instances have been reported in which sufficient zinc was present to be toxic to plants; such areas of organic soils in New York were studied by Staker and Cummings.[32] One unproductive soil was found to contain 67,073 p.p.m. of the element. Zinc has been found to be less available in alkaline than in acid soils. However, the factors that affect the availability of soil zinc are not well understood. Available information concerning the problem has been discussed by Camp.[33] It is noteworthy that any factor that restricts the development of, or impairs, the root system of a plant which is not an efficient absorber of zinc may induce the development of deficiency symptoms even though the supply of available zinc is ample for many other plants.

Removal of Zinc in Crops. Many more determinations have been made of the zinc content of crops than of soils. In a compilation of the results of the analysis of some 90 plants and plant parts Beeson [34]

[31] *Soil Sci.*, 49: 63, 1940.
[32] *Soil Sci. Soc. Amer. Proc.*, 6: 206, 1941.
[33] *Soil Sci.*, 60: 157, 1945.
[34] *U.S.D.A. Misc. Pub.* 369, 1941.

gives the smallest quantity found as 2 p.p.m. in the edible portion of prunes and the largest amount 360 p.p.m. in the seeds of Kentucky bluegrass. The quantities in several crops and groups of crops, as compiled from Beeson's tables, are given in Table 52.

TABLE 52. ZINC CONTENT OF SEVERAL CROPS AND GROUPS OF CROPS

Material	Number of Samples	Zinc Content, p.p.m. Max.	Min.	Avg.
Alfalfa, cut for hay	4	112	14	57
Redtop, cut for hay	13	60	10	23
Soybean, cut for hay	31	80	27	42
7 grains	...	63	12	24
Wheat, grain	27	100	19	63
Corn, stover	15	80	5	27
Oat, straw	8	193	4	83
Wheat, straw	24	25	7	17
6 fruits	...	9	2	6
6 roots and tubers	...	47	10	23
6 green vegetables	...	119	8	34

The wide variation in the quantity of zinc reported in different samples of the same plant material is quite amazing. That the intake of zinc by plants is greatly affected by the available supply in the soil has been shown by Lucas [35] and Stoker,[36] but, also, possibly the methods of sampling and analysis are not well standardized. Fruits appear to be low in zinc content and leguminous plants relatively high. Among green vegetables lettuce is unusually rich in zinc, according to the analyses available. There is no regularity in the relative amounts of zinc in the straw and grain of cereals. For example, wheat grain contains much more of the element than does the straw, but with oats the situation is reversed.

There is a vast difference in the ability of different plants to extract zinc from the soil. For example two different weeds in Florida have been reported to contain up to 700 p.p.m. with an average of 140 p.p.m. when growing on soil from which *Crotalaria* extracted only from 4 to 11 p.p.m.

Functions of Zinc in Plant Growth and Symptoms of Deficiency. It is generally agreed that zinc has something to do with chlorophyll formation, but nothing more is definitely known concerning the functions of the element in plant nutrition. In all reported

[35] *Soil Sci. Soc. Amer. Proc.* 10: 269, 1945.
[36] *Soil Sci. Soc. Amer. Proc.* 6: 206, 1941.

cases in which plants have recovered from zinc-deficiency diseases after an application of the element there has been an increase in the zinc content of the leaves. Furthermore, leaves from zinc-deficient plants are always below normal in zinc content. Leaf development is also restricted by an insufficient supply of zinc.

Chlorosis is the most commonly reported symptom of zinc deficiency. The chlorotic tissue varies in different plants from light green to white, and the discoloration usually occurs between the veins.[37] In

Fig. 29. Orange showing acute zinc deficiency (*right*) and normal development (*left*). Note the small, pointed leaves with distinct color pattern. The normal specimen came from a tree that was treated a year earlier for zinc deficiency. Florida Agr. Exp. Sta. Courtesy of A. F. Camp.

tobacco, however, there may be a faint chlorosis between the veins of the older leaves or at the tips and along the margins, which is followed quickly by small necrotic areas which enlarge and ultimately involve the entire leaf including the veins.[38] Some of the diseases that have been cured through applications of zinc are: bronzing of the leaves of tung trees; mottling, little leaf, or rosette in citrus; white bud of corn; little leaf of deciduous fruit trees; and pecan rosette. Figure 29 shows the small, discolored leaves of a zinc-deficient orange twig.

In corn the older leaves first show yellow streaks, which are followed by the development of necrotic areas. In extreme cases the unfolding leaves are light yellow or white, which phenomenon gave rise to the designation of white bud.

[37] *Soil Sci.,* 60: 157, 1945.

[38] McMurtrey, in *Diagnostic Techniques for Soils and Crops*, p. 242. American Potash Inst., Washington, D. C., 1948.

Camp [37] points out that zinc-deficiency symptoms are usually observed in plants growing on heavy soils, on sands in which the colloidal material is organic, on clays with low exchange capacity, and on mucks. The difficulty is usually encountered at slightly acid or alkaline reactions, although it has been found in Brazil on plants growing in soil with a pH of 4.0. Camp is of the opinion that there is a difference in characteristics of the deficiency symptoms in plants growing on soils with a pH below or above 6.0.

Zinc deficiency may be corrected by additions of soluble zinc salts to the soil or by spraying the affected plants with zinc sulfate solution. The difficulty may be prevented by growing plants which are efficient accumulators of zinc and then plowing them under in preparation for the crop which extracts the element sparingly from the soil.

MOLYBDENUM

There has been much discussion as to the essentiality of molybdenum for plant growth. Evidence of its need by plants has been accumulating in recent years, however, and most workers in the field of plant nutrition now list it as an essential element. The work of Arnon and Stout [39] contributed quite conclusive evidence that certain plants require molybdenum. The need of certain microorganisms, primarily *Azotobacter, Rhizobium,* and *Aspergillus,* for molybdenum was demonstrated a number of years ago.

Molybdenum in Soils. There is very little information concerning the molybdenum content of soils. Allison and Gaddum [40] report detectable quantities of the element in 8 out of 11 soil types collected in states other than Florida. On the other hand Rogers [41] and associates did not find the metal in examining spectrographically 77 samples representing 8 soil types in Florida. Both cropped and uncultivated soils were sampled usually, as well as different horizons of the profiles. Ter Meulen [42] reported from 0.1 to 0.3 p.p.m. in fertile soil and as little as 0.005 p.p.m. in barren sandy soil.

The most extensive study of the molybdenum content of soils was made by Barshad,[43] who determined the quantity in 20 surface soils of California and found a variation of from 0.1 p.p.m. to 9.7 p.p.m. Ten of the samples contained less than 1.0 p.p.m., and six contained more

[39] *Plant Physiol.,* 14: 599, 1939.
[40] *Soil Sci. Soc. of Florida Proc.,* II: 68, 1940.
[41] *Florida Agr. Exp. Sta. Bull.* 341, 1939.
[42] *Nature,* 130: 966, 1932.
[43] *Soil Sci.,* 66: 187, 1948.

than 2.0 p.p.m. There appeared to be no correlation between soil texture or pH value and content of molybdenum. High solubility of the
element, however, was found to be associated with alkalinity. Usually
there was more molybdenum in the surface than in the lower soil
horizons. A great variation was found in molybdenum content of
samples from different areas of the same soil type.

There is little evidence of molybdenum deficiency in soils, although
in a few instances there have been indications of crop benefit from applications of the element. For example, Bortels [44] reported an apparent
benefit to several legumes from application of molybdenum salts. Likewise, Anderson [45] found an increase in growth and a darker green in
pasture grasses, alfalfa, and subterranean clover, as a result of applications of very small quantities of molybdenum to an ironstone soil in
south Australia. Also Fairchild [46] has observed deficiency symptoms
of the element in cauliflower in West Virginia.

Molybdenum Content of Plants. As a whole plants contain very
small quantities of molybdenum. For example, Ter Meulen [47] reported
only small quantities of the element in many kinds of plants he examined,
the amounts varying from 0.01 p.p.m. to 8.0 p.p.m. in the dried tissue.
Peas and beans contained the largest quantity, from 3 to 9 p.p.m., with
cereals ranking second with 0.2 to 0.6 p.p.m. The content of fruits and
vegetables was very low. It is significant, however, that molybdenum
was always present. It is also of interest that plants are able to accumulate considerable amounts of the element if the supply in the soil permits. Ter Meulen [47] found 1 p.p.m. of the element in the dry tissue of
Azolla when the water in which the plant was growing contained only
0.0009 p.p.m.

In England [48] pasture grasses were found to contain sufficient molybdenum to cause disease in cattle. Britton and Goss [49] found evidence
of a similar difficulty in parts of California. It appears that cattle,
especially young dairy animals, are sensitive to an appreciable molybdenum content in green plants but are unaffected by similar quantities in cured hay. Ferguson [50] and associates set 20 p.p.m. as the lower
limit of molybdenum in plants, which is detrimental to cattle, but
Robinson and Edgington [51] consider this amount too high.

[44] *Arch. Mikrobiol.,* 8: 13, 1937.
[45] *J. Australian Inst. Agr. Sci.,* 8: 73, 1942.
[46] Personal letter.
[47] *Nature,* 130: 966, 1932.
[48] *J. Agr. Sci.,* 33: 44, 1943.
[49] *J. Amer. Vet. Med. Assoc.,* 108: 176, 1946.
[50] *J. Agr. Res.,* 33: 44, 1943.
[51] *Soil Sci.,* 66: 197, 1948.

In studying the soil and plant content of molybdenum in parts of California where cattle were poisoned by the element Barshad [52] found that growing plants and legumes in particular were able to accumulate sufficient molybdenum to prove toxic to cattle when growing in soils containing from 1.5 to 5.0 p.p.m. of the element. Studies of the molybdenum content of the parts of plants showed accumulations in leaf blades and growing parts. Plants also accumulate more of the element as they grow older. Variations in the molybdenum content in several plants collected from different locations and at different seasons are shown in Table 53.

TABLE 53. MOLYBDENUM CONTENT OF SEVERAL PLANTS AT DIFFERENT SEASONS AND FROM DIFFERENT LOCATIONS *

Plant	Number of Locations	Season and Variation in Mo Content, p.p.m.		
		Spring	Summer	Fall
Alfalfa	4	5.2–16.0	7.5–20.0	12.9–28.4
Rye grass	3	2.5– 4.3	4.3–14.0	6.5–25.0
Rhodes grass	1	8.1	14.0	25.0
Orchard grass	3	1.7– 4.7	4.9 †	9.8 †
Lotus corniculatus	2	20.6–30.0	31.0–43.6	72.0–92.9

* Prepared from data of Barshad. *Soil Sci.*, 66: 190, 1948. Used with permission.

† One location only.

The molybdenum content of 9 plants growing in soils containing 5–10 p.p.m. of total molybdenum was 5–200 p.p.m., whereas the same plants growing in soils with total molybdenum contents varying from a trace to 0.5 p.p.m. contained 0.8–22 p.p.m. of the element. The quantity of soluble molybdenum was much greater in the first group of soils than in the second.

Robinson and Edgington [53] determined the molybdenum content of 36 plants or plant parts from 12 states, Alaska, and Colombia. The quantities found varied from 1.0 to 137.0 p.p.m. They call attention to the conclusion of Ferguson and associates that appreciable quantities of the element are taken up by plants from alkaline soils only and not from acid soils. Robinson also notes that samples of vegetation from Colombia grown on soils with a high selenium content also contain large quantities of molybdenum. There is a question as to how much of the toxicity of such plants is due to molybdenum.

[52] *Ibid.*, p. 187.
[53] *Soil Sci.*, 66: 197, 1948.

Symptoms of Molybdenum Deficiency.   Studies are too few to permit of the identification of molybdenum-deficiency symptoms in more than a few plants.   Arnon and Stout [54] found a characteristic mottling of the lower leaves of tomato followed by necrosis and curling of the leaf edges.   Also the dropping of blossoms resulted in a poor set of fruit.

Fig. 30.   Cauliflower leaves showing (*left*) normal development and (*right*) molybdenum deficiency.   From West Virginia Agr. Exp. Sta.   Courtesy of H. W. Fairchild.

Similar symptoms have been reported for tobacco.   Leaves of oats receiving insufficient molybdenum bent smoothly backwards, but later a break or "kink" developed at the affected point and necrotic areas appeared.   A cauliflower plant showing characteristic symptoms of molybdenum deficiency, as observed by Fairchild, is shown in Fig. 30.

SODIUM

There are many well authenticated cases in which additions of sodium salts have increased the yield or otherwise improved various

[54] *Plant Physiol.,* 14: 599, 1939.

crops. Nevertheless the evidence is not sufficient to prove that the element is essential for the normal growth of plants. Most plants contain considerable quantities of sodium, and certain groups of crops absorb quite large quantities of it when the supply in the soil permits.

A considerable number of crops are benefited to a greater or less extent by additions of sodium when the amount of available potassium is insufficient, and on the other hand certain crops are improved by sodium applications when ample potassium is present. Table 54, showing the response of crops to sodium when the potassium supply is deficient

TABLE 54.   RELATIVE RESPONSE OF CROPS TO APPLICATIONS OF SODIUM

Response When Potassium Is Deficient		Response When Potassium Is Adequate	
None to Very Slight	Slight to Medium	Slight to Medium	Large
Lettuce	Asparagus	Cabbage	Celery
Onion	Broccoli	Celeriac	Mangel
Parsnip	Caraway	Horseradish	Sugar beet
Spinach	Carrot	Kale	Swiss chard
Squash	Rutabaga	Kohlrabi	Table beet
Potato	Tomato	Mustard	Turnip
Corn	Barley	Radish	
Rye	Oat	Rape	
Soybean	Vetch		
Buckwheat	Wheat		

and when it is ample, was prepared from data presented by Harmer and Benne.[55]   The beneficial effect of sodium in the absence of sufficient potassium apparently lies in its ability to perform some of the functions within the plant usually performed by potassium. Why sodium functions in this way in some plants and not in others is not clear. Another way in which sodium may be of service to certain crops which are insufficiently supplied with potassium is by limiting the absorption of other cations which may be toxic in too large amounts.

When sodium salts are applied for certain crops receiving ample potassium the percentage of the latter element in the plant is reduced, although the total quantity taken up per acre may be larger because of increased yield. The beneficial effects of sodium in plants well supplied with potassium are ascribed by Harmer and Benne to: (1) greater vigor and improved color and the persistence of these characteristics

[55] *Soil Sci.,* 60: 137, 1945.   Used with permission.

for a longer growing period, (2) greater resistance to disease, and (3) resistance to wilting in hot, dry weather. The last phenomenon may be due to an increase in the bound-water content of the plant tissue.

Plants vary greatly in the relative amounts of potassium and sodium absorbed when there is an ample supply of both nutrients. Analyses of crops grown to maturity on organic soil, which was fertilized with both potassium and sodium salts, gave the following ratio of the two elements (K/Na): celery 0.78, table beets 0.91, sugar beets 1.17, turnips 1.66, rape 2.48, cabbage 3.21, kale 3.59, kohlrabi 4.82, onions 12.60, and asparagus 13.29. Commenting on the data Harmer and Benne [55] suggest that crops which absorb relatively large amounts of sodium are benefited by the nutrient.

SILICON

Plants normally contain a comparatively high percentage of silicon, and the essentiality of the element for plant growth has been widely discussed. Early workers believed that silicon strengthened the stems of cereals and grasses, but work at the Rothamsted experiment station [56] proved the assumption to be incorrect.

Raleigh [57] has shown that it is extremely difficult to exclude silicon in nutrient solution studies, and when he was apparently able to accomplish this end he obtained marked increases in plant growth from additions of the element. Wagner's [58] results with rice, barley, corn, tomatoes, and several other plants are in agreement with those of Raleigh. Evidence, therefore, exists that plants are benefited by at least small quantities of silicon, but plant physiologists in general consider the essentiality of the element to be an unanswered question.

Silicon has proved beneficial to certain crops when the supply of phosphorus was limited. For example, Rothamsted experiments with barley for the period 1864–1900 gave a yield of 28.6 bushels of grain when the fertilizer contained nitrate and potassium but no phosphorus or silicon. However, with the addition of silicate the yield was increased to 36.4 bushels. [56] There is difference of opinion among workers as to whether silicon increases the assimilation of phosphorus within the plant or whether it increases the availability of phosphorus in the soil. There is also evidence that silicon may render plants less susceptible

[56] *Soil Conditions and Plant Growth,* eighth edition, 1950, pp. 44–45.
[57] *Plant Physiol.,* 14: 823, 1939.
[58] *Phytopathol. Z.,* 12: 427, 1940.

to attack by fungi and certain insects by impregnating the cell walls and so hardening them and making them less inert chemically.[59]

OTHER ELEMENTS

There have been reports of beneficial effects to plant growth from additions of a number of other elements not recognized as essential or considered as possibly essential in plant nutrition. Some of them are iodine, bromine, arsenic, aluminum, cobalt, nickel, lead, chlorine. These reports as a whole have not been supported by results from sufficiently well-controlled experiments to warrant their acceptance. The need of soils for additions of certain of these elements and the response of crops to such additions are being carefully investigated by workers in some experiment stations, notably New Jersey.[60] Perhaps chlorine has received as much attention as, or more than, the other elements mentioned, and a brief review of some of the results obtained is given in the following section.

Effects of Chlorine on Plant Growth. There has been considerable discussion concerning the essentiality of chlorine for plant growth. If it is needed, which is doubtful, the quantity required is small. Nevertheless, under proper conditions the growth of some plants is increased by applications of suitable amounts of the element, and plants vary considerably in their response to such applications.

Garner et al.[61] have studied in detail the effects of applications of chlorides on the growth of tobacco. As a result of field tests covering a considerable period of years and involving some 193 comparisons between plants receiving fertilizers containing sulfates and chlorides, an increase in growth amounting to approximately 10 per cent was observed in the plants treated with chlorides. This result was ascribed in part to an increase in absorption of magnesium and in part to an increased turgor. The greater moisture content of the leaves of plants receiving chlorides was well defined and resulted in some drought resistance, as evidenced by a lack of "burning" of leaf margins, which was marked in dry periods in plants receiving sulfates. Atlhough the use of KCl enabled plants to absorb more magnesium from sandy soils containing small amounts of the element, the absorption of potassium was equal from KCl and K_2SO_4. However, there was appreciably

[59] *Introduction to Plant Physiology,* by Curtis and Clark, p. 375. McGraw-Hill Book Co., New York, 1950.
[60] *Soil Sci.,* 73: 127, 1952.
[61] *J. Agr. Res.,* 11: 627, 1930.

less SO$_4$ absorbed than Cl.   Similar results were obtained for several plants by Hoagland and Davis.[62]

The application of chlorides resulted in leaves of greater spread, a lighter green color, and with a smoother surface.   However, the combustibility of the dried leaves was poor due, probably, to a low content of potassium in combination with organic acids.   An excess of chlorine interfered with carbohydrate metabolism to an extent sufficient to check growth.   Also the cured leaves were of poor color and their toughness and elasticity were reduced.   A careful study of the effects of chlorine on the growth characteristics of other plants may throw more light on its functions in growth processes.

REFERENCES

Albers, A. O., and Boggs, H. M.   Zn content of soils in relation to pecan rosette. *Soil Sci.,* 41: 329, 1936.

Allison, R. V., Bryan, O. C., and Hunter, J. H.   The stimulation of plant response on the raw peat soils of the Florida Everglades through the use of CuSO$_4$ and other chemicals. *Fla. Agr. Exp. Sta. Bull.* 190, 1927.

Arnon, D. I., and Stout, P. R.   Molybdenum as an essential element for higher plants. *Plant Physiol.,* 14: 599, 1939.

Barshad, I.   Molybdenum content of pasture plants in relation to toxicity to cattle. *Soil Sci.,* 66: 187, 1948.

Beeson, K. C.   The mineral composition of crops with particular reference to the soils in which they were grown. *U.S.D.A. Misc. Pub.* 369, 1941.

Brenchley, W. E.   The essential nature of certain minor elements for plant nutrition. *Bot. Rev.,* 2: 173, 1936.

Camp, A. F.   Zinc as a nutrient in plant growth. *Soil Sci.,* 60: 157, 1945.

Fujimoto, C. K., and Sherman, G. D.   Behavior of manganese in the soil and the manganese cycle. *Soil Sci.,* 66: 131, 1948.

Gammon, N., Jr., Volk, G. M., McCubbin, E. N., and Eddings, A. H.   Soil factors affecting molybdenum uptake by cauliflower. *Soil Sci. Soc. Amer. Proc.,* 18: 302, 1954.

Harmer, P. M., and Benne, E. J.   Effects of applying common salt to a muck soil on the yield, composition, and quality of certain vegetable crops and on the composition of the soil producing them. *J. Amer. Soc. Agron.,* 33: 955, 1941.

Harmer, P. M., and Benne, E. J.   Sodium as a crop nutrient. *Soil Sci.,* 60: 137, 1945.

Hoagland, D. R.   Molybdenum in relation to plant growth. *Soil Sci.,* 60: 119, 1945.

Lucas, R. E.   The effects of the addition of sulfates of copper, zinc, and manganese on the absorption of these elements by plants grown on organic soils. *Soil Sci. Soc. Amer. Proc.,* 10: 269, 1945.

Lucas, R. E.   Chemical and physical behavior of copper in organic soils. *Soil Sci.,* 66: 119, 1948.

[62] *New Phytol.,* 24: 99, 1925.

Lyman, C., and Dean, L. A.   Zinc deficiency of pineapples in relation to soil and plant composition. *Soil Sci.,* 54: 315, 1942.

McHargue, G. S.   The occurrence of copper, manganese, zinc, nickel, and cobalt in soils, plants, and animals and their possible functions as vital products. *J. Agr. Res.,* 30: 193, 1925.

Purvis, E. R.   Present status of boron in American agriculture. *Soil Sci. Soc. Amer. Proc.,* 4: 316, 1939.

Raleigh, G. J.   Silicon in plant growth. *Soil Sci.,* 60: 133, 1945.

Reeve, E., and Shive, J. W.   Potassium-boron and calcium-boron relationships in plant nutrition. *Soil Sci.,* 57: 1, 1944.

Rogers, L. H., Gall, O. E., Gaddeum, L. W., and Barnette, R. M.   Distribution of macro and micro elements in some soils of peninsular Florida. *Florida Agr. Exp. Sta. Bull.* 341, 1939.

Shive, J. W.   Boron in plant life—a brief historical survey. *Soil Sci.,* 60: 41, 1945.

Somers, I. I., and Shive, J. W.   The Fe-Mn relation in plant metabolism. *Plant Physiol.,* 17: 582, 1942.

Sommer, A. L.   Copper and plant growth. *Soil Sci.,* 60: 71, 1945.

Thorne, D. W., Laws, W. D., and Wallace, A.   Zinc relationship of some Utah soils. *Soil Sci.,* 54: 463, 1940.

Walker, J. C.   Histologic-pathologic effect of boron deficiency. *Soil Sci.,* 57: 51, 1949.

Whetstone, R. R., Robinson, W. O., and Byers, H. G.   Boron distribution in soils and related data. *U.S.D.A. Bur. Plant Ind. Tech. Bull.* 797, 1942.

13

Soil Deficiencies and Determination of Nutrient Needs of Crops

With the recognition of the fact that plants obtain their mineral nutrients from the soil came the demand for methods to determine the quantities of available nutrients in soils. It is interesting to note that, although the search for such methods has been under way for over a century it still continues. Much progress has been made, but a method which works satisfactorily under all conditions has not yet been devised. When, to the inquiry concerning the quantities of available nutrients present in a given soil, is added the query, "how much of each nutrient should be added to give a large yield of a given crop," the problem becomes more complicated. Because of the dynamic nature of the soil system and the fact that one is dealing with a living organism, the plant, which is sensitive to all environmental conditions, a method of obtaining a definite answer to the above questions may never be developed. Nevertheless, information has been obtained which is helpful in giving approximate answers to these questions, and a brief review of proposed methods is presented in the following discussion.

Discussion Topics

Meaning of "available" plant nutrients.
Early efforts to determine supplies of available nutrients.
Rapid soil-testing methods.
Plant analysis and tissue testing.
Nutrient-deficiency symptoms in plants.
Plant-growth methods.
Growth of microorganisms as an indicator of soil-nutrient supply.
Mitscherlich's theory and present-day agrobiology.

MEANING OF "AVAILABLE" PLANT NUTRIENTS

One concept of the term "available," [1] as applied to nutrients, refers to their existence in the soil in a chemical condition in which they may

[1] The terms "available" and "unavailable" in connection with plant nutrients were introduced by Dyer in 1894.

be absorbed by plant roots or may be readily converted into such a condition. Nutrients adsorbed on the colloidal fraction in an easily replaceable state would be considered available under this definition. Likewise, organic nitrogen which is readily nitrified would be classed as available. Strictly interpreted, the term "available" may be construed to refer only to nutrients in a chemical state which permits them to be readily taken up by plants, and this is the most commonly accepted understanding of the word.

Another limitation sometimes injected into the interpretation of "available" has to do with physical location of the nutrients in the soil. For example, the root system of a plant may not be able to explore all the soil surface and hence may not come in contact with all the chemically available nutrients present. The portion of the nutrients not contacted might be considered unavailable. Also an unfavorable structural condition might prevent root penetration of certain soil areas within the normal feeding zone of the crop. Nutrients in such areas even though water-soluble could be considered unavailable. Other situations can be conceived of which would prevent roots from contacting chemically available nutrients. In general, however, little consideration is given to this physical phase of availability.

EARLY EFFORTS TO DETERMINE SUPPLIES OF AVAILABLE NUTRIENTS

Complete Soil Analysis. Early chemists, many of whom concerned themselves with plant-growth problems, turned their attention first to so-called complete soil analysis. By this expression is meant the determination of the total amounts of certain essential plant nutrients in the soil and not a determination of the amounts of all elements present. Attention was centered largely on nitrogen, phosphorus, and potassium, with less emphasis on calcium, magnesium, sulfur, and sometimes iron. The line of reasoning was that, if there were an ample amount of any element present, a sufficient quantity of it to meet the needs of a large crop would become available during the growing season. Later Hopkins [2] proposed that 2 per cent of the nitrogen, 1 per cent of the phosphorus, and 0.25 per cent of the potassium would become available during a growing season under satisfactory conditions of moisture, temperature, soil structure, etc. These availability factors were used extensively during the early years of the present century. However, as a better idea of the complexity of the soil system developed, and particularly with

[2] *Soil Fertility and Permanent Agriculture.* Ginn and Co., Boston, 1910.

some concept of the importance of the colloidal fraction, less attention was given to complete or total analysis.

Strong-Acid Extraction. Paralleling to some extent the period during which attention was directed to complete analysis, and following it, was an era of emphasis on "partial" soil analysis. Instead of entirely decomposing the soil particles, as was done in total analysis methods, the soil was extracted with a strong acid. Usually hydrochloric acid of constant boiling-point concentration (1.125 sp. gr.) was used and the soil extracted at boiling temperature.[3] Although it was admitted that this treatment dissolved more of most nutrients than a crop could absorb in the current season, it was considered that the quantities of nutrients extracted represented the amounts that would become available during a period of years. Inability to correlate the results of the strong-acid extraction method with crop yields and the demand to know what treatment a soil needs during the coming growing season led to the abandonment of the method before a great many years.

It must not be inferred that the results of total analysis and strong-acid extraction methods are valueless. These data have served many useful purposes in the development of soil science.

Extraction with Weak Acids. Strong-acid extraction studies were followed by extraction with less concentrated acids in an effort to determine immediately available supplies of plant nutrients. The first use of a weak acid was by Dauberry, who employed a solution of carbonic acid in 1845 and suggested the use of the terms "active" and "dormant" to distinguish between the readily and more difficultly soluble soil constituents. Nitric acid of one-fifth normal strength was widely used as an extractant. Many studies were made concerning the duration of extraction and procedures to keep the strength of the acid constant when dealing with soils containing different amounts of soluble bases, principally calcium. Many other extracting solutions were proposed, including different strengths of various acids.

During the time of the early efforts to determine "available" nutrients in soils it was commonly believed that the cell sap of the roots seeped through the cell walls and dissolved nutrients from the soil particles. In an effort to find a solvent that would simulate the action of the root sap, Dyer (1894) determined the acidity of the root sap of a large number of species. The average result was approximately 1 per cent.

---

[3] The method suggested by van Bernmelen and Hissink (1929) called for boiling 10–20 grams of soil in a flask fitted with a reflux condenser for 2 hours with 25 times the volume of 25–35 per cent HCl. Later the method was modified to provide for boiling 20 grams of soil passing a 2-mm. sieve with 200 cc. constant boiling-point HCl in a tall, covered 500- or 600-cc. beaker for 1 hour.

Accordingly he proposed extracting the soil with a 1 per cent citric acid solution on the basis that many plants contain this acid. Although used in England quite extensively the citric acid method was not used in the United States to an appreciable extent. In its place $N/200$ HCl solution was recommended in this country and a 2 per cent HCl solution in Sweden.

Efforts to determine available phosphorus by extraction with dilute acids led to confusion. It was found that extraction for a short period with different acids of equivalent strength gave comparable but not equal quantities of phosphorus. However, if the extraction continued for a long period, less phosphorus was usually obtained and results with different acids varied. This phenomenon was explained by Russell and Prescott [4] on the basis of the adsorption of the dissolved phosphorus by the soil, the extent of the adsorption varying with the different acids and the time of contact with the soil. Less phosphorus was adsorbed from the citric acid solution than from solutions of HCl and HNO_3. Other workers do not accept this theory but think that iron and aluminum are dissolved by the weak acids and that these precipitated the phosphorus. If less iron and aluminum were dissolved by citric acid there would be less of the extracted phosphorus precipitated.

The weak-acid extraction methods were cumbersome and time-consuming, and attention was soon turned to more rapid procedures.

Extraction with Water and the Soil Solution. During the first third of the present century considerable attention was given to extracting soils with distilled water. A procedure used extensively was to shake, stir, or mascerate in a mortar a given weight of soil (often 100 grams) with 5 times the weight of water. The suspension was then filtered through a Pasteur-Chamberland filter cone by use of air pressure. Nitrates and sometimes other constituents were determined in the extract by colorimetric methods.

Another method was to obtain a soil extract by dialysis through collodion sacks.

An effort was also made to obtain the soil solution in an unchanged condition by displacing it from a column of soil by means of another fluid. A procedure frequently used was to bring a given weight of soil to a predetermined moisture content, usually near or below field capacity. The soil was then packed firmly into a glass cylinder and the system allowed to stand until it was assumed that an equilibrium had been established between the solid and liquid phases. Another liquid was then applied on the top of the soil column and allowed to perco-

[4] *J. Agr. Sci.,* 8: 65, 1916–1917.

late downward either by gravity or under slight pressure, and the displaced soil solution was collected at the bottom. Various liquids including water, alcohol, and oil were used as displacing agents. It was demonstrated that liquids so applied at the surface of the soil column would displace the solution in the soil and drive it downward without intermixing of the two liquids beyond a short distance from the contact face. The soil solution so obtained was submitted to analysis for various constituents by suitable methods. Studies of the displaced soil solution were not directed particularly toward a determination of the fertilizer needs of soils.

RAPID SOIL-TESTING METHODS

In recent years attention has centered largely on methods of determining the readily available nutrients in soils quickly and frequently in the field as well as in the laboratory. Most procedures involve shaking the soil for a short time with an acid solution varying in strength from just sufficiently acid to coagulate the colloids to a value of 0.7 N HCl. Also, some soil chemists add salts to the extractant in order to replace at least a portion of the nutrients adsorbed on the colloidal material. A salt to replace the cations is most frequently used, but sometimes replacement of the anions is also sought. In some testing systems salt solutions alone are used, no acid being present in the extractant. Some workers advocated a different extracting solution for phosphorus than is used for cations. In some western states carbonated water is used as an extracting liquid. A table showing the extracting solution recommended in different states is given on page 13 of the 1951 report of the Soil Test Work Group of the National Soil and Fertilizer Research Committee. After extraction the quantities of the nutrients present are determined by colorimetric methods. In testing procedures there is also considerable variation in the recommended ratios of soil to extractant.

Some experiment stations, notably New Jersey, submit the soil samples to electrolysis for a given period of time in order to extract the readily available nutrients. The solution so obtained is then analyzed by methods similar to those used for extracts obtained by means of acid and salt solutions. One advantage of this method is the lack of interactions between soil and extracting agent, which might change the concentration of the extracting solution. Although McGeorge [5] concluded that the method has merit in the determination of available

---

[5] *Arizona Agr. Exp. Sta. Tech. Bull.* 38, 1932.

phosphorus, Goodwin [6] found it less accurate than extraction with water or with a solution of K_2CO_3 for the determination of available phosphorus in calcareous soils.

The details of the various "rapid" methods should be discussed in a book dealing with soil chemistry rather than here. It should be stated, however, that each method needs to be carefully standardized by reference to results from field experiments. Usually this has been done, at least for given conditions of climate, cropping systems, and to a certain extent soil conditions. A method standardized by results from sandy soils with low organic-matter content could not be expected to give satisfactory results on soils highly buffered with both inorganic and organic colloids, at least not without careful restandardization. Methods adequately standardized give results which are very helpful in ascertaining the nutrient needs of soils for crops commonly grown in the community. The tests are especially useful in detecting the presence of certain harmful substances in the soil or of excessive or very small amounts of the different nutrients.

For several reasons results from rapid or "quick" tests are not infallible. For instance, they do not anticipate climatic conditions during the growing season, and hence they may not measure accurately the quantities of various nutrients which may become available during that period. Also a soil is a complex and dynamic system, and changes in the solubility of various materials may alter the availability of certain nutrients. Likewise all crops do not have equal capacities for extracting nutrients from the soil, and these capacities may be influenced by variations in climate as well as in soil conditions. Regardless of its limitations soil testing is a useful tool, especially when accompanied by plant-tissue tests and observation of nutrient-deficiency symptoms.

PLANT ANALYSIS AND TISSUE TESTING

Early Concepts. With the development of analytical chemistry attention was turned to the analyzing of crops as well as of soils. The customary procedure was to ash the plant tissue and then analyze the ash and to express the results in terms of the percentage of the ash. It was assumed that the ash from plants of a particular species was virtually constant and, furthermore, that nutrients in the soil were equally available to all plant species. Both these assumptions have since been proved inaccurate. It is also known that the process of ashing as car-

[6] *Colorado Agr. Exp. Sta. Tech. Bull.* 12, 1935.

ried out at that time resulted in the volatilization of portions of certain constituents, especially sulfur.

It was in connection with the work on plant ash that Liebig advanced his "mineral theory" and prepared a patent mineral fertilizer. Liebig believed that if the minerals found in plant ash were added to the soil there would be no decrease in fertility. Although correct in his theory that a supply of available mineral elements is essential, Liebig's theory overlooked various other factors that contribute to soil productivity. His fertilizer failed to give the expected results in part because it was fused at a temperature which caused some of the elements to combine into insoluble compounds.

The accepted opinion that the composition of plant ash indicates the amounts of the various nutrients required by the plant was given a severe shock by the results of experiments at the Rothamsted experiment station (1851).[7] One of the most convincing pieces of evidence was the great response of turnips to phosphate fertilizer even though turnip ash contained a small amount of this nutrient. Nevertheless, the idea of determining soil deficiencies by means of the analysis of plant ash persisted for many years. As late as 1905 we find Hall[8] commenting on the problem somewhat as follows: The scheme involves taking a plant from the soil under study and determining the proportion of phosphoric acid, potash, and other constituents in its ash. A deficiency or excess of a particular constituent is indicated by the variation of the amount present from the normal.

After his study of the composition of crops grown upon the Rothamsted plots and elsewhere, Hall reached the conclusion that results of analyses of plant ash could not be used to interpret soil conditions and thus to replace soil analysis, until "constants" for the quantities of nutrients in a test plant growing naturally on the untreated soil were determined.

When one considers the many factors that influence the uptake of nutrients by plants, among which are nature of soil, climate, age and nature of plant, management, interaction of nutrients, it appears that Hall's conclusion is justified. Salter and Ames[9] state the situation in the following terms:

Doubtless the factors influencing the intake of any given nutrient by a plant are so numerous as to preclude the hope of using plant composition as a guide to soil requirements unless steps are taken either to control or measure the influence of these factors.

[7] *J. Roy. Agr. Soc. Engl.*, 12: 1, 1851.   [9] *J. Amer. Soc. Agron.*, 20: 808, 1928.
[8] *J. Agr. Sci.*, 1: 65, 1905.

Leaf Analysis. Although dependence on the analysis of a mature plant as a means of determining soil deficiencies has been largely abandoned, interest has increased in the analysis of leaves for this diagnostic purpose. The leaf has been selected because it is the organ in which mineral nutrients are incorporated into plant food in conjunction with the products of photosynthesis. Lundegardh [10] has explained why leaf analysis is considered an index of the nutrient status of both the plant and soil. He points out that the absorbing power of the roots regulates in part the concentration of salts in the leaves and that the nutrient salt transformations taking place in the green assimilating leaves control the growth of the plant, including seed formation. Also, he believes that leaf analysis not only gives a summation of the extraction of salts from the soil during a period of several weeks but in addition presents a picture of soil saturation at the time of sampling. This conclusion is based on the fact that the vegetative parts of the plant are still vigorous, although fully grown when the samples are taken.

In selecting leaves for analysis much stress is placed on the stage of maturity of the plant when samples are taken and also on the location of the leaves chosen. Shear and his associates [11] sum up these ideas essentially as follows:

When proper consideration is given to the position of the leaves on the shoot and to the sampling time, leaf composition presents a measure of both internal and external environmental factors that influenced nutrient accumulation by the plant. And, because gradients occur in the amounts of each element contained in the leaves that vary (a) during the growth and fruiting season, (b) between shoots producing and those not producing fruit, and (c) in leaves from basal to terminal positions, it is necessary that leaf samples be taken from the same position on modal shoots and at a time when all shoots are at approximately the same stage of development.

Specific directions for the collection of leaf samples will vary with the nature of the plant under consideration and to some extent with the individual investigator. For example, in the sampling of leaves from citrus trees Chapman and Fullmer [12] recommended taking 20 to 25 spring-cycle leaves from fruit-bearing twigs from each of 10 trees that are representative for the orchard or part of the orchard being sampled. The leaves will constitute a composite sample. Ulrich,[13] in taking leaf samples from grapevines, selects the most recently mature

[10] *Nature,* 151: 310, 1943.
[11] *Proc. Amer. Soc. Hort. Sci.,* 47: 239, 1945.
[12] *Citrus Leaves,* February 1951.
[13] *Proc. Amer. Soc. Hort. Sci.,* 41: 213, 1943.

leaf found when working back from the tip of the shoot. The reason for this choice is that such a leaf will reflect changes in the nutritional status of the plant more accurately than older leaves because it is near the growing point. Thomas questions the validity of this reasoning. He admits that deficiency symptoms appear in the leaf at emergence, when demand for nutrients overtakes the supply, but does not think this fact furnishes a basis for considering that the younger leaves indicate the nutritional status of the plant better than older ones. He is of the opinion that internal starvation is indicated by older leaves earlier than by younger ones because of the rapid translocation of nutrients from the older leaves when growth is taking place. The selection of older leaves also permits of earlier sampling.

In sampling leaves of forest trees Mitchell [14] prefers the period a few weeks before yellowing, because at that time the maximum amounts of nitrogen, phosphorus, and potassium are present. It is evident that the objectives of foresters and the growers of fruits or field crops are different and hence their procedure will vary. Accordingly, Thomas [15] arrives at the conclusion that for fruit and field crops the earlier the leaf samples are taken the better when only one sampling is to be made. He bases this conclusion on these considerations: (1) The earlier the sampling, the better the chance of correcting deficiencies. (2) In the early stages of growth, especially before flowering, the rate of nutrient uptake is greater than when the plant is more mature. (3) As maturity approaches the various nutrients are not always removed from the leaves in proportion to the amounts present. Thus, if the demand for a particular nutrient is less than the supply the percentage in the leaf will increase. (4) The translocation of nutrients from mature leaves is greatest during the period of rapid growth, hence the greatest changes in nutrient concentration are occurring at this time. All workers are not in agreement with this point of view.

There is almost as much variation in methods of treatment of leaf samples as there is in collection procedures. Some workers separate the petioles and analyze the blades only. Others remove the midribs also. Some investigators extract the dry leaf tissue with hot water and others use alcohol as an extractant. It is to be expected that the analytical procedure will vary with the objective of the investigator. For determination of the nutrient status of crops and the soils in which they grow it is customary to analyze the entire leaf, after drying at a low temperature (70° C.), for the total quantities of the various nutrients.

[14] *Black Rock Forest Papers,* 1: 1, 1936.
[15] *Soil Sci.,* 59: 353, 1945.

Appropriate gravimetric and colorimetric procedures are used and the spectrograph is called into service, particularly for the determination of the microelements. Much work is being done to improve methods and shorten them. Results may be expressed as percentage of the ash or of the dry leaf tissue. The latter method is favored.

In the interpretation of leaf analyses it is recognized that plant growth is a function of both the quantity of nutrients, sometimes designated as "intensity," and the nutrient balance. Shear et al.[16] maintain that the purpose of leaf analysis is to find out both the extent of nutrient unbalance in the plant and whether excesses or deficiencies exist. Various workers have proposed limits for the contents of the principal nutrients. For example, Chapman and Brown[17] state that for citrus trees a leaf content between 1.30 and 2.50 per cent potassium indicates an ample supply, with no likelihood of an increase in either yield or size of fruit as a result of potash application. In orange trees[18] the presence of less than 0.07 per cent of phosphorus in the dry matter of the leaves indicates that an increase in yield and quality of fruit would probably result from phosphate fertilization. From 0.07 to 0.10 per cent phosphorus indicates a slight deficiency of this element. The optimum range for phosphorus content lies between 0.10 and 0.14 per cent, and more than 0.14 per cent indicates an excess of this element, which may cause a decrease in the availability of other nutrients with a concomitant decrease in yield and size of fruit. Potassium has received more attention in this regard than have the other nutrients, and a table setting forth the levels of this element in plant parts, which various investigators have found associated with pronounced potassium deficiency in different crops, is given on pages 175–177 of *Diagnostic Techniques for Soils and Crops*.

Tissue Testing. In the early attempts to use plant analyses as indicators of soil deficiencies it was customary to take the entire plant at maturity or, at times, the seed or stems. Because it is well known that several of the nutrients are translocated from one part of the plant to another during different stages of growth, and that plants in general do not need nor do they take up nutrients at a uniform rate during their life cycle, later studies have been directed toward the content of given nutrients in certain parts of plants at definite growth ages. In other words, the quantities of soluble nutrients in certain organs at given periods of growth have come to be considered indicative of

[16] *Proc. Amer. Soc. Hort. Sci.,* 47: 239, 1945.
[17] *Hilgardia,* 19: 501, 1950.
[18] *Citrus Leaves,* February 1951.

the adequacy of supply of the certain nutrients. This concept has given rise to the application of "quick tests" to growing plant tissue or to "tissue testing" as it is commonly called.

The first problem was to ascertain what part of a plant should be tested for a certain nutrient and at which stage of growth. For woody plants attention has centered on the leaf petioles, although much study has been devoted to the leaf blades. Working with small grains of the grass family it is customary to sample the stems, including leaf sheaths, but not the leaves themselves. Samples from the corn plant have been taken from different locations by different workers. For example, Tyner [19] used the blade of the sixth leaf from the bottom of the stalk. Other scientists recommend a nitrate test on the stalk near the ground, because this portion of the plant is depleted of nitrogen if a scarcity develops. The stalk near the tassel is tested for phosphorus, and a leaf sheath near the ear is sampled for the potassium test.

The time in the life of a plant at which tests are made is important. For example, winter wheat or early oats may be attempting a rapid growth when the soil is yet cold and nitrification is slow. A nitrate test at that time may prove more advantageous than one made later. On the other hand, if one wishes to know whether a plant which has completed its vegetative growth contains, or is obtaining, a sufficient supply of nutrients for the full development of its fruit or seed, tests should be made at the flowering period or when the seed is forming.

Because the potassium in a plant is water-soluble, tests are made on this basis. There is some question, however, whether nitrogen and phosphorus tests should include only nitrates and water-soluble phosphorus. Some workers feel that certain organic compounds of these two elements should be included also. Customary procedures, however, involve tests for nitrates and the phosphorus which is soluble in weak acid.

There are objections to tissue testing. Some of them are based on the fact that the results are obtained when it is impractical to correct deficiencies by applications to the soil. This is not true for all crops, however, and sometimes the needed nutrient may be applied as a spray on the leaves. Another objection is the assertion that the tests are for excess and not required nutrients. In other words, a plant may be utilizing all of a nutrient that is available and may be adequately supplied, with the result that a test will show none of the nutrient available. A pertinent objection to the test for nitrates is the fact that the quantity present is greatly modified by the rate of photosynthesis as well as by

[19] *Soil Sci. Soc. Amer. Proc.,* 11: 317, 1945.

the supply in the soil. Other objections have also been advanced, and it must be admitted that there are definite limitations in the tests themselves and in the interpretation of the results. Nevertheless, tissue testing is being utilized by many workers and it is to be inferred that useful information is being obtained. Tissue testing in conjunction with soil testing affords much information concerning the nutrient status of plants and the soil supporting them.

The reagents used for soil testing may be used in making tissue tests according to Cook et al.[20] On the other hand some workers prefer to use an entirely different set of testing reagents. A variation in procedure introduced by Bray is to utilize papers impregnated with the reagents. A freshly broken or slightly mascerated plant part may be pressed against the paper and the color resulting from the interaction of the sap and the reagent noted.

NUTRIENT-DEFICIENCY SYMPTOMS IN PLANTS

Basis for Deficiency Symptoms. It is recognized that each element essential for plant growth plays a specific role in the growth processes of plants. This statement should not be interpreted to mean that two or more elements may not perform the same duties in certain essential plant processes, but no nutrient can take over *all* the functions of another one. With this point established it is logical to assume that an insufficient supply of any nutrient will result in some abnormality of growth. These manifestations of abnormal growth offer a means of detecting nutrient deficiencies in plants and frequently in soils.

The first problem in utilizing this procedure is the identification of the specific plant symptoms that indicate a limited supply of a given nutrient. Much study has been devoted to this problem and much progress has been made. In a number of cases the identification of specific deficiency symptoms is relatively simple, but occasionally complications are encountered and one experienced in this diagnostic procedure is always watchful for them. Some causes of complications may be listed as follows:

1. A deficiency of several nutrient elements will result in chlorosis, and it is necessary, if possible, to distinguish the specific pattern of discoloration caused by an undersupply of each element. An excess of moisture or some other unfavorable environmental condition may also cause a yellowing of the foliage, possibly because the condition results in a deficiency of one or more nutrients.

[20] *Soil Sci. Soc. Amer. Proc.,* 12: 379, 1947.

2. An insufficiency of one or more elements may prevent the utilization by the plant of another element present in ample amount. The result may be the development of deficiency symptoms characteristic for the latter element.

3. When more than one element is deficient the result may be an overlapping or blending of symptoms which are difficult to identify.

4. Occasionally an infestation by insects may produce symptoms indistinguishable from those resulting from the deficiency of a nutrient. Or results from an insect attack may obscure the nutrient-deficiency symptoms.

5. Likewise a plant disease may prevent the identification of a deficiency symptom, and, on the other hand, a disease may prevent the utilization of an element and hence cause a deficiency symptom to develop when the supply of that element in the soil is adequate.

6. It must also be remembered that a correctly identified deficiency symptom may result from the inability of the plant roots to absorb the nutrient in question even though an ample supply is in the soil. For example, root damage due to grape colaspis may prevent the intake of phosphorus by corn during the early stages of growth.

In addition, it must be recognized that a symptom commonly ascribed to a deficiency of a certain element may actually be caused by the antagonistic action of the element on some other nutrient. In this case the second element is actually deficient. Furthermore it is possible that an excess of one or more nutrients may produce growth characteristics which are considered a deficiency symptom of another element. In other words a lack of nutrient balance or a toxicity effect may be mistaken for a deficiency symptom.

Notwithstanding the limitations in identifying nutrient-deficiency symptoms, the method is widely used and is proving of much assistance to scientists and to many farmers in the study of soil deficiencies.

Not a New Method. Although it is only within the last few years that much attention has been focused on foliar symptoms as a means of determining nutrient deficiencies, the method is not new. As early as 1844, the French scientist Gris called attention to chlorosis due to iron deficiency. Somewhat later (1849–1851) Salm-Horstman described plant-growth characteristics resulting from each of the elements that were known to be essential at that time. He went so far as to prepare a table listing the symptoms exhibited by oats when each of the required elements was limited in supply. In 1930 two Frenchmen, H. Lagatu and L. Maunré,[20a] emphasized the value of deficiency symptoms in studying nutrient requirements of potatoes. As was to be

[20a] *Ann. Sci. Agron.,* 47: 595, 1930.

expected, objections to the procedure were and still are voiced. Two of the earlier critics were Murneek and Gildehaus, who published an article in *Science* in 1931. Nevertheless, increasing attention has been given to this method of diagnosing nutrient deficiencies.

Identification of Deficiency Symptoms. An intimate knowledge of the characteristics of the plant symptoms indicating deficiencies of the various essential elements can only be obtained by careful studies of plants exhibiting these deficiencies at various stages of growth and under diverse environmental conditions. It should be pointed out, however, that the deficiency symptoms are fundamentally the same regardless of environment. It is not feasible to include in this discussion a detailed description of the symptoms exhibited by plants as the result of a deficiency of the various nutrients. McMurtrey [21] has compiled in chart form the symptoms exhibited by numerous plants that various workers have established as indicative of deficiencies of boron, calcium, copper, iron, magnesium, manganese, nitrogen, phosphorus, potassium, sulfur, and zinc. A long list of references to papers on foliar symptoms is also included. Also Wallace [22] has prepared a colored atlas and guide illustrating the deficiency symptoms exhibited by many plants. In the following paragraphs a few of the most readily recognized indications of an insufficient supply of nutrients will be discussed.

Nitrogen. A deficiency of nitrogen results in a limited development of chlorophyll; thus the yellow pigments are in evidence and the plant turns lighter green or yellow, depending on the intensity of the nitrogen deficiency. Nitrogen is also a constituent of protoplasm and hence the demand for it is great where new plant tissue is developing. The element is subject to translocation in the plant, and hence there is a movement from the older plant parts to the points where new tissues are being formed. The result is a yellowing of the older leaves. The discoloration may be exhibited first by certain portions of the leaf, as in corn, or more commonly it may affect the entire leaf. If the deficiency continues the older leaves may become dry and drop off. If the lack of nitrogen occurs early in the life of members of the grass family, the stems of the plants will be slender and the whole plant will show a general lack of vigor. Cold weather, excessive moisture, and continued deficiency of moisture may result in a yellowing of plants similar to that produced by lack of nitrogen. It is probable that these conditions prevent the formation of available forms of nitrogen and that the plant is actually exhibiting nitrogen-deficiency symptoms.

[21] *Diagnostic Techniques for Soils and Crops.* American Potash Institute, 1948.
[22] *Diagnosis of Mineral Deficiencies in Plants by Visual Symptoms, a Color Atlas and Guide.* H.M. Stationery Office, London, 1943; also, Supplement, 1944.

Phosphorus. Plants exhibit less definite indications of an insufficient supply of phosphorus than they do of nitrogen or potassium, or at least scientists have been less successful in observing specific indications of lack of phosphorus. In consideration of the vital functions of phosphorus in plant growth and reproduction, it is surprising that a deficiency of it does not result in very evident growth abnormalities. As with several other elements an extreme and early limitation in phosphorus supply results in a stunted growth. Many plants turn dark green when

Fig. 31. Lemon leaves showing a spotted condition indicative of an insufficient supply of phosphorus. California Agr. Exp. Sta. Courtesy of D. G. Aldrich, Jr.

insufficiently supplied with phosphorus, and sometimes this phenomenon is followed by a reddish or purplish coloration, especially on the underside of the leaves. The purple colors are often noted on the leaf petioles of pome and stone fruit trees. A loss of luster and bronzing of the leaves are frequently evident in some trees, especially citrus. Workers at the California experiment station have observed spots on lemon leaves when the phosphorus supply is insufficient, as is shown in Fig. 31.

Plants insufficiently supplied with phosphorus usually show a yellow coloration later in the growth period, frequently about blossoming time. This result is especially evident with alfalfa, white pea beans, and corn. Beets also turn yellow in the early fall when phosphorus is in short supply. With both corn and beets the yellowing appears on the older leaves first. Whenever there is reason to suspect a phosphorus deficiency, tissue testing should be employed to substantiate or disprove the diagnosis.

Potassium. Although not a constituent of the organic compounds within the plant, potassium performs several essential services in the growth process. Accordingly it is not surprising that a limitation in potassium supply is manifested by very distinct foliar characteristics. The symptoms usually appear on the older leaves first and frequently take the form of a yellowing of the edges. Later the leaf edges turn brown. With members of the grass family a yellowish green streaking between the veins may be the first evidence of insufficient potassium, but this condition rapidly gives place to the browning of the leaf tips and edges. With legumes yellow spots appear near the leaf edges. These become brown and necrotic and ultimately merge, affecting the entire leaf edge.

A mottling of the leaves of tobacco, usually evident on the lower leaves first, is evidence of potassium deficiency in this plant. Very shortly, however, the characteristic necrotic spots appear on the margins and tips. The yellowing of the leaf tips and margins is also the first indication of potassium deficiency generally observed on potato and tomato plants. The dying of the leaf margin, while the remainder of the leaf continues to grow, usually results in cupping of the leaf with the brown edges turned downward. The characteristic potassium-starvation symptoms of a number of plants are described and illustrated by Eckstein and his associates.[23]

Calcium. Not so much progress has been made in identifying plant characteristics which specifically indicate a deficiency of calcium as there has been for several other elements. A lack of calcium appears to cause a deterioration in the meristimatic tissue of both roots and stems. Calcium pectate is a constituent of the middle lamella of the cell wall, and when insufficient calcium is present new cell walls are not developed or if formed they are imperfect. Accordingly, calcium deficiency could be expected to result in a deterioration or death of the tissues near and at the terminal growing points, and this is so. The lower leaves of cereals have been observed to exhibit an inrolling of the edges, and brown spots may appear on such leaves. A peculiar hooking downward of the tips of the younger leaves of tobacco was reported by McMurtrey as an indication of calcium starvation (Fig. 32). A chlorotic condition of the leaves sometimes accompanied by development of necrotic areas has been observed in several plants. Green veins with the intervening tissue yellow is a characteristic pattern. A calcium deficiency results in a breakdown of the petiole tissue in alfalfa and ladino clover with a consequent drooping of the leaflets. Also there is frequently some

[23] *Potash Deficiency Symptoms.* B. Westermann Co., New York, 1937.

reddish coloration particularly on the underside of the leaves. The interrelationships of calcium with other cations, notably magnesium, manganese, and potassium frequently make the identification of deficiency symptoms difficult.

Magnesium. Although long recognized as an essential plant nutrient element, a deficiency of magnesium in soils was not suspected until

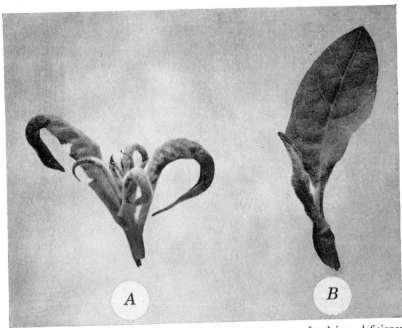

Fig. 32. Tobacco showing abnormal development because of calcium deficiency (*A*) and boron deficiency (*B*). Note how the bud leaves hook downward when calcium is needed. A boron deficiency is manifested by a breakdown of the tissue at the base of the leaves. From *Hunger Signs in Crops.* Used with permission. Courtesy of J. E. McMurtrey, Jr.

1904, when Wheeler and Hartwell showed that various plants were benefited by the addition of magnesium compounds to certain Rhode Island soils. Impetus to the study of magnesium deficiency was given by the discovery of Garner, McMurtrey, and Moss (1922) that sand drown of tobacco and of other plants was due to a limitation in supply of this element. McMurtrey has also observed that dark patches on the leaves of flue-cured tobacco result from a magnesium deficiency, as is shown in Fig. 33.

Magnesium deficiency is manifested by some type of chlorosis with the chlorotic pattern varying with different plants. Usually the discoloration occurs in the interveinal tissue, which may result in a streaked effect in members of the grass family. With some plants a reddish or purplish coloration is also reported, and the development of necrotic spots frequently follows the chlorotic condition. A yellowing and

Fig. 33. A deficiency of magnesium results in irregular dark patches on the leaves of flue-cured tobacco (*B*). A normal leaf is uniform in color (*A*). From *Hunger Signs in Crops*. Used with permission. Courtesy of J. E. McMurtrey, Jr.

browning of the leaf margins is often observed. The discoloration usually affects the older leaves. Inasmuch as magnesium appears to function as a carrier of phosphorus and also occurs in seeds in larger amounts than other cations it seems strange that a magnesium deficiency is not evidenced by some abnormality in the growing points and seed-producing portions of the plants.

Manganese. There has been much discussion concerning the services performed by manganese in plant growth. Because it is an element which passes readily from the reduced to the oxidized state, and vice versa, it is believed to be involved with the activity of oxidizing enzymes in the plant and also with the mobility of iron. A manganese deficiency is generally manifested by a chlorosis of the younger leaves. The pattern exhibited is usually a mottling of the tissue between the veins, the veins themselves and sometimes a band of tissue next to them remaining green. This characteristic coloration is one of the distinctive features used to identify a lack of manganese. Because certain virus diseases produce a similar color pattern on plant leaves care must be taken to distinguish between the two causes.

The first mention of chlorosis due to insufficient manganese appears to be that of Maze in 1914. This was followed by reports from McHargue in 1922 and 1923. By 1927 Carne had identified the gray-speck disease of oats as a manganese-deficiency symptom. In this disorder a gray, oval spot develops on the edge of a new leaf some distance from the tip. With the enlargement of the spot the color turns to yellow and eventually it covers the width of the leaf, which then droops or breaks over. The fact that the leaf tip remains green is an interesting and characteristic feature of the disease.

In the case of wheat and barley, which are also sensitive to insufficient manganese, streaks of yellow appear in the upper leaves, but the characteristic gray spots do not form as in oats. But because the yellow streaks enlarge in places something of a spotted appearance is produced. Also the leaf tips may change color, but the yellowing does not begin at this point.

Alfalfa and clover do not appear as sensitive to manganese deficiency as do the small grains, but soybeans, garden beans, and white field beans develop the characteristic discolored leaves with green veins unless well supplied with this element. Likewise manganese-deficiency symptoms have been observed on potatoes, tomatoes, and various tree fruits.

There seems to be a close relationship between soil reaction and lime supply and manganese deficiency. The quantity of available manganese is usually low in slightly acid and alkaline soils. Some workers place the critical reaction at around pH 6.5 to 6.8. Undoubtedly other factors such as aeration, temperature, clay content, phosphate content, and presence of other reducing and oxidizing compounds must be taken into consideration.

Iron. There are apparently few soils which do not supply sufficient iron for the normal growth of commonly grown crops. Iron-deficient soils may be classified as abnormal in that they contain excessive quantities of manganese or lime. Nevertheless, iron-deficiency symptoms were the first to be reported (Gris, 1844). A lack of iron is manifested by a chlorosis which affects first the young leaves or terminal growth. The difficulty may spread later to older parts of the plant. Although no breakdown of the chlorotic tissue occurs there appear to be no definite characteristics which enable the observer to identify the chlorosis as due to lack of iron.

Fig. 34. The three onions on the left were grown on slightly acid muck (pH 6.0) deficient in copper. Note the erect growth habit and the dying back of the leaf tips. The fourth plant from the left was grown on the same soil to which $CuSO_4$ had been applied. The three onions on the right grew on alkaline soil (pH 7.8). Note the curled tops and delayed formation of the bulb. The fourth plant on the right grew on originally alkaline muck to which sulfur had been added. The same quantities of phosphate and potash were applied in all cases. Michigan Agr. Exp. Sta. Courtesy of Paul M. Harmer.

Copper. Copper is reported to occur in greatest abundance in the parts of the plant where active growth is taking place. It is not surprising, therefore, that a deficiency of copper results in discoloration or dying of the terminal leaves and tips in many plants. The disease of citrus trees originally known as "dieback" is a typical example. Trees other than citrus, such as apple, peach, apricot, pecan, exhibit similar symptoms when not supplied with copper. The tips of onion leaves die back, and the scales of the yellow varieties are thin and pale yellow in place of golden or brownish yellow when insufficient copper is available. Figure 34 shows the characteristic growth of onions when receiving insufficient copper and the distinctly different growth habit when the plants are growing in alkaline muck.

Zinc. Evidence of a zinc deficiency has been reported more frequently for tobacco, pecan, citrus, and corn than for other crops. Rosette of the pecan, "mottle leaf" or "frenching" of citrus, and "white bud" in corn have all been shown to result from zinc starvation. In a number of plants the older leaves become discolored and sometimes necrotic areas develop as the first evidence of zinc deficiency.

Boron. Boron-deficiency symptoms have been studied extensively in many plants. Usually the terminal bud, twig, or leaves die. Rosette of alfalfa, cracked stem in celery, heart rot in sugar beets, internal black spots in table beets, "witches'-broom" and internal corky spots of apples, internal browning of cauliflowers, and numerous other plant disorders have been shown to result from an insufficient supply of boron. A boron deficiency is usually associated with a high soil pH value.

PLANT-GROWTH METHODS

The Neubauer Method. A method utilizing the capability of rye plants to extract potassium and phosphorus from soil as a means of measuring the available supplies of these elements in a given soil was proposed by Neubauer and Schneider [24] in 1923. Briefly, the method consists of mixing 100 grams of dry soil with 50 grams of pure sand [25] and growing 100 rye plants on the mixture for 17 days under controlled conditions of temperature and humidity. The plants are then ashed and the quantities of phosphorus and potassium determined in the ash. These amounts minus the quantities contained in rye plants grown on sand alone represent the available nutrients in the soil.[26]

A number of criticisms of the method have been advanced, and although it has been used extensively in Germany it is not commonly employed in the United States.

Plant-House Tests. A method widely used at present to study the nutrient status of soils, and one which has been used for almost two hundred years,[27] is to grow plants in small quantities of soil in contain-

[24] *Z. Pflanzenernährung u. Düng.,* 2A: 229, 1923.
[25] McGeorge has introduced some modifications of the method. *Soil Sci.,* 62: 61, 1946.
[26] For a detailed discussion of the method and interpretation of the results see *Purdue Univ. Agr. Exp. Sta. Bull.* 399, 1935.
[27] Francis Home made pot experiments in 1757.

ers of various sizes and made of various materials. The cultures may be kept in a glass house or in a wire enclosure to keep out birds. At times they are maintained in the open and may be buried in soil to within an inch or so of the top or just set on benches or the ground. A very satisfactory procedure is to set the jars on small benches or tables which are mounted on large castors. These benches may then be rolled out into a net-wire enclosure during fair and warm weather and rolled back into a glass house in stormy weather. During winter or cold periods the benches may remain in the greenhouse.

Glazed earthenware jars are most commonly used and a 2-gallon capacity is a favorite size, but sometimes the 3-, 4-, or 5-gallon sizes are preferred and occasionally 1-gallon jars or even smaller ones are considered sufficiently large. Unglazed pots and metal containers of various sizes are sometimes selected, and then they are coated inside with asphalt paint or some other compound which is waterproof, contains no plant nutrients, and is non-toxic to plant roots. One objection to large containers is the difficulty in weighing them to determine the quantities of water to be added. A modification of the pot test is to set metal cylinders into the ground to within a few inches of the top. These cylinders are coated with asphalt paint, or other suitable preparation, and may be from about one to several feet in length. The soil to be tested is packed into them and may be dug out and replaced with other soil when desirable.

Quantities of fertilizers or other materials to be added are usually calculated on the basis of surface area of the container rather than on the pounds of soil in the jar. It is customary to use a moisture content near the field capacity of the soil unless soil-moisture content is one of the problems involved in the study. In extreme cases the jars are weighed and made up to weight with water every day. A more common practice is to weigh the cultures about once a week and calculate the daily loss of water. This amount of water is added each day. Distilled water is used when the study involves nutrient supply.

A number of limitations in the application of results from pot experiments to field conditions have been pointed out. Some of them follow: (1) The area of the pots is so small that a large error is involved in raising results to an acre basis. (2) The small quantity of soil in a pot permits the plant roots to investigate virtually all the soil surface, which may not be true in the field. (3) Plant root systems are greatly restricted in pots. (4) The root systems of plants in pots are submitted to greater fluctuations in temperature, if the cultures are out of doors, and to higher and more uniform temperature in the greenhouse, than is true under field conditions. (5) Plants in pot cultures are supplied with adequate moisture. (6) Activities of microorganisms are probably different in potted than in field soil. (7) In pot tests plants are not influenced by subsoil conditions as they are in the field.

On the other hand there are advantages in pot tests compared to field-plot experiments, which are considered by many to be the best procedure for studying the nutrient status of soils. Some of the advantages of pot cultures may be listed as follows: (1) Many more treatments can be employed than usually are practical in the field. (2) A larger number of replications can be carried on than is customary in field-plot work. (3) The expense is much smaller than for field experiments. (4) One man can study the requirements of many more soils in pot tests than he can by the field-plot method. In other words the time requirement is much less by the former method. (5) By controlling soil-moisture conditions the results of greenhouse tests are not influenced so much by climatic variation as are those from field studies. Accordingly field tests may need to be repeated several years in order to establish what may be called "average" results whereas in pot tests an idea of soil response under approximately optimum conditions may be obtained in one trial. (6) It is usually possible to control insect pests and plant diseases more completely in pot cultures than in field plots.

The selection of a suitable indicator crop is an important item in pot-culture work. Because of growth characteristics some plants are not well adapted to growth in small containers. For example plants with a vine-like habit of growth make handling of the jars difficult and plants with weak stems are objectionable. Large plants, only a very few of which may be grown per jar, are not favored by some workers on the basis that if one plant is damaged the results for that jar are unduly decreased. However, other investigators think that, in the event of injury to one plant, the remaining plants will make a proportionately larger growth, so that the result will reflect satisfactorily the influence of the limiting nutrient or other factor. In some studies all the crops to be grown in the rotation under field conditions are grown either in succession in the same jars of soil or in jars filled with fresh soil. Other workers have selected a special crop which they consider a good indicator of soil fertility regardless of the crops to be grown in the field. For example, scientists in Germany use romaine lettuce, Stephenson and Schuster use sunflower, etc.

Regardless of the criticisms directed against pot tests, the method has been and is used extensively in studying plant response to various soil treatments. Some research workers consider the method valuable primarily as a preliminary procedure for the purpose of determining what treatments should be tried in field plots.

GROWTH OF MICROORGANISMS AS AN INDICATOR OF SOIL-NUTRIENT SUPPLY

Azotobacter-Plaque Method.[28] The relative growth of certain bacteria and fungi on cultures containing soil in place of given amounts of different nutrients has been used as a measure of the nutrient supply in soils. The method was first suggested by Winogradsky (1927) who maintained that the growth of *Azotobacter* was a more delicate indicator of the supply of available calcium, potassium, and phosphorus in soils than chemical determinations. Somewhat later (1931) Sackett and Stewart, acting on Winogradsky's suggestion, developed a procedure for studying the mineral deficiencies of soils by the growth of *Azotobacter*.

The method consists of growing the organism on 50-gram samples of soil for 72 hours at 30° C. The texture of the soil is modified by adding kaolin to sandy soils and sand to clays, and $CaCO_3$ is added to acid soils. K_2SO_4 solution is supplied to a sample of the soil being tested, $Na_2HPO_4 \cdot 12H_2O$ solution to another, K_2HPO_4 solution to a third, and no nutrient to a fourth. *Azotobacter* colonies on the four cultures are compared and the degree of deficiency of phosphorus and potassium determined.

Although Stewart et al.[29] found the results from this method to be equally satisfactory with those of the Neubauer method in testing 108 soils, Dalberg and Brown [30] were not pleased with the results they obtained for soils containing a relatively high phosphorus content. Extensive comparisons of the results from this method with those from field plots or from pot experiments have not been made, and many experiment stations have used the procedure little if at all.

Methods Using Fungi. In 1909 the Russian Butkewitach suggested using the growth of *Aspergillus niger* as a measure of the supply of available nutrients in soils. It was 1928, however, before the method was put into use when Berrecke and Soding developed a procedure for determining phosphorus and potassium deficiencies in soils. The method

---

[28] For a detailed description of the method see *Diagnostic Techniques for Soils and Crops*, p. 199. Amer. Potash Institute, 1948.

[29] *Colorado Agr. Exp. Sta. Bull.* 390, 1932.

[30] *J. Amer. Soc. Agron.*, 24: 460, 1932.

was further improved and used for the quantitative determination of available phosphorus, potassium, and to some extent magnesium by Niklas, Poschenrieder, and Trischler during the period 1930–1936. Mehlich, Truog, and Fred (1932) made additional modifications of the procedure and applied it especially for the determination of available potassium.

In essence the method consists in mixing a 2.5-gram soil sample with 30 ml. of a special nutrient solution in an Erlenmeyer flask and inoculating the mixture with *Aspergillus niger*. After an incubation period of $4\frac{1}{2}$ days at 35° C., a pad of mycelium develops which may be removed, washed, dried, weighed, and analyzed. By comparing the data obtained from a series of soils with those from Neubauer tests and chemical tests on the same soils, Mehlich [31] prepared a table from which the relative need of a soil for potassium may be determined. Mulder [32] has also modified the method for the determination of copper and magnesium.

Cunninghamella-Plaque Phosphorus Method.   Mehlich et al.[33] developed a method for estimating the quantity of available phosphorus in soils by measuring the growth of the fungus *Cunninghamella* sp. Fifty-gram samples of the soil are placed in petri dishes and moistened with a nutrient solution containing K, Mg, S, Fe, and Zn. On the center of the smoothed surface of each culture a small drop of a rich spore suspension of the fungus is placed. After incubation for $4\frac{1}{2}$ days at 28° to 29° in a moist atmosphere, the diameter of the fungus colony on each culture is measured. Through use of data from soils of known crop response to phosphate fertilization, it was determined that colony diameter is a reliable indicator of growth response to available phosphorus supply.

By using the data obtained from adding increasing increments of phosphate to samples of a series of soils, Mitscherlich grow-curves were constructed. The investigators proposed the construction of an average curve from the data. By referring the diameters of colonies developed on a soil test to this curve, the parts per million of available phosphorus could be estimated.

Notwithstanding the fact that most workers in the United States who have tried the methods involving growth of microorganisms as a measure of the nutrient status of soils have reported favorably on the results obtained, the methods have not been widely used in this country.

[31] *Soil Sci.*, 35: 259, 1933.
[32] *Diss. Landbouwhoogeschool*, p. 38. Wageningen, Holland, 1938.
[33] *Soil Sci.*, 38: 445, 1934.

MITSCHERLICH'S THEORY AND PRESENT-DAY AGROBIOLOGY

Mitscherlich's Theory. In the early part of the present century the German scientist Mitscherlich [34] proposed to calculate the effect of different quantities of various growth factors on the yield of plants by means of a mathematical formula. The formula was based on the observation that the addition of each successive equal increment (Baule) [35] of a given growth factor gives just one-half as much increase in crop growth as was obtained by the preceding increment. For example, if the addition of one Baule of P_2O_5 increased the yield of cotton 100 pounds, the addition of another equal increment of P_2O_5 would give an additional increase of only 50 pounds, and the third increment of the nutrient would result in a 25-pound increase, etc. Furthermore, if the original increment of P_2O_5 applied had been 2 Baules, the increased yield of cotton would have been 150 pounds, and a second addition of 2 Baules of P_2O_5 would have produced 37.5 pounds more cotton. Results from a large number, some 30,000, field experiments and a large number of pot tests support the reliability of this observation.

A "theoretically highest possible yield" is assumed for each set of growth conditions when an optimum supply of any one growth factor is present. This yield, designated as A, will vary with the supply of other nutrients, climatic conditions, system of cultivation, etc.

The equation proposed by Mitscherlich to express this relationship of growth to growth factors is as follows:

$$\log (A - y) = \log A - c \cdot (x + b)$$

In this equation A represents maximum yield, y = actual yield, x = quantity of a given nutrient applied, b = quantity of the given nutrient in the soil in an available form, and c = an effectiveness factor. By antilogarithizing the equation we get:

$$\frac{A - y}{A} = 10^{-c \cdot (x+b)}$$

and

$$y = A \cdot [1 - 10^{-c \cdot (x+b)}]$$

[34] Mitscherlich was a professor of agriculture in the University of Königsberg in East Prussia. He was also the director of an experiment station devoted to the solving of soil problems. His efforts to find a method for determining the quantities of plant nutrients farmers should apply in order to obtain increased crop yields led to his study of the old law of diminishing returns and the determination of c values.

[35] See pp. 274–275 for a definition of a Baule unit.

Curves showing the relation of available N, P_2O_5, and K_2O to yield in per cent of A, according to this equation, are shown in Fig. 35. The different gradients of the curves are indicated in the equation by different values of an effectiveness factor c. They are 0.6 for P_2O_5, 0.4 for K_2O, and 0.122 for N.[36] This effectiveness factor c, which is specific for each growth factor, was determined by a great deal of experimental work and was found to be independent of the kind of plant involved. The assigning of a specific value to c for a considerable number of

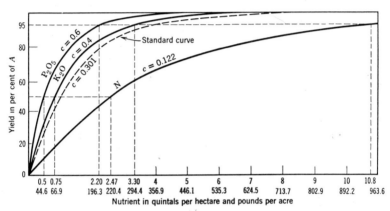

Fig. 35. A correlation between available nutrient in quintals per hectare and yield in per cent of A. The values are also given in pounds per acre. The broken line shows the standard curve upon which the Baule units are based. From *Easy Lessons in Mitscherlich* by Heinz Krause, a mimeograph distributed by the Davison Chemical Corporation, Baltimore.

growth factors constitutes Mitscherlich's real contribution. The values are applicable for soils free from characteristics which are harmful to plant growth, "normal soils," as Mitscherlich designated them.

Contributions of Baule. A mathematician from Göttingen by the name of B. Baule assisted Mitscherlich with his calculations. Baule pointed out that, while A represented the maximum yield obtainable with a full supply of one growth factor x for any set of conditions, consideration should be given to the maximum yield obtainable if all growth factors were in full supply. The maximum yield under perfect or ideal conditions could be designated as A_n or Q. Under such conditions y would approach Q, and we could write $y = 0.9999 Q$.

The Baule Unit. The quantity of any growth factor which will produce one-half of the theoretically highest yield A (Fig. 35) is termed

[36] The *values* are in terms of quintals per hectare. When reduced to pounds per acre they become 0.00135, 0.00664, and 0.00442 for N, P_2O_5, and K_2O, respectively.

a Baule. These quantities for N, P_2O_5, and K_2O in pounds per acre are: 220.4, 44.6, and 66.9, respectively. The corresponding values in quintals per hectare are 2.47, 0.5, and 0.75. It should be pointed out that these values include the amounts of the available nutrients in the soil in addition to any that are supplied in fertilizers. The method of arriving at the value of a Baule for each of the three nutrients is shown in Fig. 35.

Instead of using a separate growth response curve for each of the three nutrients it is much simpler to use one curve, which may be designated as a "standard curve." Such a curve may be constructed as follows: if the maximum yield A, with a value of 100, is divided by 50 (one-half the maximum yield) the figure 2 is obtained, the log of which is 0.301. By using this equality factor as the curve gradient (c) the standard curve as shown in Fig. 35 is obtained. This curve can be utilized in determining quantities of individual nutrients *in terms of Baule units only,* because both the curve and Baule units are based on quantities which give equal amounts (one-half) of the maximum growth.

Maximum Crop Yields. Mitscherlich conducted a large number of experiments with different plants, making use of pots 7.87 inches in diameter and 7.87 inches deep. By adding what he considered a sufficiency of all growth factors but one, and then increasing the amounts of this one factor or nutrient by given increments, he determined the quantity of this nutrient that would give the maximum yield. By this procedure it was determined that 3.50 grams of N, 0.70 gram of P_2O_5, and 1.30 grams of K_2O gave maximum yields in these pots. Converting these quantities into pounds per acre gives 995.1 pounds of N, 199 pounds of P_2O_5, and 369.6 pounds of K_2O as the quantities required for maximum crop yields.[37] As a matter of convenience it is considered that the quantity of any growth factor which will give maximum yield is 10 Baules. Accordingly, 1 Baule of N is $\frac{1}{10}$ of 995.1 pounds per acre, or 99.5 pounds. Likewise, 19.9 pounds of P_2O_5 constitutes 1 Baule of this nutrient and 36.96 pounds a Baule of K_2O. Spurway [38] determined by calculation that 6.0 pounds constitutes 1 Baule of Mg, and 0.8 pound 1 Baule of S.

In determining maximum crop yields it was thought that a given plant, let us say corn, for example, is only inherently capable of producing a given amount of plant tissue regardless of how favorable all exterior factors such as nutrient supply, soil conditions, water supply, and

[37] These values vary from those given by Dr. Wilcox in the *ABC of Agrobiology,* which the writer believes are incorrect.

[38] *Soil Fertility Diagnosis and Control for Field, Garden, and Greenhouse Soils,* by C. H. Spurway. Edwards Brothers, Ann Arbor, Mich., 1948.

climate may be. The maximum yields of several crops as given by
O. W. Wilcox are shown in Table 55.

TABLE 55. MAXIMUM YIELDS PER ACRE OF SEVERAL CROPS WHEN ALL
GROWTH FACTORS ARE AT THE OPTIMUM *

Crop	Yield	Crop	Yield
Corn	225.0 bu.	Potatoes	1,550.0 bu.
Wheat	171.2 bu.	Rice	252.5 bu.
Oats	395.0 bu.	Sugar beet	54.0 tons
Barley	308.0 bu.	Sugar cane	192.0 tons
Rye	198.0 bu.	Cotton	4.6 bales

* *ABC of Agrobiology.* W. W. Norton & Co., New York, 1937. Used with
permission.

Calculation of Crop Yield in Per Cent of the Maximum. It was
pointed out previously that 1 Baule of any growth factor is equal in
effect on growth to the effect of 1 Baule of any other factor and furthermore that 10 Baules of any factor give maximum growth so far as that
factor is concerned. Accordingly the effect of any quantity, in Baule
units, of any factor on growth can be calculated in terms of per cent of
maximum crop yield by use of the yield formula of Mitscherlich, which
is:

$$y = 100 - [0.1 \times 2^{(10-x)}]$$

where y = per cent of maximum crop yield and x = plant nutrient in
Baule units per acre. By this procedure Spurway derived the values in
Table 56.

The potential or expected yield of any crop may be calculated by use
of the factors in Table 56 if the growth factors in Baule units are known.
For example, assume N supply is 0.7 Baule, P_2O_5 supply is 1.0 Baule,
K_2O supply is 2.0 Baule, and climatic and soil factors are 4.5 Baule.
The crop to be grown is wheat, the maximum theoretical yield of which
is 171.2 bushels. The calculation would then be:

$$\frac{37.0}{100} \text{ N} \cdot \frac{48.8}{100} P_2O_5 \cdot \frac{74.4}{100} K_2O \cdot \frac{95.5}{100} \text{ climate} + \text{soil} = y = 12.83\%$$

$$0.1283 \times 171.2 = 21.96 \text{ bu.}$$

It is seen that with this formula one may readily calculate the increase
in yield that can be expected from the addition of a given amount (in
Baule units) of the nutrient which is in shortest supply. Likewise, when
the deficiency of one nutrient is supplied, the results to be obtained from

TABLE 56. POTENCY OF A SINGLE PLANT NUTRIENT IN TERMS ŏF BAULE UNITS AND PER CENT OF MAXIMUM CROP YIELD, ALL OTHER PLANT-GROWTH FACTORS BEING AT THE OPTIMUM *

Baule Units	Per Cent of Maximum Crop Yield	Baule Units	Per Cent of Maximum Crop Yield	Baule Units	Per Cent of Maximum Crop Yield
0.1	4.5	1.3	58.4	3.0	87.2
0.2	10.9	1.4	61.2	3.5	90.9
0.3	16.9	1.5	63.8	4.0	93.6
0.4	22.4	1.6	66.2	4.5	95.5
0.5	27.6	1.7	68.5	5.0	96.8
0.6	32.5	1.8	70.6	6.0	98.4
0.7	37.0	1.9	72.6	7.0	99.2
0.8	41.2	2.0	74.4	8.0	99.6
0.9	45.2	2.2	77.7	9.0	99.8
1.0	48.8	2.4	80.6	10.0	100.00
1.1	52.3	2.6	83.1		
1.2	55.5	2.8	85.3		

* From *Soil Fertility Diagnosis and Control for Field, Garden, and Greenhouse Soils.* C. H. Spurway, East Lansing, Michigan. (Edwards Brothers, Ann Arbor, Mich., 1948.) Used by permission.

additions of other nutrients, as needed, may be determined. Furthermore, the quantities of the various nutrients which can be profitably applied may be calculated by giving consideration to the costs of the nutrients and the value of the crop increase obtained. It should also be noted that the addition of a nutrient which is present in considerable quantity, K_2O in the above example, will give some increase in yield even if no N is added.

Detrimental Effect of Excess Nitrogen. In later work Mitscherlich points out that, whereas P_2O_5 and K_2O are readily fixed in the soil when applied in a soluble form, nitrogen is not fixed but remains readily available. As a result over fertilization with N is much easier to accomplish with heavy applications than is true with either K_2O or P_2O_5. Furthermore, grain crops are more susceptible to damage from excessive amounts of N than are root crops. In consideration of these facts Mitscherlich supplemented his equation with a factor *K*, to be used primarily in dealing with grain crops.[39]

A Simplified Field Experiment. In place of the replicated and randomized field-plot experiment which is considered rather "standard"

[39] The nitrogen problem is discussed and curves presented showing the depressing effect of increasing nitrogen application on yields of wheat, rye, and oats in *Düngungsfragen*, by E. A. Mitscherlich, Berlin, 1949.

today, Mitscherlich proposes a simple 7-plot series without replication. The treatments in the order of occurrence are tabulated.

Plot	Nutrient	Lb. per Acre	Plot	Nutrient	Lb. per Acre
1	None	0.0	5	Nitrogen	107.1
2	Nitrogen	107.1		Phosphorus (P_2O_5)	142.8
3	Nitrogen	107.1	6	Nitrogen	107.1
	Potassium (K_2O)	142.8	7	None	0.0
4	Nitrogen	107.1			
	Potassium (K_2O)	142.8			
	Phosphorus (P_2O_5)	142.8			

A root crop is recommended as the test plant because of the effect of nitrogen on grain crops when used in excessive amounts.

In interpreting the results some consideration should be given to soil variability. For example, should the yield from Plot 1 be 10 per cent higher than that from Plot 7, and the Plot 2 yield proportionately higher (less than 10 per cent) than the Plot 6 yield, then the difference is supposed to be due to a soil variation, and the yield for each plot should be adjusted on a percentage basis before evaluating the results of the test. Table 57 presents hypothetical results from such a field trial. No soil variation is assumed in this example.

TABLE 57. RESULTS FROM A 7-PLOT FIELD EXPERIMENT AS SUGGESTED BY MITSCHERLICH

Plot No.	Yield, lb. per acre	Increase in Yield Due to	In Lb.	Per Cent Increase in Yield Based on Yield of Plot	Per Cent Increase
1	8,921.6	O	0.0	0	0.0
2	16,772.6	N	7,851.0	1	88.0
3	19,181.4	K_2O	2,408.8	2	14.4
4	23,991.0	P_2O_5	4,809.6	3	25.1
4	23,991.0	K_2O	3,025.2	5	14.4
5	20,965.8	P_2O_5	4,193.2	6	25.0
6	16,772.6	N	7,857.0	7	88.0
7	8,921.6	O	0.0	0	0.0

It will be noted that the data permit of a check on the increased yield due to each nutrient element. Assuming that the area of soil selected for the experiment is uniform in chemical and physical condition throughout the profile, that it is representative of average conditions in the field, and that the crop on the different plots has not been appreciably affected by differences in surface drainage, or the attack of insects or plant diseases, or in plant population, the results from such a simple test could be quite reliable. However, the statistical treatment of data from such an experiment would be difficult.

Calculation of Amounts of Available Nutrients in Soil. A method is also proposed for calculating the amounts of available nutrients in soils from the results of the simplified experiment, but space does not permit of its presentation here.

Application of Mitscherlich's Work. Mitscherlich's proposals have been received favorably by some American workers and with much opposition by others. American workers in general have given little attention to his studies. The fact that the experimental data used to support his contentions were obtained under East Prussian conditions raises a question as to how generally his values for c may be applied. Commenting on this point in *Die Ertragsgesetze* in 1948, Mitscherlich calls attention to the fact that results from more than 28,000 field experiments carried on by German fertilizer companies support the validity of the value given to c. It is maintained that c is independent of climate and of the type of plant used.

Mitscherlich's proposal to use 1 series of 7 plots in the field to determine the fertilizer needs of a soil in place of several series, using increasing amounts of the different plant nutrients, will not be accepted readily by workers carrying on field experiments under the prevailing procedures.

Perhaps a careful checking of Mitscherlich's work by several scientists under American conditions would prove fruitful.

REFERENCES

Anderson, M. S., and Noble, W. U. Comparison of various chemical quick tests on different soils. *U.S.D.A. Misc. Pub.* 259, 1937.

Barnette, R. M., Camp, J. P., Warner, J. D., and Gall, O. E. The use of zinc sulfate under corn and other field crops. *Florida Agr. Exp. Sta. Bull.* 292, 1936.

Blake, M. A., Nightingale, G. T., and Davidson, O. W. Nutrition of apple trees. *New Jersey Agr. Exp. Sta. Bull.* 626, 1937.

Bray, R. H. Requirements for successful soil tests. *Soil Sci.,* 66: 83, 1948.

Bray, R. H. Correlation of soil tests with crop response to added fertilizers and with fertilizer requirements. *Diagnostic Techniques for Soils and Crops,* p. 53. American Potash Institute, Washington, D. C., 1948.

Camp, A. F., and Fudge, B. R. Some symptoms of citrus malnutrition in Florida. *Florida Agr. Exp. Sta. Bull.* 335, 1939.

280 Soil Fertility

Chapman, H. D., and Brown, S. M. Analysis of orange leaves for diagnosing nutrient status with reference to potassium. *Hilgardia,* 19: 501, 1950.

Chapman, H. D., Brown, S. M., and Rayner, D. S. Effect of potash deficiency and excess on orange trees. *Hilgardia,* 17: 619, 1947.

Chapman, H. D., and Fullmer, F. Potassium and phosphorus status of California citrus orchards as indicated by leaf analysis surveys. *Citrus Leaves,* February 1951.

Cook, R. L., and Millar, C. E. Plant nutrient deficiencies. *Michigan Agr. Exp. Sta. Spec. Bull.* 353, 1953.

Eckstein, O., Bruno, A., and Turrentine, J. W. *Kennzeichen des Kalimangels.* (*Signes des manque de potasse. Potash Deficiency Symptoms.*) B. Westermann Co., New York, 1937.

Emmert, E. M. Plant tissue tests as a guide to fertilizer treatment of tomatoes. *Kentucky Agr. Exp. Sta. Bull.* 430, 1942.

Goodall, W. D., and Gregory, F. G. Chemical composition of plants as an index of their nutritional status. Tech. Com. 16, *Imp. Bur. Hort. Plantation Crops,* I. A. B. Penglais, Aberystwyth, Wales, 1947.

Graham, E. R. Testing Missouri soils. *Missouri Agr. Exp. Sta. Cir.* 345, 1950.

Haas, A. R. C. Deficiency chlorosis in citrus. *Soil Sci.,* 42: 435, 1936.

Hunger Signs in Crops. Amer. Soc. Agron. and the National Fertilizer Assoc., 1949.

Jenny, H., Vlamis, J., and Martin, W. E. Greenhouse assay of fertility of California soils. *Hilgardia,* 20, No. 1, May 1950.

Johnson, M. O. Manganese chlorosis of pineapples; its cause and control. *Hawaii Agr. Exp. Sta. Bull.* 52, 1924.

Krantz, B. A., Nelson, W. L., and Burkhart, L. F. Plant tissue tests as a tool in agronomic research. *Diagnostic Techniques for Soils and Crops,* p. 137. American Potash Institute, Washington, D. C., 1948.

Krause, H. *Easy Lessons in Mitscherlich.* A mimeograph. Distributed by V. Sauchelli of the Davison Chemical Corp., Baltimore, Maryland.

Laurie, A., and Wagner, A. Deficiency symptoms of greenhouse flowering crops. *Ohio Agr. Exp. Sta. Bull.* 611, 1940.

Lundegardh, H. Leaf analysis as a guide to soil fertility. *Nature,* 151: 310, 1943.

Lunt, H. A., Swanson, C. L. W., and Jacobson, H. G. M. The Morgan soil testing system. *Connecticut Agr. Exp. Sta. Bull.* 541 (revised), 1950.

Lynd, J. Q., Turk, L. M., and Cook, R. L. Application of soil tests, tissue tests, and foliar analysis to field experiments. *Soil Sci. Soc. Amer. Proc.* 14: 236, 1949.

Mehlich, A., Fred, E. B., and Truog, E. The *Cunninghamella*-plaque method of measuring available phosphorus in soil. *Soil Sci.,* 38: 445, 1934.

Mehlich, A., Truog, E., and Fred, E. B. The *Aspergillus niger* method of measuring available potassium in soils. *Soil Sci.,* 35: 259, 1933.

Mitscherlich, E. A. *Die Bestimmung des Düngebedürfnisses des Bodens.* P. Parey, Berlin, 1930.

McGeorge, W. T. Modified Neubauer method for soil cultures. *Soil Sci.,* 62: 61, 1946.

McMurtrey, J. E., Jr. Visual symptoms of malnutrition in plants. *Diagnostic Techniques for Soils and Crops,* p. 231. American Potash Institute, Washington, D. C., 1948.

McMurtrey, J. E., Jr. Symptoms on field-grown tobacco characteristic of the deficient supply of each of several essential chemical elements. *U.S.D.A. Tech. Bull.* 612, 1938.

Niklas, H., and Poschenrieder, H. Zur Feststellung der Magnesia-düngebedürftig-keit und Magnesia-düngewirkung in Boden mittles *Aspergillus niger, Boden-kunde u. Pflanzenernähr.*, 1: 235, 1936.

Niklas, H., Poschenrieder, H., and Trischler, J. Die Kulture des Acimmelspilzes *Aspergillus niger* zur biochemischen Bestimmung der Kali und Phosphorsäure Bedürftigkeit der Boden. *J. Ernähr. Pflanzen.*, 26: 97, 1930.

Official Methods of Analysis of the Association of Official Agricultural Chemists, seventh edition, 1950.

Peech, M. Chemical methods for assessing soil fertility. *Diagnostic Techniques for Soils and Crops,* p. 1, American Potash Institute, Washington, D. C., 1948.

Peech, M. Methods of soil analysis for soil fertility investigations. *U.S.D.A. Cir.* 757, 1947.

Rogers, H. T. Iron deficiency of crimson clover on a calcareous soil and method of diagnosis. *J. Amer. Soc. Agron.*, 39: 638, 1947.

Russell, E. J., revised by Russell, E. W. *Soil Conditions and Plant Growth.* Longmans, Green & Co., New York, 1950.

Salter, R. M., and Ames, J. W. Plant composition as a guide to the availability of soil nutrients. *J. Amer. Soc. Agron.*, 20: 808, 1928.

Scarseth, G. D. Plant tissue testing in diagnosis of the nutritional status of grow-ing plants. *Soil Sci.*, 55: 113, 1943.

Shear, C. B., Crane, H. L., and Myers, A. T. Nutrient-element balance: A fundamental concept in plant nutrition. *Proc. Amer. Soc. Hort. Sci.*, 47: 239, 1945.

Spurway, C. H. *Soil Fertility Diagnosis and Control for Field, Garden, and Greenhouse Soils.* C. H. Spurway, East Lansing, Mich., 1948. (Edwards Brothers, Ann Arbor, Mich.)

Spurway, C. H., and Lawton, K. A practical system of soil fertility diagnosis. *Michigan Agr. Exp. Sta. Tech. Bull.* 132 (fourth revision).

Thomas, W. Present status of diagnosis of mineral requirements of plants by means of leaf analysis. *Soil Sci.*, 59: 353, 1945.

Thomas, W., and Mack, W. B. Misconceptions relative to the method of foliar diagnosis. *Proc. Amer. Soc. Hort. Sci.*, 44: 355, 1944.

Thornton, S. F. Soil and fertilizer studies by means of the Neubauer method. *Purdue Univ. Agr. Exp. Sta. Bull.* 399, 1935.

Tyner, E. H. The relation of corn yields to leaf nitrogen, phosphorus, and po-tassium content. *Soil Sci. Soc. Amer. Proc.*, 11: 317, 1945.

Tyner, E. H., and Webb, J. R. The relation of corn yields to nutrient balance as revealed by leaf analysis. *J. Amer. Soc. Agron.*, 38: 173, 1946.

Ulrich, A. Plant analysis as a diagnostic procedure. *Soil Sci.*, 55: 101, 1943.

Ulrich, A. Plant analysis: Methods and interpretation of results. *Diagnostic Techniques for Soils and Crops,* p. 157. American Potash Institute, Washing-ton, D. C., 1948.

Vandecaveye, S. C. Biological methods of determining nutrients in soils. *Ibid.,* p. 199.

Wallace, T. Diagnosis of Mineral Deficiencies in Plants by Visual Symptoms, a Color Atlas and Guide. H. M. Stationery Office, London, 1943; also Supple-ment, 1944.

Wilcox, O. W. A conspectus of quantitative agrobiology. A mimeograph. Also various other mimeographs prepared by Dr. Wilcox and distributed by Dr. V. Sauchelli of the Davison Chemical Corp., Baltimore, Maryland.

Wilcox, O. W. *ABC of Agrobiology.* W. W. Norton & Co., New York, 1937.

Wright, C. H. *Soil Analysis: Physical and Chemical Methods.* Thomas Murby & Co., London, 1934.

14

Activities of Soil Organisms That Affect Productivity[1]

The chemical and physical processes of the soil are so intriguing and have such visible effects on plant growth that much more study has been devoted to them than to the activities of the numerous organisms which live in the soil. Nevertheless, biological activities play an indispensable role in the formation of available nutrients from complex compounds and also bring about changes in the physical condition of the soil. The contribution of soil organisms to many soil processes that influence productivity is becoming better recognized as research in the field progresses.

Although suggestions were made during the first century B.C. concerning the existence of minute forms of life, particularly in swamps and in water, which cause diseases, the actual existence of microorganisms was not established until about 1671, when Kircheus made use of a crude microscope in studying decomposing substances. The name "animalcules" was applied to such organisms. During the following years the expansion of knowledge of microorganisms went hand in hand with the development of the microscope. The study of larger soil organisms dates primarily from the work of Darwin on earthworms around 1880, and the contribution of plant roots to soil improvement is a still more recent study.[1]

The classification, characteristics, and general activities of soil organisms are discussed in introductory soil science courses. Accordingly, only the activities of organisms inhabiting the soil that bear specifically on soil productivity will be considered in this chapter.

Discussion Topics

Improvement in soil physical condition by organisms.
Chemical changes in soil constituents produced by organisms.
Additions of nitrogen to soils through biological fixation.

[1] This topic is discussed fully by Clark in *Advances in Agronomy,* 1: 241, 1949.

IMPROVEMENT IN SOIL PHYSICAL CONDITION
BY ORGANISMS

There is some direct improvement in the physical condition of soils through the activities of certain organisms as, for example, the growth of plant roots, the passage of soil through the digestive tract of earthworms, and the envelopment of soil particles by the mycelium of fungi. In general, however, the by-products of biological activity bring about more physical improvement than results directly from the growth of organisms inhabiting the soil.

Soil Improvement Through Root Development. Since about 1945 emphasis has been placed on the value of deep-rooted plants, especially those with taproots, for the development of drainage channels into fine-textured subsoils and for improved soil aeration. Locally this action may be of much importance, but of far more general significance is the granulating action of the fibrous roots of plants. It has been shown repeatedly that the extensive development of fibrous roots in the soil is one of the most effective processes of granulation. Furthermore, the granules so produced have been found to be more stable than those formed by tillage operations or through freezing and thawing.

Activities of Earthworms.[2] Aside from plant roots, earthworms undoubtedly contribute more to the improvement of soil structure than other large forms of life in the soil. Although there are various species of earthworms which vary markedly in size, the work they do in the soil is similar. Likewise the number of earthworms in an acre of soil varies greatly with soil conditions. Loams with an above-average organic-matter content appear to be most favorable for a large worm population. Although they require a supply of calcium, soil acidity does not appear to affect them greatly unless the pH is below 4.5, according to Russell.[2] Cropping systems which include a high proportion of pasture and hay crops, with a large amount of crop residues left on the soil surface, are conducive to earthworm development. Some 10 worms per square foot of soil have been reported in Maryland,[3] with the total weight amounting to 500 pounds per acre. Data collected by Slater and Hopp [4] indicate similar numbers in soils of the Middle Atlantic and North Central states.

[2] Russell gives an excellent summary of information concerning earthworms and their activities in *Soil Conditions and Plant Growth,* p. 178, 1950.

[3] *J. Soil and Water Cons.,* 1 (2): 85, 1946.

[4] *Soil Sci. Soc. Amer. Proc.,* 12: 508, 1947.

The feeding habits of earthworms result in a more thorough inter-mixing of the organic matter and mineral portion of the soil than would otherwise be the case.   Some species come to the surface and drag leaves and other plant parts down into their burrows.   This action is one of the main processes by which organic matter becomes mixed with the surface soil in forests.   Also earthworms show a decided preference for the leaves of certain species such as elm, ash, and birch.   Other worm species do not come out onto the surface but obtain food material near the surface and pull it deeper into the soil.

As a whole earthworms work in the surface or humus-rich portion of the soil although in dry weather and during cold winters they may burrow to depths of 4 or even 8 feet.   Only small quantities of subsoil are, accordingly, brought up and mixed with the surface soil.   These deep burrows have some effect on drainage and aeration, but primarily the improvement of the physical condition is confined to the surface horizon.

Quantities of Soil Moved by Earthworms.   In productive areas con-taining many earthworms the quantity of soil passed through their bodies is large, but in unproductive fields the soil is modified very little by their action.   Darwin, the first scientist to give serious study to earth-worm activity, concluded that as much as 15 tons of dry soil per acre per year might pass through their digestive tract.   Lunt and Jacobson [5] found 8 tons of casts on the surface of cultivated soil in Connecticut. In considering these figures, large though they may seem, it should be remembered that the estimate was made on the basis of the worm casts found on the soil surface.   Studies have shown, however, that only a few species excrete casts on the surface.   It is possible, therefore, that much larger quantities of earth are passed through the digestive tract of these worms if species which do not come to the surface are present in large numbers.   For example, it was estimated that in an old pasture at Rothamsted from 33 to 45 per cent of the worm casts were excreted below the surface.[6]

Soil Changes Produced by Earthworms.   In feeding, earthworms pass small mineral particles and organic matter through their digestive tract. During the process a part of the organic matter is destroyed to furnish energy and nutrients for the worms and the remainder is thoroughly intermixed with the soil particles.   Also calcium carbonate is excreted

[5] *Soil Sci.,* 58: 367, 1944.

[6] *Soil Conditions and Plant Growth,* p. 184.   Longmans, Green & Co., London, 1950.

from glands in the digestive tract and mixed with the contents of the intestine. The worm casts are, accordingly, richer in calcium, nitrogen, carbon, and phosphorus than the surrounding soil. They also have a higher pH value. This change in composition is due primarily to the mixing of the finer soil particles with organic matter, which is rich in nutrients, and with calcium carbonate, rather than to the effect of the digestive process on the mineral particles. No increase in fertility as a whole can be proved as the result of worm action although the casts are more productive than the soil containing them. However, the physical condition of the soil is improved.

Other Animals. Although other worms, small animals, and insects play some part in the decomposition of organic matter and its incorporation into the soil, their effect is not great except in an occasional small area where the population is exceptionally high. Some subsoil is brought to the surface by the activities of these forms of life, and their burrows may improve drainage and soil aeration to a limited extent, but on the whole they have little effect on productivity.

Effects of Microorganisms on Soil Physical Condition. Organisms improve soil structure directly by inducing granulation and indirectly by the production of humus. The mycelium of filamentous fungi, and to some extent of *Actinomyces,* binds soil particles into various sized groups or clusters and hence produces a form of granulation. Although these structural units are somewhat temporary, since they disintegrate with the decomposition of the hyphae, they are at times important in decreasing wind and water erosion and in increasing the permeability of the soil. It is not necessary to discuss here the value of humus in the improvement of the physical condition of the soil.

The part played by bacteria in soil aggregation is not fully understood, but there is evidence that it is much more extensive than was formerly thought. The granulating effect of plant residues appears to be greatest shortly after their incorporation into the soil and hence cannot be ascribed to humus or other products of their decay. Norman [7] calls attention to the belief that polysaccharides with adhesive properties are produced extracellularly by bacteria and that these substances produce aggregation of the soil particles. The granulating effect of a sod is well recognized, and it is believed the influence on soil structure is much greater than would result from plowing under a similar weight of plant material. It is suggested, accordingly, that the great aggregating effect of the sod is due to adhesive products of the large bacterial population in the rhizosphere.

[7] *Soil Sci. Soc. Amer. Proc.,* 11: 9, 1946.

CHEMICAL CHANGES IN SOIL CONSTITUENTS PRODUCED BY ORGANISMS

The soil constituent affected most extensively by direct action of soil organisms is the organic matter. The mineral material of the soil is changed chemically indirectly through the action of the products of biological activity by oxidation of some constituents by autotrophic bacteria and by reduction of some highly oxidized compounds.

Decay of Organic Matter. Through the growth processes of plants many organic compounds are synthesized, some of which contain mineral elements. In addition, various mineral compounds occur in the different plant structures although they may not be constituents of them. If such plant materials did not decay and so set free the constituent elements in forms usable by other plants, the available supply of several mineral nutrients would soon be exhausted and in consequence plant growth would be inhibited. Animal tissue also must be decayed if the nutrients it contains are to be used by plants. This process of organic-matter decomposition is primarily a function of microorganisms. The decay process consists in the breaking down of complex compounds into simpler ones and ultimately into simple inorganic compounds and elements. *The latter process is known as mineralization.*

Decay of Non-Nitrogenous Compounds. Non-nitrogenous compounds such as starches, sugars, cellulose, and hemicelluloses are converted into intermediate compounds the nature of which depends largely on the organisms attacking them, on the supply of oxygen, and of course on the compound being decomposed. For example, Waksman [8] points out that glucose is converted into citric acid and water by fungi when the oxygen supply is limited, but with better aeration oxalic acid and water are the products. On the other hand anaerobic bacteria and yeasts may produce lactic acid, butyric acid, alcohol, carbon dioxide, and hydrogen from glucose. Regardless of the nature of the intermediate products, under aerobic conditions the carbohydrates are ultimately reduced to carbon dioxide and water. Organic matter containing elements other than carbon, hydrogen, and oxygen upon decomposition by aerobic organisms gives rise to various salts as calcium phosphate, sulfates, nitrates, and chlorides of calcium, potassium, sodium, and magnesium, and carbonates of some of the same metals. These salts may then serve as nutrients for higher plants and also for microorganisms.

Under anaerobic conditions attack of soil organisms on organic matter results in the formation of complex intermediate compounds most

[8] *Soil Microbiology,* p. 109. John Wiley & Sons, New York, 1952.

of which are quite resistant to further decomposition. Some water, carbon dioxide, and ammonia are formed, but few simple compounds are produced which can serve as plant nutrients. The decomposition process is also much slower than under aerobic conditions.

Many of the compounds found in plant and animal tissue are readily decomposed by most soil organisms, but some are quite resistant to the attack of all but a relatively few specific forms. For example, starches and sugars and many proteins are decomposed by most soil microorganisms, but cellulose is resistant to the attack of many of them. Only specific forms of bacteria, fungi, and actinomycetes decompose it readily, and such organisms are sometimes referred to as "cellulose destroyers." The aerobic bacteria and fungi break down cellulose quite completely, producing mainly carbon dioxide with a high percentage (30–40 per cent) of the material being built into cells of the decomposing organisms.[9] Anaerobic bacteria produce various organic acids and alcohols from cellulose. In contrast, the hemicelluloses are decomposed by a great many types of bacteria and fungi. Again lignin is very resistant to decomposition by soil organisms, especially under anaerobic conditions. With good aeration, lignin is broken down more readily, but still the process is slow compared to the rate of decomposition of other organic substances. Some of the higher fungi are most effective in lignin decay.

Decomposition of Nitrogenous Compounds. Although a number of substances found in plant and animal tissue contain nitrogen, including urea, purine bases, lecithin, and alkaloids, a large part of the nitrogen is present in the form of proteins. These amino acid complexes contain, according to Waksman,[10] an average of 50–55 per cent carbon, 15–19 per cent nitrogen, 6–7 per cent hydrogen, and 21–23 per cent oxygen, in addition to small quantities of sulfur and sometimes phosphorus. The first step in protein decomposition by soil organisms is an hydrolysis into polypeptides and then into amino acids by the action of enzymes. Under aerobic conditions these are converted into ammonia, carbon dioxide, organic acids, and alcohols by the action of many types of bacteria and fungi. Under anaerobic conditions putrefaction occurs with the formation of various vile-smelling compounds, including mercaptans.

In the decomposition of amino acids with the formation of ammonia, *known as ammonification,* the proportion of the nitrogen converted into ammonia varies largely with the active organisms and the amount of carbohydrate present. The more carbohydrate there is the greater will be the increase in microbial population and hence the utilization of nitro-

---

[9] *Soil Microbiology,* p. 111. John Wiley & Sons, New York, 1952.
[10] *Ibid.,* p. 117.

gen in the formation of cell substance with correspondingly less ammonia production. According to Waksman [11] from 50 to 80 per cent of the nitrogen in protein may be ultimately liberated as ammonia in the decomposition process. Plant residues must contain from 1.5 to 1.7 per cent of nitrogen if any ammonia is to be liberated immediately. If the percentage falls below 1.5 little if any ammonia will be liberated until further decay occurs. In the decomposition of matter having smaller percentages of nitrogen the organisms concerned will require additional nitrogen for the development of cell substance. The ammonia produced during the decay of soil organic matter does not accumulate in the soil under conditions which are favorable for the growth of most plants. Some of it may be absorbed by plant roots and some may be utilized by organisms decomposing organic matter containing little or no nitrogen, but the major part is oxidized, mostly to nitrates.

Oxidation of Ammonia. Although ammonification is brought about by many kinds of soil organisms, the oxidation of ammonia is accomplished by specific bacteria only. The first step consists in the production of nitrite and is accomplished mainly by bacteria of the *Nitrosomonas* and *Nitrosococcus* groups. The nitrite is then oxidized to nitrate by a bacterial group called *Nitrobacter.* An appreciable concentration of nitrite nitrogen is toxic to plants, and seldom is there an accumulation of nitrite in soils harmful to crop production. The nitrous and nitric acids produced by the *nitrification process* are immediately neutralized by cations commonly found in soils thus producing the corresponding salts.

The nitrifying bacteria, although they appear to be present in all arable land, occur in greater numbers in fertile than in infertile soils but are never abundant. They are quite sensitive to soil conditions, especially aeration and reaction. In poorly drained land nitrification may be greatly impeded by lack of sufficient air and crops may suffer from a lack of nitrogen. Some strains of nitrifiers will grow in a pH range of 3.5 to 10, but the optimum reaction for the group is pH 7.0 to 8.0. In general their activity is limited in strongly acid or highly alkaline soils. An abundant supply of mineral nutrients, especially phosphorus and calcium, is required for maximum activity of nitrifying bacteria, and they obtain their carbon from carbon dioxide. Their energy is derived from the oxidation process.

Changes in Mineral Elements Caused by Microorganisms. During the decay of organic matter many significant changes are brought about in the mineral elements contained in the material, and micro-

[11] *Ibid.,* p. 118.

organisms are responsible for changes in mineral compounds which are not a part of the soil organic matter. As a whole, changes in the mineral constituents of plant and animal tissue result in the formation of simple compounds which can be utilized by plants or microorganisms or may be leached from the soil in humid climates.

Calcium, magnesium, and potassium usually are ultimately converted into the respective carbonates or bicarbonates. The potassium is either absorbed by growing organisms, adsorbed by the soil colloids, or, because of the high solubility of its salts, is dissolved and carried out of the soil profile unless precipitation is extremely small. The calcium and magnesium may likewise be adsorbed or absorbed, but because of the low solubility of their carbonates they are often reprecipitated in the soil profile in that form. Because the bicarbonates have a relatively low solubility, a much higher precipitation is needed to remove an equal quantity of them from the soil than is true for potassium.

Iron and manganese may also be converted into soluble salts during decay of organic matter and be utilized by living organisms. The tendency for these elements to form relatively insoluble oxides, however, prevents the leaching of appreciable quantities from well aerated soils. These elements may also be oxidized by soil microorganisms.

The phosphorus in decaying organic matter finally appears as $H_2PO_4^-$ or $HPO_4^=$ ions which rapidly unite with basic ions to form various phosphates. Because of the low solubility of virtually all phosphates little loss of the element by leaching occurs, and that portion of it which is not utilized by living organisms remains in the upper horizons of the soil. It is reasonable to conclude, however, that because of the small quantity of available phosphorus in most soils any portion of the element made soluble through organic-matter decay is quickly absorbed by growing life forms.

Under conditions of poor aeration, sulfur in organic matter is reduced to various forms including hydrogen sulfide, carbon disulfide, and elemental sulfur. Under aerobic conditions these substances are quickly oxidized. Decay under anaerobic conditions results in the formation of foul-smelling sulfur compounds such as the mercaptans.

The role of microorganisms in the liberation of mineral elements through the decay of plant and animal tissue is of great importance in plant growth.

Sulfur Oxidation. The sulfur-bearing amino acids, cystine and cysteine, are constituents of many plant proteins. When these proteins are decomposed in the soil much of the sulfur remains as a constituent of humus, but part of it is converted into hydrogen sulfide with possibly some free sulfur being liberated. Under aerobic conditions these products are then oxidized to sulfurous acid and then to sulfuric acid. *This process is known as sulfofication.* A specific group of bacteria known as *Thiobacillus* is primarily responsible for this oxidation although it is believed that certain fungi are also capable of causing the oxidation. These bacteria are widely distributed in soil.

The importance of this process is evident from the fact that plants absorb their sulfur in the sulfate form. Furthermore, in reducing the alkalinity of arid soils and also of slightly acid or alkaline mucks and peats an application of elemental sulfur is frequently made. This is rapidly oxidized to sulfuric acid with the consequent decrease in soil *p*H. A similar procedure is followed in preparing potting soil or in setting plants in the open when it is desired to grow an acid-requiring decorative plant in soil which is not sufficiently acid. The oxidation of sulfur proceeds slowly at first but accelerates as the soil becomes acid.[12]

Oxidation of Other Elements and Compounds. Ferrous compounds may be oxidized to ferric salts by certain soil bacteria, which use the energy so liberated for the assimilation of carbon dioxide. Manganous salts may also be oxidized to the manganic state in a similar way. In fact cases have been reported in which the oxidation of manganese by bacteria in the rhizosphere was sufficient to cause a deficiency of the element for oats.[13] Certain organisms are also capable of oxidizing carbon monoxide and others oxidize hydrogen.

Microbiological Reduction in the Soil. When the supply of air in the soil is limited certain aerobic organisms can obtain their supply of oxygen by reducing highly oxidized compounds such as sulfates and nitrates. With nitrates the reducing action may result in the formation of lower oxides of nitrogen, or it may continue until free nitrogen is produced. Also many organisms can reduce nitrates with the formation of ammonia and oxygen as end products. The production of an appreciable quantity of nitrite is highly detrimental to plant growth because of its high toxicity. In fact the anaerobic soil condition that gives rise to reduction is unfavorable for the growth of most plants. The reduction of nitrates to nitrite or ammonia does not necessarily mean a loss of nitrogen from the soil, as these products can be reoxidized when conditions are favorable. Also the nitrogen in nitrate assimilated by soil organisms is merely stored in their cell substance and may be liberated in available form later.

Although ammonia and gaseous nitrogen can escape from the soil into the atmosphere the losses of nitrogen through denitrification is

[12] *Ibid.,* p. 66.
[13] *Soil Sci. Soc. Amer. Proc.,* 11: 284, 1947.

considered insignificant in normal cultivated soils unless heavy applications of nitrogen are made. When crops such as rice are grown under flooded conditions, however, considerable loss of nitrogen as ammonia may result from alkaline soils under high temperatures. Russell [14] also calls attention to the loss of ammonia from English soil when considerable quantities of easily decayed organic matter high in nitrogen content were worked into a shallow layer of the surface.

A number of organisms can also reduce sulfates to hydrogen sulfide under conditions of poor soil aeration. In addition, ferric iron may be reduced to the ferrous state by biological action and manganese to the manganous form. In the reduced state these nutrients are more soluble and more available to plants. To what extent biological reduction contributes to the utilization of these nutrients is not known. It is known, however, that an appreciable concentration of ferrous or manganous compounds in the soil is toxic to most plants. In all the reduction processes mentioned a supply of readily decayable carbohydrate is necessary to serve as a source of energy for the reducing organisms.

ADDITIONS OF NITROGEN TO SOILS THROUGH BIOLOGICAL FIXATION

Deep-rooted plants may obtain nutrients, chiefly calcium and phosphorus, from the lower soil horizons and deposit portions of them in the surface horizons as constituents of leaves and stems. Although this process may benefit crops that follow in the rotation, it is a translocation rather than a direct addition of nutrients. Nitrogen is the only nutrient element which plants take from the soil and which may be increased in supply through the activity of living organisms. Nitrogen is obtained from the soil air by two groups of organisms: (1) those that live independently of other plants and (2) those that live in association with other plants.

Direct Fixation of Nitrogen. The ability of bacteria to fix nitrogen without living in symbiosis with higher plants was demonstrated by Winogradsky in 1891. His work was with the anaerobic *Clostridium pasteurianum*.[15] Other members of the butyric acid group of bacteria also have nitrogen-fixing ability but to varying degrees. In addition nitrogen is fixed by *Azotobacter,* an aerobic bacterium. *Clostridium* is much more tolerant of acidity than is *Azotobacter* and is found in strongly acid soils, although the optimum reaction for its activity is near

[14] *Soil Conditions and Plant Growth,* p. 297. Longmans, Green & Co., London, 1950.
[15] Often spelled *pastorianum*.

neutrality. *Azotobacter,* on the other hand, is highly sensitive to acidity, with the optimum reaction for its growth between *p*H 7.0 and 8.0. It is usually considered that a *p*H of 6.0 is the lower limit for the development of the organism although there are reports of strains that are active in soils of higher acidity. The tolerance of *Clostridium* for acidity doubtless accounts for its wider distribution in soils and in larger numbers. Although the numbers of bacteria will vary with conditions, some idea of the relative populations of the two organisms may be gained from the fact that in a soil receiving potassium and phosphorus fertilizer some 1,120,000 *Clostridium* were found per gram of soil compared to 98,700 *Azotobacter*.[16] Other workers have reported counts of *Azotobacter* as low as 18 per gram and 100 of *Clostridium*. In a few soils no *Azotobacter* were found. This organism has been shown to live in symbiotic relation with certain algae and also with some bacteria including *Clostridium*.[17] In the latter relationship *Azotobacter* produce anaerobic conditions by using oxygen, and salts of organic acids produced by *Clostridium* serve as a source of energy for *Azotobacter*.

Soil conditions other than those mentioned, which favor the activity of non-symbiotic nitrogen-fixing bacteria, are similar to those desirable for the growth of acid-sensitive legumes, namely, good aeration, an adequate supply of mineral nutrients, especially of calcium and phosphorus, sufficient but not excessive moisture supply, and a moderate soil temperature. In addition both *Clostridium* and *Azotobacter* require a supply of readily decayable organic matter, and carbonaceous material is more effective for nitrogen fixation than is organic matter rich in nitrogen.

Both groups of organisms fix appreciable quantities of nitrogen under laboratory conditions, but how much they fix under field conditions is undetermined. Neither organism can decompose humus as a source of energy, and therefore relatively undecomposed plant or animal residues are required. The quantity of nitrogen fixed is influenced by the nature and the supply of energy food available. A trace of molybdenum is also essential for the fixation process. Unfortunately the bacteria will use combined nitrogen, if present, in preference to obtaining their supply from the atmosphere. Although these two groups of bacteria are probably responsible for much of the nitrogen added to the soil through non-symbiotic fixation, it is known that some species of blue-green algae of the genera *Nostoc* and *Anabaena* use atmospheric nitrogen, and it is considered probable that some fungi (genus *Phoma*) and several other

---

[16] *Soil Microbiology*, p. 194. John Wiley & Sons, New York, 1952.
[17] *Ibid.*, p. 199.

groups of bacteria (*Rhodospirillum rubum,* purple S-bacterium) are capable of doing so. The quantities of nitrogen fixed non-symbiotically in field soils is discussed on pp. 125–126.

Symbiotic Nitrogen Fixation. The cause for the beneficial effect of legumes on crops following them puzzled scientists for 75 years or more. The presence of nodules on the roots of legumes was observed about the middle of the last century, and the production of these nodules through the action of bacteria was reported by Lachmann in 1858. Other workers observed a relationship between nodule formation and bacterial activity and that the organisms inhabited the nodules. However, it remained for Hellriegel and Wilfarth, in 1886, to demonstrate the fixation of nitrogen by bacteria living in the nodules and for Beijerinck to isolate the organism and name it *Bacillus radicicola* in 1888. The bacillus is now commonly known as *Rhizobium.*

Eventually it was shown that the organisms in the soil attack root hairs of the legumes and so gain entrance to the root system. Infection takes place when the tip of the root hair is deformed and an abundance of nitrate appears to prevent this deformation. According to Fred et al.,[18] the bacteria congregate on one side of the root hair and secrete an auxin-like substance or hormone which causes the curling of the root hair tip. However, Wilson[19] points out that the same deformation results when the roots are treated with extracts of the bacteria. Responding to the abundant supply of food afforded by the plant the organism increases rapidly in numbers and penetrates the root cortex by means of an infection thread. The plant in turn is stimulated by the infection to produce a cluster of cells in the meristematic tissue which develops into a nodule. The steps in the process are illustrated in Fig. 36. Because the nodules are connected with the vascular system of the root, products of photosynthesis are carried to them and secretions from bacteria living in the nodules are transferred to other parts of the plant.

Waksman[20] points out that certain relationships between the host and the bacteria influence the fixation of nitrogen. For example, a given strain of *Rhizobium* may cause the formation by a given host of substances which inhibit the development of bacteria, and as a result little nitrogen is fixed because the nodules contain a small quantity of bacterial tissue. On another host, however, of a different species, normal

[18] *Root Nodule Bacteria and Leguminous Plants.* University of Wisconsin Press, Madison, 1932.

[19] A full discussion of symbiotic nitrogen fixation is given by Wilson in *Biochemistry of Symbiotic Nitrogen Fixation.* University of Wisconsin Press, Madison, 1940.

[20] *Soil Microbiology,* p. 219. John Wiley & Sons, New York, 1952.

nodules may be caused by the same strain of *Rhizobium* and efficient nitrogen fixation may take place. This relationship between host and bacteria has been designated "host-plant specificity." [21] It is evident that the presence of nodules on the roots of a legume does not necessarily mean that appreciable quantities of nitrogen are being fixed. Also nematodes or crown-gall bacteria may cause growths similar to nodules on the roots of legumes and, furthermore, nodule-like enlargements may be produced by mycorrhiza, nematodes, or crown-gall organisms on the roots of non-legumes. In addition nodules have been found on the roots of some non-legumes, including redroot and alder, and it is maintained by some workers that the organisms in them fix nitrogen.

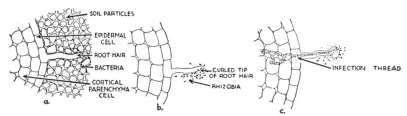

Fig. 36. Infection of a root by *Rhizobium*. (*a*) Movement of the bacteria toward a root hair, (*b*) curling of the root hair, (*c*) penetration of the root by an infection thread. From *Biochemistry of Symbiotic Nitrogen Fixation,* 1940. Courtesy of P. W. Wilson and the University of Wisconsin Press.

Nitrogen fixation is also controlled by the rate of photosynthesis of the host plant and by the supply of combined nitrogen. According to Waksman,[22] nitrogen fixation is at a maximum with a moderate rate of photosynthesis and the quantity of nitrogen fixed may exceed that needed for protein formation, and hence combined nitrogen will be excreted. An excessive rate of photosynthesis, however, depresses nitrogen fixation as does also a low rate. Too large a supply of nitrate is also detrimental to the process, and it reduces the number of nodules formed by preventing the deformation of the root hair, as mentioned on page 295. The quantity of nitrogen fixed by symbiotic organisms is discussed on pages 122–125. That much energy is needed for the fixation process is evidenced by Wilson's [23] estimate of 20 pounds of carbohydrate assimilated for each pound of nitrogen fixed. Nitrogen accumulated by nodule

---

[21] A summary of the relationship between host plant and bacteria is given by Wilson on p. 82 of *Biochemistry of Symbiotic Nitrogen Fixation.* University of Wisconsin Press, Madison, 1940.

[22] *Soil Microbiology,* p. 220. John Wiley & Sons, New York, 1952.

[23] *Biochemistry of Symbiotic Nitrogen Fixation.* University of Wisconsin Press, Madison, 1940.

bacteria may pass into the sap of the host plant and be used directly; it may be built into bacterial cells and released when the nodules decay; or it may diffuse into the soil and be absorbed by the roots of other plants. The stimulation of a non-legume growing in association with a legume by the nitrogen excreted from the nodules was noted many years ago by Lipman.[24]

As is indicated in the preceding discussion different species of *Rhizobia* must be used for the inoculation of different legumes or groups of legumes if efficient nitrogen fixation is to occur. Some of the more common species with the legumes upon which they will produce nodules are shown in Chart 1. There are a number of species of the organism that produce nodules on the roots of less commonly grown legumes.

CHART 1. COMMON SPECIES OF *Rhizobia* AND SOME LEGUMES ON WHICH THEY FORM NODULES

Species	Legumes Nodulated
R. trifolii	Red, alsike, crimson, mammoth, and Dutch clovers
R. Meliloti	Sweet clover (white and yellow) and alfalfa
R. phaseoli	Many kinds of beans but not soybeans, lima, or velvet beans
R. japonicum	Soybeans
R. leguminosarum	Vetches and many kinds of peas but not cowpeas
R. sp.	Cowpeas, velvet and lima beans, peanuts, and lespedeza

The many strains of *Rhizobium* that infect the roots of different species of legumes have quite a wide range of tolerance for soil reaction. The optimum reaction is from pH 5.5 to 7.0, although it has been reported that they can grow in a soil with a pH of 4.0 if combined nitrogen is available. Nitrogen fixation is thought to be limited below a pH of 5.0, although Albrecht[25] reports active fixation by soybeans at a pH of 4.2 when adequate calcium was supplied. The organisms are especially sensitive to a deficiency of calcium and phosphorus. The upper limits for the activity of *Rhizobium* are pH 9.0 to 10.0. The variation in acidity tolerance of strains of the organism causing nodulation on the roots of different legumes is puzzling. Those strains infecting lupine are among the most tolerant and those infecting alfalfa are among the most sensitive to acidity. Other factors detrimental to the organisms are: absence of at least a small quantity of molybdenum; drying of the soil; temperatures below 0° C. or above 50° C.; and poor aeration. The contribution of molybdenum to nitrogen fixation is not understood and its essentiality to

[24] *New Jersey Agr. Exp. Sta. Bull.* 253, 1912.

[25] *J. Amer. Soc. Agron.*, 25: 512, 1933. Also *Soil Sci. Soc. Amer. Proc.*, 7: 247, 1942.

the process has only been recognized in recent years. There is evidence that unless the supply of this element is abundant it will be found concentrated in the nodules. Diffused light is not harmful to *Rhizobium* and direct sunlight is tolerated for a limited time. Although the organisms can exist in the soil for a number of years without the presence of their host plant the bacteria appear to be rejuvenated by the symbiotic association every few years.

Fig. 37. A lack of inoculation often causes failure of a crimson clover seeding. The two plants in the figure are of the same age. However, the one on the right was not inoculated whereas the left one was well inoculated. From *Georgia Agr. Ext. Serv. Bull.* 452. Courtesy of the Nitragin Co.

Bacteriophage. Strains of phages occur in soils which attack nodule bacteria. Usually a given strain of phage can only feed upon one group of nodule bacteria, but there are indications that some strains are not so limited in their activity. Organisms which escape the attack of the phage may in time develop a resistant strain of bacteria. It has not yet been established that bacteriophage is responsible for "sickness" of soils for the growing of given legumes.

REFERENCES

Clark, F. E. Soil microorganisms and plant roots. *Advances in Agron.*, 1: 241, 1949.
De, P. K., and Sulaiman, M. Fixation of nitrogen in rice soils by algae as influenced by crop, CO_2, and organic substances. *Soil Sci.*, 70: 137, 1950.

Happ, H. The ecology of earthworms in cropland. *Soil Sci. Soc. Amer. Proc.,* 12: 503, 1947.

Lipman, J. G. Broad relationships between microorganisms and soil fertility. *Trans. 3rd Internatl. Congr. Soil Sci.,* Oxford, England, 3: 29, 1935.

Lipman, J. G., and Starkey, R. L. Broad relationships between microorganisms and soil fertility. *New Jersey Agr. Exp. Sta. Bull.* 595, 1935.

Lunt, H. A., and Jacobson, H. G. M. The chemical composition of earthworm casts. *Soil Sci.,* 58: 367, 1944.

Lutz, H. J., and Chandler, R. F., Jr. *Forest Soils,* p. 90. John Wiley & Sons, New York, 1946.

Norman, A. G. Recent advances in soil microbiology. *Soil Sci. Soc. Amer. Proc.,* 11: 9, 1946.

Russell, E. J., revised by Russell, E. W. *Soil Conditions and Plant Growth,* eighth edition, p. 169. Longmans, Green & Co., London, 1950.

Teotia, S. P., Duley, F. L., and McCalla, T. M. Effect of stubble mulching on number and activity of earthworms. *Nebraska Agr. Exp. Sta. Res. Bull.* 165, 1950.

Waksman, S. A. *Soil Microbiology.* John Wiley & Sons, New York, 1952.

Wilson, P. W. *Biochemistry of Symbiotic Nitrogen Fixation.* University of Wisconsin Press, Madison, 1940.

15

Green Manures, Crop Residues, and Composts

Many benefits may result from the use of green manures and crop residues, and some of them are mentioned here. (1) These materials constitute the chief source of organic matter added to the soil and they may increase or decrease the humus content depending on the amount and nature of the material added. For example, the incorporation into the soil of small amounts of immature plant tissue, even though leguminous, may sometimes result in a more rapid decay of the humus.[1] On the other hand, mature plant residues may be expected to increase the supply of humus, especially when sufficient nitrogen is present. (2) An increase in the supply of available nitrogen sometimes is possible through green manuring, and mineral nutrients may be accumulated in available form in the plow soil. (3) The decay of green manures and plant residues produces carbon dioxide which aids in the liberation of nutrients from the soil particles, and the minerals contained in these materials are made available in addition. (4) Further benefits result from green manures which occupy the soil during periods when regular crops are absent. Under such conditions a reduction in erosion and in loss of nutrients through leaching may be accomplished. (5) Improvement in soil structure can also be listed as a benefit arising from the incorporation of residues and green manures.

Composts have been considered valuable soil-improvement materials for many generations, and in recent years additional emphasis has been placed on their virtues.

In the following pages some of the information accumulated through experimental work concerning the composition, utilization, and value of green manures, crop residues, and composts will be reviewed. The discussion may be undertaken under three headings.

[1] *Soil Sci. Soc. Amer. Proc.,* 17: 365, 1953.

Discussion Topics

   Green crops for soil protection and improvement.
   Crop residues and sods.
   Composts and municipal wastes as fertilizers and soil amendments.

GREEN CROPS FOR SOIL PROTECTION AND IMPROVEMENT

   Green manuring is a very old practice, and yet this method of soil protection and improvement is not followed as widely in America as it should be. The use of green manures appears to be growing in favor, however, and it is hoped that additional experimental work and experience will lead to a wider adoption of the practice.

   Crops to Use. Because non-legumes contain no minerals or nitrogen which were not taken from the soil, they should only be used as cover or green-manure crops under circumstances which do not permit the growing of a legume crop. The reduction in soil erosion and loss of nutrients through leaching frequently warrant the use of non-legumes as cover crops. Also the products of their decomposition are beneficial, as pointed out on page 287. However the demand of the decay organisms for nitrogen during decomposition of these carbonaceous materials sometimes results in a deficiency of this element for the growing crop unless a nitrogen fertilizer or manure is applied. Heavy fertilization usually leads to a much increased growth of the green-manure and so to a greater addition of organic matter to the soil. If the fertilizer contains a high percentage of nitrogen the nitrogen content of the green manure may be increased so that a deficiency of the nutrient will not develop during decomposition.

   From the leguminous crops one should be selected that will make a vigorous growth under the prevailing climatic conditions and on the soil under consideration. Whenever feasible a legume should be chosen that has a large root system, and one that fills the surface soil with fibrous roots and so simulates a sod. Various members of the clover family, alfalfa, and lespedeza are particularly desirable in this respect, even though the soil may require liming to grow them. On the other hand, some annual legumes such as cowpeas and soybeans have small root systems and are not considered so desirable as green manures. The division of the dry matter of several legumes between the roots and tops and the percentages of nitrogen in these plant parts are shown in Table 58. Not only do the root systems of the clovers and alfalfa constitute a much greater proportion of the entire plant than is true for annual legumes, but the root systems of the former crops are much more

TABLE 58. DISTRIBUTION OF DRY MATTER BETWEEN TOPS AND ROOTS OF SEVERAL LEGUMES AND THEIR NITROGEN CONTENT *

Percentage of Total Dry Matter

| | Clovers | | | | | Cow-pea | Velvet Bean | Soy-bean |
	Red	Sweet	Crimson	Alfalfa	Vetch			
Tops	66.5	73.5	75.6	66.5	82.7	85.5	86.8	87.8
Roots	33.5	26.5	24.4	33.5	17.3	14.5	13.2	12.2

Nitrogen Content, per cent

| Tops | 2.70 | 2.41 | 2.85 | 2.56 | 3.34 | 2.70 | 2.34 | 2.58 |
| Roots | 2.34 | 2.04 | 2.29 | 2.03 | 2.16 | 1.45 | 1.27 | 1.91 |

* Prepared from data in *Root Nodule Bacteria and Leguminous Plants*, by E. B. Fred, I. L. Baldwin, and E. McCoy. Univ. of Wisconsin Press, Madison, 1932, p. 221. Used with permission.

extensive than those of the annuals. Furthermore the nitrogen content of the roots of legumes which tend to form sods is greater than is true for the other crops mentioned. The Ohio station has collected further information concerning the weight of roots of some of the crops mentioned in Table 58 and of several other crops. Table 59 contains the results. The distribution of organic matter and nitrogen between the roots and tops of plants will of course vary with the stage of growth. For example, on October 1 of the year of seeding, red clover roots were found [2] to contain 16.7 per cent of the weight of the plant, and between April 24 and May 12 of the next year the percentage had increased to 44.8. In contrast, on the same dates alfalfa roots constituted 39.3 per per cent and 30.9 per cent, respectively, of the plant weight.

The distribution of the roots of soil-building crops in different soil depths is also of interest. An extensive study of sweet clover by Willard [3] has supplied such information for that plant. Some of the data are shown in Table 60. The results for two years are given because seasonal conditions have much influence on the root development of plants. It will be noted that in 1923, a dry year, there was a greater development of roots in the lower soil depths than occurred in 1925, which was a wet year. The large proportion of the roots in the surface foot of soil is rather surprising, and the high percentage of roots concentrated in the surface 4 inches in 1925 is still more at variance with popular belief. Willard states that sweet-clover roots normally penetrate

[2] *Ohio Agr. Exp. Sta. Book* Series B-1, p. 152, 1951.
[3] *Ohio Agr. Exp. Sta. Bull.* 405, 1927.

TABLE 59. WEIGHT AND NITROGEN CONTENT OF THE ROOTS OF SEVERAL
PLANTS *

Crop	Time of Sampling	Roots	
		Pounds per Acre	Content of Nitrogen, per cent
Red clover	48 dates and stages, avg.	1,000	2.2
Alfalfa	Late fall, seeding year	1,270	2.8
Alfalfa	Late fall, first hay year	2,680	2.3
Alfalfa	Late fall, second hay year	3,400	2.3
Sweet clover	November, seeding year	2,640	3.6
Sweet clover	July, year after seeding	800	1.7
Korean lespedeza	August 15	560	1.4
Soybeans	Pods well filled and 3,800 pounds of tops	550	1.5
Bromegrass	July, 2-year-old sod	3,740	. . .
Timothy	December, unfertilized	4,180 †	1.7
	December, fertilized	6,080 †	1.9
Bluegrass	Old sod	6,770 †	2.1
English rye-grass	Sown in corn and sampled the next spring before plowing	6,000 †	0.7

* *Ohio Agr. Exp. Sta. Book* Series B-1, 1951.
† Includes all underground parts as well as true roots.

TABLE 60. DISTRIBUTION OF ROOTS OF SECOND-YEAR SWEET CLOVER

	Year	Depth, in.					
		1–4	4–8	8–12	1–12	12–24	24–36
Pounds per acre: air-dry	1923 *	. . .	. . .	. . .	1,210	240	120
	1925 †	682	124	64	870	78	23
Pounds nitrogen	1923	. . .	. . .	. . .	22.6	3.8	1.8
	1925	11.2	2.3	1.0	14.5	1.0	0.3
Per cent nitrogen	1923	. . .	. . .	. . .	1.87	1.58	1.44
	1925	1.64	1.75	1.54	1.67	1.33	1.44

* July 19, plants 72 in. high.
† July 13, plants 60 in. high.

almost, if not entirely, to their full depth during the first year. It will also
be noted that the percentage of nitrogen in the roots reaching a lower
depth is less than that of the surface roots.

Weaver [4] points out that the distribution of red and white clover
roots is similar to that of sweet clover although the total depth of

[4] *Root Development of Field Crop.* McGraw-Hill Book Co., New York, 1926.

penetration may not be so great. Alfalfa, on the other hand, develops a greater proportion of its roots at lower depths. There is, however, considerable variation in the root system of different varieties.

Relation of Age to Weight and Composition of Green Manures. Changes in weight and composition of plants with age have been studied because of their relationship to the best time for incorporating green manure into the soil. In studies previously referred to, Willard determined the weights and nitrogen content of the roots and tops of second-year sweet clover at different dates. Table 61 contains some of the data collected. It is observed that, as the tops increase in

TABLE 61. WEIGHT AND NITROGEN CONTENT OF SWEET CLOVER TOPS AND ROOTS AT DIFFERENT DATES *

Date	Height, in.	Air-Dry Weight, lb. per acre		Nitrogen Content, lb. per acre		Per Cent Nitrogen	
		Tops	Roots †	Tops	Roots	Tops	Roots
April 26	4–6	1,100	1,620	54.0	70.5	4.91	4.35
May 31	25	4,260	1,270	138.6	32.5	3.56 ‡	2.56
June 28	60	6,990	960	162.5	19.9	2.55 ‡	2.07

Ohio Agr. Exp. Sta. Bull. 405, 1927. † To depth of 12 in. ‡ Per cent in hay. Per cent in stubble was much lower.

weight rapidly with growth, the weight of the roots decreases. Willard reports little further decrease when root weight was reduced to 800–1,000 pounds per acre. Total nitrogen content of the roots also decreased as that of the tops increased. Evidently the second-year spring growth of sweet clover is made largely by utilizing the food reserves of the root system. Similar data were reported by Davis and Turk.[5] Nevertheless, there is an appreciable increase in the total nitrogen content of the plant as growth progresses, although the increase is not in proportion to the increase in weight. This fact is shown by the decrease in nitrogen percentage of the tops and roots.

Albrecht and Allison [6] found the cellulose, and lignin content of the roots and tops of soybeans, to increase with age and the nitrogen content to decrease. Similar changes in the composition of rye with age were reported by Blair and Waksman,[7] and Table 62 presents some of their findings. The data are sufficient to show that with advancing age both legumes and non-legumes become lower in mineral content and nitrogen but increase in lignin and cellulose. The proportion of the plant con-

[5] *Soil Sci. Soc. Amer. Proc.*, 8: 298, 1944.
[6] *Soil Sci.*, 32: 271, 1931.
[7] *New Jersey Agr. Exp. Sta. Bull.* 653, 1938.

TABLE 62. PARTIAL COMPOSITION OF RYE PLANTS AT DIFFERENT GROWTH
STAGES, PER CENT

		Soluble in Cold Water		Cellular			
				Cellular			
		Carbo-	Min-	Carbo-	Lig-	Nitro-	Min-
Stage of Growth	Total	hydrates	erals	hydrates	nin	gen	erals
10–14 in. high	34.2	3.5	5.1	34.7	9.1	2.50	7.7
Just before head formation	22.7	6.0	4.6	48.2	11.8	1.86	5.9
Just before bloom *	18.2	2.8	2.4	53.3	18.0	1.01	4.9
Mature plants *	9.9	2.1	2.1	59.2	19.8	0.24	3.9

* At the two latter stages of growth only the stems and leaves were used.

stituents that is water-soluble also decreases. The increase in nitrogen content of soybean tops in October was probably due to seed formation. Unfortunately sufficient data showing total weight of different crops per acre at different stages of growth and the composition are not available to make possible a determination of the stage at which the greatest weight of readily decayable material and of nitrogen may be added to the soil. The data for sweet clover are more complete in these respects than are those for other crops.

Relationship between Age and Rate of Decomposition of Plant Tissue. Many studies have been made which show that the rate of decay of plant tissue decreases with age. A few examples will serve to illustrate the rate at which plant material decomposes and how rapidly the decay process slows down with age. Table 63 below presents some

TABLE 63. EFFECT OF STAGE OF MATURITY OF CROP ON QUANTITY OF NI-
TRATES PRODUCED IN 5 MONTHS *

Crop	Stage of Growth	Dry Matter Added, grams †	Nitrates Produced from Plant Tissue, p.p.m.	Per Cent of Nitrogen in Plant Nitrified
Rye	Before boot stage	36.3	137	12.4
	Blossoming	78.0	114	7.3
	Almost ripe	150.0	50	0.4
Oats	Boot stage	34.4	225	15.6
	Well headed	63.0	132	9.3
	Almost ripe	122.0	102	6.2
Buck-wheat	Blossoming	27.2	352	35.4
	Well blossomed	69.0	498	20.8
	Almost ripe	100.0	416	18.2

* *Cornell Univ. Agr. Exp. Sta. Bull.* 406, 1921.
† The amount of tissue added increased as the crops grew.

of the data collected by Martin during an experiment in which the plant tissue grown on equal areas of soil was harvested at different stages of growth, cut up, and mixed with 3,600 grams of clayey silt loam. The mixtures were placed in 1-gallon jars and kept in a greenhouse for 5 months. The nitrate content was then determined. The small quantity of nitrates produced from the more mature plant tissue and the low percentage of the nitrogen in the tissue that was nitrified are of interest from the standpoint of using green manures as a source of nitrogen for following crops. Additional data showing the slowness with which the nitrogen in mature plants nitrifies are supplied by Pinck and associates. Table 64 contains some of the data they obtained. In

TABLE 64. RECOVERY OF NITROGEN CONTAINED IN GREEN MANURES OF DIFFERENT MATURITIES BY 5 FOLLOWING CROPS *

Age of Green Manure	Per Cent of Added Nitrogen Recovered in Following Crops †					
	1st Crop	2nd Crop	3rd Crop	4th Crop	5th Crop	5 Crops Average
Young	9.4	25.9	20.4	9.9	38.6	20.8
Intermediate	−43.0	−0.6	0.6	3.9	21.0	−3.9
Mature	−46.9	−7.7	−6.1	1.7	9.4	−9.9

* Soil Sci., 66: 39, 1948. Used with permission.
† Forty pounds of nitrogen in urea was added for the green-manure crops, and calculations of recovered nitrogen are based on the nitrogen added.

the experiment a green crop of millet or rye was grown in 20 pounds of loamy sand to the stage of maturity indicated. It was then turned under and an indicator crop grown. This process was repeated 5 times. Three of the following crops were sudan grass and two were wheat. It is evident that when mature plant tissue was added to the soil the 3 following crops obtained no nitrogen from it, but by the time the last 2 indicator crops were grown some of the nitrogen of the first green manure added had become available. In a similar experiment the same investigators [8] found that 6 indicator crops recovered 3.6 per cent, 9.0 per cent, and 28.0 per cent, respectively, of the nitrogen contained in mature, intermediate, and young millet used as green manure.

In studying the changes in composition and rate of decay of the soybean with age Turk [9] found that the roots decomposed more slowly

[8] J. Amer. Soc. Agron., 40: 237, 1948.
[9] Missouri Agr. Exp. Sta. Res. Bull. 173, 1932.

as the plants aged.   The entire plant also showed a greater resistance
to decay during July and August, but with seed formation in September the rate of decomposition again increased.   The decayability of
the tops increased in September to a greater extent than did that of the
entire plant, and this property carried over into October.   Evidently the
formation of seed has a marked effect on the ease of decomposition of
soybeans.   In this connection it must be remembered that the soybean would be incorporated with the soil before seed formation when
the crop is used as a green manure.

**Effect on Nutrient Availability of Turning Under Green Ma-
nure *vs.* Use as a Mulch.**   At various times studies have been made
of the advisability of incorporating green manures in the soil compared
to leaving the material on the surface as a mulch.   Hill reports one of
the most complete experiments on this subject.   Mature and green rye
was mixed with silt loam in lysimeter tanks in one experiment and
applied as a mulch to the soil surface in another.   The rate of application was 3 tons per acre, and the young rye contained 4.05 per cent
nitrogen and the mature plants 0.32 per cent.   The nitrate content of
the soil was determined at monthly intervals during the growing season,
and the loss of nitrogen and several mineral nutrients in the drainage
was measured.   The experiment covered 4 years but only 1 application
of green manure was made.   Table 65 [10] presents some of the results.

TABLE 65.   COMPARATIVE NITRATE PRODUCTION FROM GREEN AND MATURE
RYE MIXED IN SOIL AND APPLIED AS A MULCH, AND EFFECT ON LOSS OF NU-
TRIENTS IN DRAINAGE

Nitrate Nitrogen Content of Soil for 4 Years Following Green Manuring, lb.
per acre

Year or Nutrient	Green Rye		Mature Rye		No Green Manure
	Mulch	Mixed in Soil	Mulch	Mixed in Soil	
1929	238	362	57	65	90
1930	147	103	78	109	95
1931	65	69	45	42	63
1932	58	61	50	49	55

Loss of Nutrients in Drainage, 4-Year Total, lb. per acre

Nitrogen	360	356	239	232	198
Calcium	538	507	395	349	317
Magnesium	80	102	76	74	61
Potassium	33	36	33	31	23

[10] *Virginia Agr. Exp. Sta. Tech. Bull.* 53, 1934.

These data again illustrate the slow rate of decay of the mature plant tissue and the rapid decomposition of the young material. It is noteworthy that to break down the mature rye the decay organisms drew nitrogen from the soil. There was very little difference in the rate of decay of either the young or mature plant tissue when mixed with the soil or when applied as a mulch. Doubtless the quantity of material would influence this result, as would also the humidity of the climate. Little if any effect of the green manure on the nitrate content of the soil was evident after the second year.

Losses in drainage water of the four nutrients listed were appreciably increased through application of the rye. Decay of the green tissue caused a greater loss of calcium, magnesium, and nitrogen, but not of potassium, than decay of the mature rye. A study of the yearly data reported by the investigators shows that the greatest losses of minerals occurred during the first year after application of the green manure.

System of Using Green Crops. Crops grown for increasing the yields of following crops may be fitted into the rotation in various ways. Occasionally, it may be advisable to devote an entire season to the growing of crops to be incorporated with the soil. Seldom, however, is such a practice warranted unless the land is being prepared for a high value-per-acre crop. When a full year is devoted to soil improvement it is usually possible to grow several crops. For example, rye may be seeded in the fall and incorporated in the soil the following spring or early summer. A summer crop as buckwheat, millet, cowpeas, or soybeans may then be planted, plowed under in the fall, and rye seeded again. Other combinations of crops to suit the climatic conditions could be used.

Three other procedures are commonly followed. When climatic conditions permit, a catch crop may be seeded after harvesting an early summer crop. This green manure may be worked into the soil for a fall-seeded crop or may be left on the ground as a cover until the following spring. A fast-growing and usually an annual plant is used. Such green manures transpire large amounts of moisture, and their utilization is limited to regions with considerable summer and early fall rain. Also a rather long growing season is desirable.

A somewhat similar practice to that just described is to seed the green manure in the fall, or in mild climates in early winter, after the harvest of a major crop. A frost-resistant plant is needed for this purpose. The green manure is worked into the soil for a late spring or early summer crop.

A third system of using green crops is to seed them with a major crop and permit them to grow after the crop is harvested. For example, a clover is frequently seeded in the spring in a small grain and plowed under the next spring. Also a clover or a grass may be seeded in a row crop at the last cultivation and worked into the soil the following spring.

In clean-cultivated orchards or vineyards a green manure is often seeded in the late summer in order to utilize excess nitrates and so to hasten the maturity of the new growth in addition to supplying organic matter to the soil and protecting it during the winter. If a crop is used which is not killed during the winter, it must be destroyed by cultivation before the trees or vines require large amounts of water the following season.

Crop Response to Green Manures. So many factors influence the response of crops to green manuring that any general statement concerning the effect of the practice is of questionable value. For example the plowing under of a non-legume such as rye-grass for oats frequently reduces the oat yield unless a nitrogen fertilizer is applied. On the other hand a clover used in the same way usually increases the yield. Also any green manure which is allowed to grow until it is time to plant the main crop may reduce the yield unless timely rains fall during the growing season. When well managed, however, green manures will usually increase the yield of the following crop but will not appreciably increase soil organic-matter content. Some illustrations of the effect of green crops on yields will be of interest.

In a rotation of corn silage and soybeans for hay, various green-manure crops were seeded in the corn at the last cultivation and after the soybeans were cut. Pohlman and Henderson [11] report a 13-year average yield increase in corn silage of 0.57, 0.24, and 0.20 ton from rye, rye and vetch, and vetch respectively used as green manure. For the same period soybean hay was increased by 0.29, 0.31, and 0.23 ton, respectively, by the green manures mentioned above. These increases are small, but it is noteworthy that they were greater during the latter years of the experiment than they were during the first years. Crimson clover and sweet clover were also used in the experiment, but they winter-killed so badly that they had little value.

Much greater yield increases in corn were obtained by Sprague.[12] The green-manure crops were seeded in corn during the last half of August and were plowed under approximately May first. The 5-year average results are given in Table 66. In the experiment the workers were unusually successful in obtaining stands of the green-manure crops in corn, as is evidenced by the large weights of dry matter turned into

[11] *West Virginia Agr. Exp. Sta. Bull.* 275, 1936.
[12] *New Jersey Agr. Exp. Sta. Bull.* 609, 1936.

TABLE 66. DRY MATTER AND NITROGEN SUPPLIED IN SEVERAL GREEN
MANURES AND THE EFFECT ON YIELDS OF CORN

5-Year Average Results on an Acre Basis

Green Manure

Green Manure	Dry Matter, lb.	Nitrogen, lb.	Dry Weight in Roots, per cent	Corn Yields		
				Stover, lb.	Grain, bu.	Increase, bu.
Winter vetch	3,812	133.0	20.8	4,100	40.9	8.9
Crimson clover	3,049	92.4	21.3	3,679	37.0	5.0
Red clover	1,786	50.4	17.8	3,594	36.7	4.7
Sweet clover	1,436	39.5	19.7	3,600	36.4	4.4
Alsike clover	1,983	53.1	20.6	3,717	33.4	1.4
Winter wheat	2,089	34.1	39.3	3,585	31.9	−0.1
Winter rye	2,463	31.8	35.5	3,235	30.5	−1.5
Weeds	1,263	18.9	7.6	3,442	32.0	...

the soil. It will be noticed that yield increases of corn were more or less in proportion to the weight of leguminous dry material plowed under, except for alsike. This crop proved less efficient as a green manure than either sweet clover or red clover. The inferior value of non-legumes for soil improvement is illustrated by the results from wheat and rye. These crops may protect the soil from erosion, but their low nitrogen content resulted in decreased yields of corn.

The Illinois station [13] reported the effect of a sweet clover catch crop in two 3-year rotations. During 13 years, corn following wheat in which the sweet clover was seeded yielded 70.0 bushels compared to 59.3 bushels when no green manure was grown. Also oats following the corn were increased in yield by 7.1 bushels and the wheat by 6.3 bushels. The corn stover and wheat straw were returned to the soil in all cases. In the second rotation a sweet clover catch crop in oats increased the yield of corn and soybeans by 36.0 bushels and 5.6 bushels, respectively, and the oats themselves by 1.3 bushels. It will be noted that the effect of the catch crop is much greater on the corn which follows immediately than on the other two crops in the rotations. The use of sweet clover proved highly profitable on the soils studied in this experiment.

The comparative effectiveness of four legumes used as a catch crop seeded in oats and followed by corn was determined at the Ohio station.[14]

[13] *Illinois Agr. Exp. Sta. Bull.* 516, 1945.
[14] *Ohio Agr. Exp. Sta. Book* Series B-1, 1951.

The 14-year average increases in yields of corn in bushels per acre following the designated legumes were as follows: red clover 8.0, mammoth clover 10.7, alfalfa 13.1, and sweet clover 13.3. The corresponding increases in oat yields in bushels were: 2.9, 4.0, 5.4, and 2.4. The superiority of alfalfa and sweet clover as a green manure for corn are shown by the results.

The great value of a legume catch crop on soils very deficient in nitrogen is brought out in the data presented by Davis [15] in summarizing the results from some of the old rotation studies at the Alabama station (see p. 418).

The Alabama experiment station [16] studied the relative value of different summer legumes seeded in alternate rows with corn and plowed under for cotton. The results for 8 years at 3 locations are given in Table 67. All the legumes proved quite beneficial to the cotton, and on the average there was little difference in their value.

TABLE 67. COMPARATIVE EFFECTS OF SUMMER LEGUMES IN CORN ON YIELDS OF COTTON

8-Year Average Cotton Yields, lb. per acre

Experiment Field	No Legume	Soybeans	Cowpeas	Velvet Beans	Crotalaria
Brewton	604	817	796	760	947
Prattville	657	947	953	1,069	914
Tennessee Valley	1,209	1,350	1,374	1,371	1,373
Average	823	1,038	1,041	1,067	1,078

The South Carolina station [17] reported a 12-year average yield of 1,298 pounds of seed cotton on soil receiving an annual application of 400 pounds of 6-12-6 plus 100 pounds of sodium nitrate. With the same fertilizer application and the inclusion of a green-manure crop of rye and vetch the yield was increased to 1,553 pounds.

In studies involving the use of kudzu the Mississippi station [18] grew the crop for 4 years before planting corn. On one area the entire growth was turned under and on another the crop was removed and the stubble only plowed under. The yields of corn on the two areas were 111.8 bushels and 113.5 bushels, respectively, when fertilizer containing 160

[15] *Better Crops with Plant Food.* Amer. Potash Institute, August–September 1949.

[16] Mimeographed release.

[17] *South Carolina Agr. Exp. Sta. Ann. Rep.* 33, 1940.

[18] Unpublished data from the Division of Soil Management and Irrigation, Bur. Plant Ind., Soils and Agr. Eng. and the Mississippi Exp. Sta.

pounds N, and 80 pounds each of P_2O_5 and K_2O was applied. With the nitrogen omitted from the fertilizer the yields were 102.1 bushels and 87.8 bushels. Corn grown continuously and fertilized as above described yielded 87.3 bushels and 19.4 bushels. Apparently the kudzu supplied a large quantity of nitrogen, which was the determining factor in corn yield on this soil. The investigators held the opinion that the corn rooted deeper in the soil which had grown kudzu.

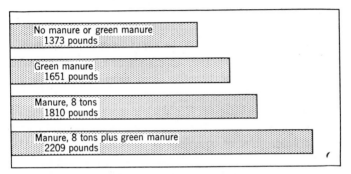

Fig. 38. Eleven-year average yields of seed cotton, in pounds per acre, grown on a Cecil sandy loam with the designated treatments. Although the green-manure crop of rye and vetch did not increase the cotton yield as much as did the manure, green manure in addition to manure produced the largest yield. All plots received 400 pounds of 6-12-6 and 100 pounds of nitrate of soda annually. Prepared from data in *South Carolina Agr. Exp. Sta. Ann. Rep. 1940.*

The use of sweet clover seeded in wheat, mowed in June, and plowed under in August of the following year for corn increased the 7-year average yields of corn and wheat from 49.3 and 20.4 bushels, respectively, to 53.5 and 29.0 bushels in South Dakota.[19] The rotation consisted of corn, oats, and wheat. The value of a green-manure crop under dry-farming conditions was also studied at the Garden City station in Kansas.[20] Milo maize grown continuously produced a 26-year average yield of 14.9 bushels. However, a green-manure crop of sudan grass raised the yield to 16.4 bushels and cowpeas increased it to 22.2 bushels. It should be noted, however, that in some years the green manure reduced the yield of milo.

The data presented show that under some conditions leguminous catch crops may be quite effective in increasing the yields of following crops but not always. The beneficial effect is more or less proportional to the amount of growth of the green-manure crop. Non-legumes are

[19] *South Dakota Agr. Exp. Sta. Cir.* 86, 1951.
[20] Mimeographed release.

not nearly so beneficial for green manuring as are the legumes. Data similar to those presented can be obtained from many other experiment stations, but space does not permit of further examples.

CROP RESIDUES AND SODS

The value of sods in improving the physical condition of soils is generally recognized. Yields of crops following the plowing of a sod are usually increased, especially if the sod crop contained a legume. However, the incorporation of crop residues into the soil has not given such universally good results. In fact, in areas of limited rainfall a detrimental effect is frequently noted. Methods of management which will result in obtaining greater benefits from crop residues need further investigation.

Effect of Crop Residue on Yields. In cash-crop systems of farming it is customary to leave the stalks and straw of grain crops and cotton in the field. Use of combines is also inclining livestock farmers to leave on the soil all the straw not needed for bedding or feed. Accordingly an increasing interest in the effect of such residues on yields has developed.

The Illinois station [21] early undertook a comparison of livestock with cash-crop systems of farming and hence has accumulated much data on the soil-improving value of crop residues. For example, a comparison of the effect of corn stover plowed under in a rotation of corn, oats, and wheat with that of the ash when the stover was burned showed a slight advantage for the ash, the relative values being 100 to 98. When a sweet-clover catch crop was included, however, the relative values of the stover and the ash were 124 and 122 (values based on yield of plot receiving stover ash only). In the same experiment, covering 13 years, returning all the crop residues gave a yield percentage of 103 without sweet clover and of 129 when the green manure was included. Evidently the supply of nitrogen is an important factor in this soil.

Average yields for the 9 years 1936–1944 for 21 of the old experimental fields well distributed over Illinois show 40.1 bushels of corn for soil receiving no fertilizers, manure, or crop residues and 47.9 bushels for soil receiving residues. These fields were started during the period 1910–1915 and hence are of long standing. The rotations all contained legumes either as main crops or catch crops or both. Some of the soils were acid and so legumes did not thrive. When lime was applied to all the fields the average corn yield rose to 58.9 bushels, but it is not

[21] *Illinois Agr. Exp. Sta. Bull.* 516, p. 161, 1945.

possible to tell how much of the increase was due to the effect of the lime on the corn crop directly, to the increased growth of the legume, or to the action of the legume in increasing the value of the residues. That soil reaction and the growth of the legumes are pertinent factors in the response of crops to crop residues is shown also by the following results.[22]

On 6 experimental fields located on dark soils which will grow sweet clover without being limed, the average increases in yields of corn, oats, and wheat from the application of crop residues were 9.6, 4.5, and 2.3 bushels, respectively, for the period 1910–1912. On the other hand, the average increases in yields of the same crops from 9 fields located on dark soils which grow red clover but not sweet clover without liming were only 5.2, 1.9, and 1.4 bushels, respectively, for the period 1911–1915. Furthermore, on 11 light-colored soils which require lime for the growth of red clover the 1910–1917 average increases in yields of corn, oats, and wheat dropped to 2.9, 1.7, and 1.1 bushels, respectively.

The Ohio experiment station has also made some studies of the value of crop residues. A rotation of corn and oats was grown both with and without a sweet-clover catch crop and with the return of part, all, or none of the crop residues. A 0-12-12 fertilizer was applied to the grain crops at the rate of 250 pounds per acre. The 8-year average yields of corn are given in Table 68. These results show the residues

TABLE 68.   EFFECT OF CROP RESIDUES WITH AND WITHOUT A SWEET-CLOVER CATCH CROP ON CORN YIELDS,* BU. PER ACRE

	No Residues or Clover	Clover Only	Residues Only	Straw plus Clover	Stover plus Clover	Straw and Stover plus Clover
Corn	65.1	83.9	68.6	87.9	86.8	89.9
Increase	. . .	18.8	3.5	22.8	21.7	24.8

* *Ohio Agr. Exp. Sta. Book* Series B-1, 1951.

alone produced a small yield increase and the sweet clover produced a large one. The combined straw, stover, and sweet-clover additions increased the yield 6.0 bushels more than did the green manure alone. Also this increase is 2.5 bushels more than that from the residues alone. It appears, therefore, that the value of the residues was increased considerably by the green-manure crop. That residues may be especially beneficial on a very heavy soil is shown by the results from a corn-oats rotation in Paulding County, Ohio. When the stalks and straw were

[22] *Illinois Agr. Exp. Sta. Bull.* 362, 1930.

returned the corn yields over a 10-year period were increased from 41.0 to 48.7 bushels and oats from 38.0 to 40.0 bushels.

The value of crop residues in a rotation of corn, soybeans, wheat, and alfalfa was studied by the Indiana experiment station. The cornstalks were plowed under for soybeans, the soybean straw was applied as a topdressing on the wheat, and the wheat straw was spread on the alfalfa sod before plowing for corn. This method of handling the soybean and wheat straw is somewhat different from the practices employed at present when combines are used. Although the experiment was started in 1922 the results for the 10-year period 1930–1940 are given.[23] The average yields, with and without the return of residues, of corn, soybeans, wheat, and hay, respectively, were 63.9 *vs.* 48.0 bushels, 31.1 *vs.* 17.9 bushels, 21.1 *vs.* 17.9 bushels, and 4,768 *vs.* 4,339 pounds. The data show that the residues caused a rather large increase in yield of all crops except alfalfa.

In general, studies in areas of moderate to heavy rainfall indicate that crop residues have an appreciable value for increasing yields when nitrogen is supplied through the growth of legumes. Without a source of nitrogen other than the soil the residues may have no effect or a depressing influence on crop yields. It seems reasonable to expect that a material increase in the benefits derived from mature crop residues would result if nitrogen fertilizer were applied with them. More data from field experiments are needed to demonstrate this point.

The plowing under of crop residues in a corn, oats, wheat rotation in South Dakota[24] caused an increase in crop yields, and the benefit is becoming more pronounced each year. However, when subsurface tillage was practiced the residues had little effect on yields. Somewhat contrary results were obtained in a corn-wheat rotation in which different amounts of straw were returned to the soil. Table 69 contains the results.

Members of the Kansas station[25] have also studied the effect of returning wheat stubble in an area of limited rainfall. Average yields of wheat at Garden City for a 19-year period were 11.0 bushels when burning of the stubble was practiced and 8.8 bushels when the stubble was not burned. The determining effect of rainfall on wheat yields in the area is indicated by the fact that there were 4 crop failures and 6 near-failures in the 19 years. In three quite favorable seasons, burning the stubble resulted in yields of 35.0, 27.8, and 41.3 bushels, compared to 30.7, 16.2, and 26.3 bushels where the stubble was not burned.

[23] *Indiana Agr. Exp. Sta. Cir.* 242, 1941.
[24] *South Dakota Agr. Exp. Sta. Cir.* 86, 1951.
[25] Unpublished data. Courtesy of A. B. Erhart.

TABLE 69. INFLUENCE OF TILLAGE METHOD AND QUANTITY OF STRAW ON CROP YIELDS, 1942–1947 *

Straw Treatment	Wheat, bu.			Corn, bu.		
Tillage Method	Sub-surface	One Way	Plow	Sub-surface	One Way	Plow
Stubble mowed	27.4	27.9	29.3	50.2	47.2	48.0
6 in. stubble	28.2	27.8	28.1	45.9	44.7	46.7
12 in. stubble	27.9	28.1	28.5	44.5	45.6	45.0
Combined	27.6	27.5	29.4	43.6	46.3	49.7
6 in. stubble + manure	29.2	30.9	29.5	49.8	48.7	49.4

* *South Dakota Agr. Exp. Sta. Cir. 86, 1951.*

At the Soil Conservation Service experiment station near Pullman, Washington, wheat following a sweet-clover green-manure crop in a 5-year rotation yielded around 51 bushels regardless of whether the wheat straw was burned or returned to the soil. Furthermore pea yields following wheat were about equal when the wheat straw was returned and when it was burned.

Crop Residues as Mulches. Members of the Soil Conservation Service have laid much stress on the value of crop residues left on the surface or partially worked into the surface soil for the control of erosion and the increased absorption of rainfall. Attention should also be given to the effect of these practices on the yields of crops. A brief review of some experiments dealing with this phase of the problem in different parts of the country is given in the following paragraphs.

At Urbana,[26] Illinois, the use of 2 tons of straw as a mulch for corn reduced the 3-year average yield from 92.7 bushels to 76.5 bushels. On the other hand the average yield of soybeans for a 2-year period was increased 2.3 bushels. The increase, however, was confined to 1 year.

Near Pullman, Washington, 2 tons of straw were used as a mulch following a fallow, with a resulting wheat yield of 28.7 bushels. Under similar conditions, but with the straw plowed under, the wheat yield was 31.4 bushels. However, burning the 2 tons of straw resulted in a yield of 34.3 bushels of wheat.

In areas of North Carolina [27] with limited moisture supply an average of 8 experiments covering a 4-year period showed an increase of 21 bushels in yield of corn as a result of mulching. The greatest yield increase was 45 bushels, and the smallest was 12.3 bushels. On the other hand, with adequate supplies of moisture the average yield increase

[26] *Soil Sci. Soc. Amer. Proc.,* 8: 97, 1944.
[27] *North Carolina Agr. Exp. Sta. Bull.* 366, 1949.

from use of a mulch was only 5.4 bushels. The corn was amply supplied with fertilizer in all cases. The mulch was applied after the last cultivation when the corn was about knee high. The relative moisture contents of the mulched and unmulched soil at a depth of 6 inches are shown by the curves in Fig. 39. The tensions with which the moisture was held by the soil at different moisture contents are also shown. The plants wilted when the tension reached about 15 atmospheres.

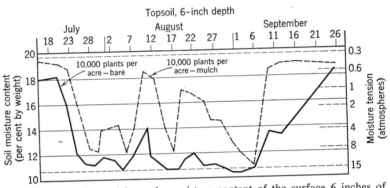

Fig. 39. Effect of a mulch on the moisture content of the surface 6 inches of a North Carolina soil growing corn. It will be noted that the mulched and unmulched soil carried the same number of plants per acre. The yields of corn on the mulched and unmulched soil were 94.9 bushels and 49.9 bushels, respectively. The moisture contents of the soils at depths of 12 inches and 24 inches showed similar but not so marked variations. At a moisture tension of about 15 atmospheres the plants wilted. From *North Carolina Agr. Exp. Sta. Bull.* 366, 1949. Used with permission.

The use of crop residues as mulches in orchards and in the growing of some small fruits and vegetables is an old practice of established value. Liberal applications of nitrogen fertilizer are usually made when such mulches are employed.

Sods for Increased Productivity. The beneficial effect of a sod plowed under for a cultivated crop has long been recognized by farmers. To get some definite idea of the value of a sod for increasing yields, a survey of some experimental studies is necessary. The benefit of a grass sod to following crops and a comparison of the benefits of a leguminous and non-leguminous sod would be an interesting study.

Unfortunately such data are not abundant, but some comparisons were made at the Cornell University station and some of the results are shown in Table 70. In this test clover, timothy, and alfalfa were mowed and removed so that only the sods were plowed under. The superiority of the legume sod is evident in each case, but no comparison can be made

TABLE 70. COMPARISON OF THE EFFECTS OF TIMOTHY SOD WITH CLOVER AND ALFALFA SODS ON YIELDS OF FOLLOWING CROPS *

Yields of Dry Matter, lb. per acre

Crop and Year	Fodder Corn 1923	Wheat 1924	Rye 1925	Oats 1926
Alfalfa 1922	9,226	8,055	3,580	3,395
Timothy 1922	6,413	5,409	3,087	3,610

	Oats 1921	Wheat 1922	Fodder Corn 1923	
Clover 1920	5,246	5,940	7,354	
Timothy 1920	2,146	5,293	6,733	

* Cornell Univ. Agr. Exp. Sta. Bull. 500, 1930.

between the value of the alfalfa and clover sods because the various crops were not grown in the same years. A similar experiment in which the effects of clover and timothy sods were compared in a rotation of corn, oats, wheat, and hay on a very sandy soil (Plainfield) was reported by the Indiana experiment station. At times, soybeans or cowpeas were substituted for oats. The results for the period 1928–1940 are shown in Table 71. Although the yields are very low because of the nature of the soil, the data indicate a decided superiority for the clover sod. No comparison was made between the rotation containing timothy and one with no sod.

TABLE 71. COMPARATIVE EFFECTS OF TIMOTHY AND CLOVER SOD ON YIELDS OF OTHER CROPS *

Yields, bu. per acre and lb. of hay

Sod Crop	Corn	Oats, Soybeans, or Cowpeas	Wheat or Rye	Hay
Clover	31.3	17.7	9.8	1,809
Timothy	24.3	12.0	8.6	920
Difference	7.0	5.7	1.2	889

* Indiana Agr. Exp. Sta. Cir. 247, 1941.

The Cornell experiment station also compared a cereal rotation with one containing timothy.[28] The rotation consisted of timothy or rye, oats, wheat, and corn fodder. The weights in pounds of the entire crop following rye and timothy, respectively, were as follows: oats 3,638 vs.

[28] Cornell Univ. Agr. Exp. Sta. Bull. 500, 1930.

Soil Fertility

4,470, wheat 4,901 *vs.* 5,779, and corn fodder 4,402 *vs.* 4,577. The superiority of the sod over the rye in increasing crop yields is evident. However, the duration of this experiment and of that reported in Table 70 is so short that too much weight cannot be placed on the results. In studying the value of non-leguminous sods it should be remembered that frequently such sods were seeded as a mixture of legumes and grasses, and, although it is assumed that the legume has disappeared after the first hay year, in reality a considerable number of legume plants are present for several years.

Value of Sods from Different Legumes. Just as many grass sods contain some legume plants, so legume sods usually contain a considerable amount of grass. Naturally the proportion of grass present will be a factor in comparing the value of sods developed from different legumes. Some of the available data concerning the relative value of sods from different legumes will be reviewed in the following paragraphs.

The Kentucky experiment station compared the value of 5 legumes, 1 non-legume, and 1 legume-grass mixture for increasing yields in a 3-year rotation. The results are given in Table 72. It will be noted

TABLE 72. COMPARATIVE EFFECT OF DIFFERENT LEGUMES IN A 3-YEAR ROTATION

Kind and Use of Legume	Soil Treatment *	Yields, bu. or lb.		
		8 Crops		9 Crops
		Corn	Wheat	Hay
Lespedeza for hay	P	36.9	11.0	2,067
Lespedeza plowed under	P	43.1	11.9	...
Cowpeas for hay	P	33.4	8.7	3,082
Soybeans for hay	P	35.2	8.8	3,313
Alfalfa for hay	LP	48.3	13.7	2,162
Clover for hay	LP	53.0	16.7	2,742
Clover plowed under	LP	55.5	17.4	...
Timothy for hay	LP	39.1	10.1	1,880
Clover and timothy for hay	LP	47.8	13.6	2,761

* P = 300 pounds of 0-16-0 for corn and wheat. L = 1 ton of limestone at the beginning of the experiment.

that higher yields of corn and wheat were obtained with clover or alfalfa in the rotation than with the other legumes. Part of this superiority may be due to the lime applied to fit the soil for growing clover and alfalfa. The data support the idea that it is a better practice to lime an acid soil and grow a crop such as clover or alfalfa than to grow an acid-tolerant legume which is inferior in soil-building capability. Professor

Roberts calls attention to the fact that a legume-grass mixture is desirable under Kentucky conditions because the grass will absorb considerable quantities of nitrogen fixed by the legume which might otherwise be lost by leaching. This danger is greater when an early-maturing legume is grown such as the annual lespedezas. It is interesting to note that there was little difference in yields of corn and wheat following lespedeza and timothy when both crops were cut for hay. Also, plowing under the entire crop of lespedeza and clover proved more advantageous than plowing under the stubble only. However, if the value of the hay is considered it is doubtful whether plowing under the entire crop is advisable. The Michigan station obtained similar results.[29]

One of the most complete experiments of this nature which has come to the writer's attention was performed by Dr. Lyon of Cornell. Some 8 legumes were grown alone or in combination with a non-legume or another legume and were followed the next year with a small grain as an indicator crop. The tests were in duplicate and were repeated for 10 years. There were also two blocks of test plots, and the experiment was started on one set a year later than on the other; thus each crop appeared every year of the experimental period. "Hay" legumes were

TABLE 73. EFFECT OF DIFFERENT SODS ON THE YIELDS OF FOLLOWING CROPS *

Lb. of Dry Matter per Acre of Harvested Portion

Legume or Crop Mixture	9-Year Average Weight of Legume or Crop Mixture	10-Year Average Yield of Rye and Barley Following Legume or Crop Mixture	Increase over Cereals Only
Red clover	4,123	5,144	2,930
Alsike clover	4,092	5,126	2,912
Alfalfa	8,842	6,068	3,854
Sweet clover	4,035	5,119	2,905
Vetch and wheat	4,700	2,805	591
Red and alsike clover	5,466	5,243	3,029
Sweet clover and vetch	4,294	4,951	2,737
Soybeans	5,873	2,953	739
Peas and oats	3,720	2,907	693
Field beans	4,247	2,760	546
Cereals only	...	2,214	...

* *Cornell Univ. Agr. Exp. Sta. Bull.* 645, 1936.

seeded in the small grain and "seed" legumes were planted in rows at the appropriate time. All legumes and legume mixtures were harvested

[29] *Michigan Agr. Exp. Sta. Spec. Bull.* 366, 1951.

and only the roots and stubble turned under. A summation of the results
is presented in Table 73. The results show the biennial and perennial
legumes to have a decided advantage over the annuals and over vetch
when seeded with a cereal. Alfalfa proved somewhat more beneficial
to the following crops than did the clovers.

A similar experiment in Indiana compared the effects of 2 legumes,
1 grass, and 3 grain crops on the following crops for a period of 19
years. The results are shown in Table 74. All of each "preceding
crop" was removed except the second growth of clover. No fertilizer
was used on the "following crops" and each one followed directly after
a preceding crop.

TABLE 74.   EFFECT OF SEVERAL CROPS ON THE YIELDS OF THOSE THAT
FOLLOW *

Average Yields of Following Crops in Bu. per Acre
and Increases Based on Yields Following Corn

Preceding Crop	Corn	Increase	Soybeans	Increase	Oats	Increase	Wheat	Increase
Corn	50.1	. . .	24.9	. . .	47.9	. . .	23.0	. . .
Soybeans	52.6	2.5	23.8	−1.1	51.4	3.5	24.0	1.0
Oats	49.8	−0.3	24.4	−0.5	40.9	−7.0	22.1	−0.9
Wheat	50.0	−0.1	23.4	−1.5	42.4	−5.5	20.3	−2.7
Clover	57.7	7.6	24.8	−0.1	51.8	3.9	31.2	8.2
Timothy	51.6	1.5	23.4	−1.5	40.7	−7.2	22.4	−0.6

* *Indiana Agr. Exp. Sta. Cir.* 242, 1941.

Clover was the best crop of those tested to precede corn, oats, and
wheat. Soybeans followed corn, oats, and clover about equally well.

During the period 1943–1949 the Ohio station [30] compared the effect
of alfalfa, red clover, and alsike on the yields of corn and oats in a
3-year rotation on Brookston soil. During the same period the value
of mixed alfalfa and grass sod compared to alfalfa alone was studied.
On this heavy soil all the legume sods caused marked increases in yields
of both corn and oats. The red and alsike clovers were about equal in
effects and both were somewhat superior to alfalfa. Also the 2-year
old alfalfa sod resulted in only slightly higher yields than the 1-year old
sod. Clover sods were as beneficial as the 2-year old alfalfa sod. The
inclusion of a grass with the alfalfa caused increases in yields of corn,
oats, and hay. The greater yield of the grain crops was probably

[30] *Ohio Agr. Exp. Sta. Book* Series B-1, 1951.

due to an improvement in soil structure resulting from the fibrous roots of the grasses.

The oldest study in this country which shows the value of a legume sod is found on the Morrow plots at Illinois University. In a rotation of corn and oats without any soil treatment corn has yielded 36.2 bushels per acre for the period 1888–1942 and oats have produced 36.9 bushels. During the same period, in a rotation of corn, oats, and red clover, the yields have been 48.0 bushels of corn and 49.6 bushels of oats.

Workers in Nebraska have compared the value of different legumes in rotations of various lengths under conditions of rather limited moisture supply. The legumes were seeded in oats, using only one-half the normal quantity of grain. As a result oat yields were not comparable to those obtained in rotations containing no legume. The 6-year average yields of corn, wheat, and barley are given in Table 75 for the 6-year rotations.

TABLE 75. CROP YIELDS WITH DIFFERENT LEGUMES IN THE ROTATION *

	Average Yields in Bu. of		
Legume Grown †	Corn	Wheat	Barley
None	45.5	36.6	14.4
Sweet clover, 2 years	53.5	40.2	19.0
Red clover, 2 years	53.3	38.6	20.7
Alfalfa, 2 years	51.6	37.2	18.0
Sweet clover, 1 year	48.2	38.4	15.9

* *Nebraska Agr. Exp. Sta. Ann. Rep. 61, 1948.*
† Removed for hay.

Because the soil was quite fertile the increased yields from growing the legumes were not so great as might have been obtained on poorer soil. Growing sweet clover for 1 year was not so beneficial to corn and barley as growing it 2 years. There was no great difference in the soil-improving value of the 3 legumes tested.

In southeastern Kansas [31] yields from a rotation without legumes were compared with those from a rotation containing a catch crop of sweet clover once in 5 years and alfalfa from 3 to 5 years. The 5-year rotation consisted of corn, soybeans, flax, wheat, oats-sweet clover. A similar area was seeded to alfalfa, and when the stand thinned (3 to 5 years) the sod was plowed and the 5-year rotation established. At the same time the former area devoted to the rotation was seeded to alfalfa. The non-legume rotation contained grain sorghum in place of soybeans and

[31] *Kansas Agr. Exp. Sta. Bull. 343, 1950.*

redtop or bromegrass in place of alfalfa. The 19-year average yield of crops from the legume rotation, in percentage of those from the non-legume cropping system taken as 100, was: corn 134, flax 146, wheat 109, and oats 106. Evidently crops on this soil were appreciably benefited by the growing of legumes.

COMPOSTS AND MUNICIPAL WASTES AS FERTILIZERS AND SOIL AMENDMENTS

The value of composts for improving soil productivity has been recognized for many generations. It is well known that liberal applications of compost lead to desirable physical conditions in most soils, including large water-absorption and holding capacity, and to the supplying of liberal quantities of plant nutrients throughout the season when climatic conditions are favorable for decay. Composts, however, do not have any mysterious capacity to make soils fertile. If well-made compost sufficient to treat all garden soils could be prepared at a cost which made its use practical, it would be highly desirable. Unfortunately this is not so, and it is still more impractical to consider the extensive use of composts on farm land.

As cities have increased in size the disposal of sewage and garbage has required increased attention. Proposals to use these materials as ingredients of commercial fertilizer have not met with favor. Accordingly the direct application of these wastes to the soil is worthy of consideration.

Composition of Composts. Generally composts are prepared from the leaves and stems of plants. These plant parts contain relatively low percentages of most plant nutrients and with few exceptions the nutrients present become available through decay. The processes taking place in the compost heap are, accordingly, the concentration of plant nutrients by the dissipation of carbonaceous plant tissue and the rendering of the nutrients more available. Some of the plant food elements may be left in a soluble state, but the large share is built into the bodies of the decay organisms or converted into other compounds that decay quite readily. Some are also adsorbed by the organic colloids. The great bulk of the compost, however, is composed of organic substances resistant to decay and similar in nature to soil humus. The changes which several components of various compost mixtures underwent during the decay process have been reported by Martin and Wang (Table 76).[32] Although there is some loss of lignin in all mixtures except the

[32] *J. Amer. Soc. Agron.,* 36: 373, 1944.

TABLE 76. LOSSES AND GAINS OF SEVERAL COMPONENTS OF COMPOST HEAPS
DURING DECAY

Loss of Materials and Change
in Nitrogen Content, per cent

Materials Composted	Oat Straw Chemicals	Oat Straw Clover Hay	Cow Manure	Cornstalk Chemicals	Leaves Timothy Hay
Loss of					
Cellulose	87	83	92	86	88
Hemicellulose	66	73	82	81	73
Lignin	14	41	47	+7	55
Dry Matter	56	66	53	51	62
Nitrogen content					
Original material *	1.36	1.24	2.16	1.28	1.13
End product	2.34	2.50	3.07	2.23	1.84

* Includes chemical added.

cornstalks and chemicals, the losses are much less than the losses of cellulose, hemicellulose, and total dry matter. The increase in percentage of nitrogen is considerable and an equal or greater increase in content of minerals could be expected.

The same changes which take place in the compost heap also occur under field conditions when the farmer plows under straw, corn stover, or other crop residues. There is this difference, however. In the compost pile the liberated carbon dioxide escapes into the air, and under farm conditions it in part combines with water and may react with soil minerals to make more nutrients available or take part in the liberation of bases from the soil colloids.

Chemicals Added to Composts. It is desirable to hasten the decay process in compost heaps by addition of materials high in nitrogen content and containing considerable available phosphorus. Manure may be used if obtainable, but the more common practice is to apply a chemical mixture containing the desired nutrients. Nitrogen fertilizers such as sulfate of ammonia or ammonium nitrate, together with superphosphate and some lime, do very well. A mixture often recommended consists of 45 pounds sulfate of ammonia, 15 pounds superphosphate (20 per cent) and 40 pounds finely ground limestone. One hundred fifty pounds of this mixture are used per ton of dry vegetable matter being composted. On the other hand there are specially prepared chemical mixtures on the market which may be purchased if one wishes to pay the price. The purpose of adding chemicals is to hasten the decay process and also to increase the plant nutrient content of the finished compost.

Municipal Wastes. The disposition of garbage and similar municipal wastes has presented a problem to most cities. That large quantities of such materials must be disposed of is evident from the fact that garbage from 7 suburban communities in the Detroit [33] area averaged 0.45 pounds a day per person and other rubbish amounted to 0.79 pounds. Thus, a daily total of 1.24 pounds of waste per person had to be disposed of. Various methods of treating such wastes have been studied, including composting, with the idea of preparing a fertilizer.[33] The University of California [34] has experimented with composts made from vegetable trimmings both alone and with additions of straw, horse manure, and lime. Representative data show that composting without any additions increased the percentage of nitrogen, phosphorus, and potassium from 1.66, 0.13, and 0.80, respectively, to 2.45, 0.27, and 1.65. The carbon-nitrogen ratio was reduced from 24.9 to 14.1 and moisture content increased from 80.7 to 85.6 per cent.

The municipal refuse varied considerably in composition. The result of composting one lot with a composition closely representing the average is presented in Table 77.

TABLE 77.   COMPOSITION OF MUNICIPAL WASTE BEFORE AND AFTER COMPOSTING *

Per Cent of

	Ash	Moisture	Nitrogen	P_2O_5	K_2O	Carbon
Original	34.5	45.3	1.2	1.05	0.89	42.2
Compost	40.8	30.9	1.3	1.20	0.84	32.6

* University of California, *Sanitary Research Project Tech. Bull.* 9, 1953.

The low nutrient content of the composts from vegetable trimmings and from municipal waste indicate that little expense in trucking and applying them would be justified unless they proved to have additional values in supplying micronutrients or in improving the physical properties of soils for the production of special crops.

Sewage Sludge. Many cities are also confronted with the disposal of the sludge prepared from sewage by several commonly used processes. Stephenson and Bollen [35] reported that shredded, sun-dried digested

[33] Second Interim Report of the Interdepartmental Committee on Utilization of Organic Wastes. *New Zealand Engineering,* 6, November–December 1951.

[34] University of California, *Sanitary Research Project Tech. Bull.* 9, 1953.

[35] *Soil Sci. Soc. Amer. Proc.,* 10: 168, 1945.

sludge had a composition and fertilizer value approximately equivalent to that of good farm manure. Lunt [36] investigated the effect of digested sewage sludge on the properties of loam and sandy loam soils and on the growth of several crops. The results showed that applications of 88 cubic yards or more per acre appreciably increased field moisture capacity, non-capillary porosity, cation-exchange capacity, and organic-matter content of the soil. Although yields of grasses and small grains were increased by applications of sludge to all soils used, most other crops were damaged on acid soils by an application of 50 cubic yards. Beneficial results were obtained, however, when the soils were limed to a pH of 6.5 or higher. The detrimental effect of the sludge in acid soils was ascribed to its microelement content. The average micronutrient content in p.p.m. of 25 to 31 samples of sludge from 13 plants was found to be as follows: boron 211; copper 758; manganese 172; and zinc 3,205. The amounts of some other nutrients found in the sludges are given in Table 78.

TABLE 78.   NUTRIENT CONTENT OF DIGESTED SEWAGE SLUDGE *

Element	Number of Samples	Average	Range
Nitrogen, %	26	2.07	1.30–2.94
Phosphorus, %	30	0.71	0.27–1.92
Calcium, %	30	2.49	0.68–10.00
Magnesium, %	30	0.23	0.14–0.45
Potassium		None detected	
Carbon-nitrogen ratio	16	13.2	10–22
pH	19	5.77	4.5–6.85

* Unpublished data.   Courtesy of H. A. Lunt.

Professor Lunt is of the opinion that it is "economically feasible" for specialty farmers to use sludge if they cannot maintain soil fertility without manure or a similar product.

Studying the sludges from some 200 sewage-disposal plants in New Jersey, Rudolfs and Gehm [37] found the product from those using the digestion process to contain 45 to 60 per cent organic matter. The activation process produced sludge containing from 62 to 75 per cent organic matter and that from plain sedimentation 60 to 80 per cent. Activated sludge contained the most nitrogen (6.2 per cent) and the most phosphorus (2.50 per cent). Settled sludge averaged 4.5 per cent

[36] *Water and Sewage Works,* August 1953.
[37] *New Jersey Agr. Exp. Sta. Bull.* 699, 1942.

nitrogen and 2.25 per cent phosphorus, and the percentages in digested sludge were 2.25 and 1.50, respectively. All the sludges contained from traces to appreciable quantities of a large number of elements, and the presence of several "growth-promoting" substances was detected in them. The investigators opined that the fertilizing value of a sludge could not be determined by chemical analysis but must be measured by the results obtained in tests with plants.

The Use of Nutrients in Composts by Plants. The idea that the nutrients in composts are more easily used by plants and are more beneficial to them than those in mineral fertilizers has no scientific basis. Before being absorbed by plant roots the nutrients in composts are largely converted into mineral compounds similar to those contained in mineral fertilizers. The plant food elements in composts are derived mainly from plant tissue, and these plants in turn obtained their supply from other decaying plant or animal tissue, or from the mineral matter of the soil, or from both. In the final analysis the original plants obtained their mineral nutrients from decomposing soil minerals. Hydroponics has proved through many years of experience that plants can obtain all their nitrogen and mineral nutrients from salts in solution and make a normal growth.

During the decay process there may be developed in composts certain organic compounds which serve a useful purpose in plant growth. These hormones, as they are sometimes called, may be utilized by plants if present in the soil or other growth medium. It should be remembered, however, that these substances may be produced in any normal soil by the activity of microorganisms. Furthermore there is no evidence that plants are dependent on the soil as a source of such "growth substances." Under favorable conditions, when satisfactory growth may be expected, there is reason to believe that plants can and do synthesize these compounds in their own structure and utilize them.

There is no reason to belittle the value of composts. They are excellent soil conditioners and satisfactory sources of plant nutrients. Every gardener utilizing mineral soil may well consider the feasibility of maintaining a compost heap. On the other hand, there is no occasion to take the extreme view that composts are essential to successful plant growth or that their use is superior to other well-planned systems of soil management.

Sawdust as a Soil Amendment. In some localities sawdust is available in considerable quantities, and the advisability of applying it as a source of soil organic matter comes into question. It should be remembered that sawdust contains very small amounts of plant nutrients and that it is particularly low in nitrogen content. As a result considerable quantities of this element will be required during the decay of the sawdust, and this must be supplied from the soil or some other source. On the other hand the material appears to exert no toxic effect on soil organisms or higher plants, and if ample nitrogen is supplied from fertilizer or some other material no detrimental effect should be experienced from incorporating sawdust into the soil. It has also been used successfully as a mulch for orchards and small fruits when an abundance of nitrogen fertilizer was applied.

Peat for Soil Improvement. Peat has frequently been used to improve the physical condition of soil and also as a source of nitrogen. There is no question concerning the beneficial effects of peat on the physical properties of both sandy and clay soils. Also the material decays fairly rapidly when mixed with well-drained soil and so liberates appreciable quantities of nitrogen. The main limiting factor in the use of peat as a soil amendment is the expense of obtaining and applying it in sufficient quantities to bring about the desired beneficial effects.

REFERENCES

Albrecht, W. A. Artificial manure production on the farm. *Missouri Agr. Exp. Sta. Bull.* 369, 1936.

Allison, F. E., and Anderson, M. S. The use of sawdust for mulches and soil improvement. *U.S.D.A. Cir.* 891, 1951.

Davis, J. F., and Turk, L. M. The effect of fertilizers and the age of plants on the quality of alfalfa and sweet clover for green manure. *Soil Sci. Soc. Amer. Proc.*, 8: 298, 1944.

Fraps, G. S. The composition and fertilizer value of sewage sludge. *Texas Agr. Exp. Sta. Bull.* 445, 1932.

Lyon, T. L. The effect of some legumes on yields of succeeding crops. *Cornell Univ. Agr. Exp. Sta. Bull.* 447, 1925.

Lyon, T. L. The residual effects of some leguminous crops. *Cornell Univ. Agr. Exp. Sta. Bull.* 645, 1936.

Martin, J. P., and Wang, Yueh. Utilization of plant residues for the production of artificial manures. *J. Amer. Soc. Agron.*, 36: 373, 1944.

McIlvaine, T. C., and Pohlman, G. G. Crop rotation experiments in the Ohio Valley (1925–1936). *West Virginia Agr. Exp. Sta. Bull.* 306, 1943.

Pieters, A. J. *Green Manuring. Principles and Practices.* John Wiley & Sons, New York, 1927.

Pohlman, G. G., and Henderson, H. O. Thirteen years' results with cover crops. *West Virginia Agr. Exp. Sta. Bull.* 275, 1936.

Rudolfs, W., and Gehm, H. W. Chemical composition of sewage sludges, with particular reference to their phosphoric acid contents. *New Jersey Agr. Exp. Sta. Bull.* 699, 1942.

Sprague, H. B. The value of winter green-manure crops. *New Jersey Agr. Exp. Sta. Bull.* 609, 1936.

Terman, G. L. Green-manure crops and rotations for Maine potato soils. *Maine Agr. Exp. Sta. Bull.* 474, 1949.

Waksman, S. A., Turney, F. S., and Diehem, R. A. Chemical and microbiological principles underlying the transformation of organic matter in the preparation of artificial manures. *J. Amer. Soc. Agron.,* 21: 535, 1929.

16

Animal Manures

Notwithstanding the high degree of mechanization that has been attained on American farms and the greatly increased use of commercial fertilizer, animal manures remain one of the main sources of plant nutrients applied to the soil. In far too many instances manure does not receive the care that its value as a fertilizer warrants. Also many farmers could profitably give more attention to rates of application and the crops in the rotation to which manure is applied. It is generally conceded that soil productivity may be more easily maintained under a well-organized system of livestock farming than under a cash-crop system. Nevertheless livestock farming can be soil-depleting unless attention is given to soil-conserving practices. Some information concerning the composition, care, and utilization of manure in relation to soil productivity is presented under the following headings.

Discussion Topics

Regional fertilizer use and nutrient content of manure.
Production and composition of manure.
Recovery in manure of nutrients in feed.
Handling and conservation of manure.
Manure and crop production.

REGIONAL FERTILIZER USE AND NUTRIENT CONTENT OF MANURE

In general, more and more dependence is being placed on fertilizers as a source of plant nutrients to increase crop yields and sometimes to restore nutrient supplies in the soil. In some areas, however, manure is considered the main soil-improving material. Accordingly, some consideration of the nutrients supplied by manure and fertilizer is in order.

Fertilizer Use. For many years the South Atlantic states have used far more fertilizer than any other area in the United States. Not only is fertilizer used by virtually every farmer, but the rates applied per acre are relatively large. Other states along the Atlantic Coast are also heavy users of fertilizer as are those bordering the Gulf east of the Mississippi River. In many sections of these areas profitable crop production is dependent on liberal fertilization. On the other hand fertilizer use has developed more slowly in the Central West, although there has been a rapid increase in demand for fertilizers since 1941. Also, with the exception of those on the Pacific Coast, fertilizers are used sparingly in the Western states.

Manure Production. The numbers of livestock in the United States are very unevenly distributed. Although the total numbers of cattle and sheep in the West are large, the number per section of land is small because of the limitation in feed supply. Also, in the densely populated Eastern states, livestock farming is confined largely to dairying and poultry raising. Numbers of livestock in the Southeastern states have been increasing rapidly in recent years, and in consequence the adoption of soil-improvement practices can be expected to expand, particularly the growing of larger acreages of hay and pasture. However, it is in the Central West that large numbers of livestock are found. The large quantities of fattening feeds produced and the geographical location between the western ranges and the densely populated East have resulted in the development of livestock feeding as a major industry. Dairying is also extensively developed because of the relatively dense population. As a result use of manure is a large factor in the soil-management program of this area.

Nutrients in Manure and Fertilizers. In view of the differences in livestock population and fertilizer use pointed out in the preceding paragraphs it is of interest to consider the relative amounts of nitrogen, phosphorus, and potassium applied to the soil in fertilizers and contained in the manure produced in different sections of our country. Information of this nature is presented in Table 79.

It is interesting to find that in all regions the quantities of nitrogen and potassium excreted in manure exceed those applied in commercial fertilizers. This situation may not be true in each individual state, but it is true in the groups of states in Table 79. It is entirely different, however, for phosphorus. The quantities of this element in fertilizers and manure are approximately equal in the South Central states, but in all areas composed entirely of states east of the Mississippi River much more phosphorus is applied in fertilizers than is contained in the manure as excreted. As is to be expected, in the Western and West North Central states fresh manure contains more phosphorus than is supplied in fertilizers.

TABLE 79. COMPARISON OF QUANTITIES OF NUTRIENTS APPLIED TO SOIL IN
FERTILIZERS AND AMOUNTS EXCRETED IN MANURE IN DIFFERENT REGIONS
OF THE UNITED STATES *

Excreted by †

	Cattle, tons	Horses, tons	Swine, tons	Sheep, tons	Total, tons	Applied in Fertilizers,‡ tons
North Atlantic States						
Nitrogen	336,803	43,580	16,235	2,158	398,775	79,477
Phosphorus	42,430	6,433	6,344	320	55,527	115,104
Potassium	273,179	31,574	14,888	1,721	321,862	119,743
South Atlantic States						
Nitrogen	338,637	36,270	67,887	2,864	445,657	288,818
Phosphorus	42,661	5,354	26,530	425	74,969	247,777
Potassium	275,168	26,278	62,260	2,284	365,990	296,504
East North Central States						
Nitrogen	831,663	122,094	184,965	12,031	1,150,753	94,509
Phosphorus	104,772	18,022	72,282	1,785	196,861	247,973
Potassium	675,791	88,458	169,632	9,599	943,476	247,698
West North Central States						
Nitrogen	1,483,074	212,065	287,303	21,045	2,003,487	59,802
Phosphorus	186,837	31,302	112,275	3,122	333,536	105,133
Potassium	1,205,112	153,643	263,487	16,783	1,639,025	49,754
South Central States						
Nitrogen	1,263,929	125,046	118,754	36,250	1,543,979	287,557
Phosphorus	159,229	18,457	46,408	5,378	229,472	222,201
Potassium	1,027,040	90,597	108,910	28,909	1,255,455	153,445
Western States						
Nitrogen	844,431	97,352	25,958	59,214	1,026,955	145,476
Phosphorus	106,381	14,370	10,144	8,784	139,679	52,465
Potassium	686,166	70,532	23,806	47,222	827,725	20,541

* It should be noted that the quantities of nutrients excreted by animals are much greater than the amounts applied to the soil in manure on most farms. The great variation in the latter amounts on different farms makes such figures of little value.

† Based on the average numbers of livestock for the period 1939–1948 given in U.S.D.A., *Agricultural Statistics 1950*. Quantities of nutrients are calculated on the basis of clear manure, assuming that the following amounts are excreted per year by different classes of livestock: cattle 13.5 tons, horses 9.9 tons, swine 3 tons, and sheep 0.31 ton.

‡ Data taken from U.S.D.A., *Commercial Fertilizers: Consumption in the United States 1949–1950*, by Scholl and Wallace.

In considering the data in Table 79 it must be remembered that the figures for manure represent the nutrients in manure as excreted. In some regions most of this manure is dropped on the land. In others most of it is voided in barns and lots, and the proportion of the contained nutrients applied to the soil is dependent on the method of handling manure employed by the individual farmer. In still other regions the proportion of manure dropped in fields and in stables and lots varies considerably, and no accurate estimate can be made of the percentages of excreted nutrients that are returned to the crop and pasture lands. It is evident, however, from the data presented that manure can be and often is an important source of plant nutrients on large numbers of American farms.

PRODUCTION AND COMPOSITION OF MANURE

Farmers keeping livestock are concerned with the quantities of manure produced by different types of farm animals and with the supplies of essential plant nutrients contained in such manures. It is also important to recognize the influence that management practices have on the quantities of manure recovered on different farms.

Quantities of Manure Excreted. The quantities of manure excreted by different types of livestock have been determined by several investigators. Although some variation in results may be expected because of differences in rations fed, quantities of water consumed, and other factors, possibly the data given by Van Slyke [1] are as serviceable as any in studying manure as a fertilizer and soil amendment. The figures in Table 80 were calculated from Van Slyke's data.

TABLE 80. QUANTITIES OF MANURE EXCRETED BY 1,000 LB. LIVE WEIGHT OF DIFFERENT ANIMALS AND THE NUTRIENT CONTENT OF THE MANURE *

Ani- mal	Tons Excreted per Year	Per Cent of						Dry Matter, lb. per	
		Urine	Feces	Water	Nitro- gen	Phos- phorus	Potas- sium	Ton	Year
Horse	9.0	20	80	78	0.71	0.105	0.514	440	3,960
Cow	13.5	30	70	86	0.49	0.061	0.394	280	3,780
Swine	15.3	40	60	87	0.38	0.148	0.348	260	3,978
Sheep	6.3	33	67	68	1.03	0.153	0.821	640	4,032
Poultry	4.3	...	...	55	1.00	0.349	0.332	900	3,870

* Fresh manure without bedding.

These data indicate the wide variations in total quantities of manure excreted by equal weights of different kinds of animals and the differ-

[1] *Fertilizers and Crop Production,* by L. L. Van Slyke. Orange Judd Publishing Co., New York, 1932. Used with permission.

ences in the percentage of the total made up of liquid manure. It is interesting to note that, although there is much variation in the wetness of the manures, the total pounds of dry matter excreted by equal weights of the different kinds of stock are not greatly different.

Composition of Manures. There are striking contrasts in the percentages of the various plant nutrients in the manures, and these are reflected in the total quantities of the nutrients excreted in a year, as shown in Table 81.

TABLE 81. TOTAL QUANTITIES OF NUTRIENTS IN THE MANURE FROM 1,000 LB. WEIGHT OF DIFFERENT ANIMALS AND THE DISTRIBUTION OF NUTRIENTS BETWEEN LIQUID AND SOLID EXCREMENT *

Kind of Animal	Lb. Nitrogen in			Lb. Phosphorus in		Lb. Potassium in		
	Liquid	Solid	Total Manure	Liquid	Solid	Liquid	Solid	Total Manure
Cow	80	76	156	. . .	17	90	16	106
Horse	49	79	128	. . .	19	37	58	95
Pig	49	101	150	5.3	40	46	73	119
Sheep	57	62	119	0.9	42	73	38	111
Hen	. . .	85	85	. . .	68	. . .	27	27

* *Ibid.* Used with permission.

The presence of an appreciable quantity of phosphorus in the urine of pigs and sheep is of interest, as is also the larger amounts of nitrogen and potassium in the urine of cows and sheep. The fact that sheep and cattle are ruminants doubtless accounts for the latter phenomenon. The high phosphorus and low potassium content of chicken manure is undoubtedly due to the concentrated nature of the feed consumed. On the other hand the low nitrogen content of hen manure would indicate a low protein diet or else a high utilization of the protein consumed. A study by Papanos and Brown [2] furnishes additional information concerning the composition of poultry manure collected under different conditions. Table 82 presents the data obtained.

In the foregoing discussion clear manure has been considered because the quantities and kinds of bedding used on different farms varies so greatly that the effect on amounts and composition of the manures is difficult to estimate. It is often considered, however, that average farm manure as drawn to the field contains approximately 10 pounds of nitrogen, 2.2 pounds of phosphorus, and 8.3 pounds of potassium per ton.[3]

[2] Taken from a mimeographed release from the Connecticut Agricultural Experiment Station, April 1950.

[3] Equivalent to 5 pounds P_2O_5 and 10 pounds K_2O.

TABLE 82.   COMPOSITION OF POULTRY MANURE WITH AND WITHOUT LITTER

Composition in Percentage

Nature of Sample	Moisture	Nitrogen	Phosphorus	Potassium	Calcium	Magnesium
Droppings less than 24 hours old	76	1.47	0.50	0.40	0.98	0.11
Dropping board manure accumulated during 4 to 28 weeks	64	1.22	0.80	0.78	1.36	0.18
Floor litter manure accumulated during 6 months	24	3.00	1.14	1.16	. . .	. . .

Considerable variation from these figures may be expected.   For example, Ames and Gaither [4] found the composition of manures, including bedding, from different kinds of animals kept at the Ohio experiment station to be as shown in Table 83.   These manures were handled

TABLE 83.   AVERAGE COMPOSITION OF MANURE, INCLUDING BEDDING, FROM DIFFERENT KINDS OF ANIMALS

Percentage of

Animal	Moisture	Organic Matter	Nitrogen	Phosphorus	Potassium
Horse	59.16	33.04	0.695	0.108	0.636
Dairy cattle	79.05	18.50	0.572	0.096	0.520
Feeder steers	77.85	18.91	0.726	0.208	0.459
Sheep	63.61	30.73	1.439	0.223	1.010
Average	69.92	25.29	0.858	0.159	0.656

much more carefully than is customary on most farms and hence could be expected to be higher in nutrients than average farm manure. The inclusion of sheep manure increases the average nutrient content shown in the table, and on many farms the excrement from sheep makes up little if any of the manure supply.   Omitting the data for this manure, an average of 13.3 pounds of nitrogen, 2.7 pounds of phosphorus, and 10.8 pounds of potassium per ton is obtained for the mixed horse and cattle manure.

Quantities of Manure Recovered.   The number of days in the year that different kinds of livestock are kept in stables or lots from which the manure may be recovered varies greatly in different parts of the country and on different farms.   Accordingly the tons of manure

[4] *Ohio Agr. Exp. Sta. Bull.* 246, 1912.

a farmer may have available to use on crops from a given number of livestock of different types cannot be estimated with any degree of accuracy. The problem is further complicated by variations in the care exercised by the farmers in collecting the manure and in the quantities of bedding used. Some information on the subject is furnished by a study made by Ross [5] on 224 dairy farms in northern Illinois. His results showed the number of loads of manure recovered from dairy animals to vary from less than 1 to 21 or 22 per mature animal per year, the average being 6.6. These farms carried an average of approximately 32 animal units [6] of dairy cattle.

On the same farms there were recovered annually 1.73 loads of swine manure, 1.89 loads of poultry manure, and 0.83 loads of sheep manure per animal unit of the various kinds of livestock. Doubtless these amounts would vary if the main livestock enterprises were poultry, swine, or sheep. Corresponding data for farms on which cattle feeding is the major enterprise have not come to the writer's attention.

Odland and Knoblauch [7] found during a 9-year period that cows in the stable produced 78.5 pounds of manure per day when bedded with 5.1 pounds of straw. This left 73.3 pounds of clear manure per animal. When sawdust was used as bedding the clear manure recovered amounted to 68.8 pounds, because of the lower absorptive capacity of the sawdust, even though much more was used than of straw.

RECOVERY IN MANURE OF NUTRIENTS IN FEED

On livestock farms the quantities of plant nutrients in manure measure, to a large extent, the possibilities of the return to the soil of nutrients removed from it by crops. Accordingly some consideration of the proportion of the nutrients in feed that are excreted by farm animals is warranted at this point.

Nutrients Excreted by Dairy Cows. So many factors influence the percentage of the nutrients in feed which are excreted in manure that average figures are of little value. However, the results of some trials under designated conditions may enable one to estimate the percentage recovery of plant nutrients under the conditions which may be encountered.

[5] *Illinois Agr. Exp. Sta. Bull.* 240, 1922.
[6] One mature cow, steer, or bull, 5 hogs, 7 sheep, and 100 hens are considered an animal unit.
[7] *Rhode Island Agr. Exp. Sta. Bull.* 251, 1935.

Forbes[8] and his associates made a careful study of the mineral nutrition of dairy cows at different stages of the lactation and gestation periods. Some of the data obtained for three cows have been recalculated to furnish the figures for Table 84.

TABLE 84. PERCENTAGES OF THE PLANT NUTRIENTS IN FEED CONSUMED BY DAIRY COWS THAT ARE RECOVERED IN THE MANURE

Condition of Cow	Lb. Milk Produced	Excrement	Percentage of Nutrient in Feed Found in the Manure		
			Nitrogen	Phosphorus	Potassium
Gestation, 49–68 days Lactation, 139–158 days	42.77	Urine	37.4	0.2	71.3
		Feces	35.2	65.7	10.9
		Total	72.6	65.9	82.2
Not bred Lactation, 55–74 days	40.63	Urine	44.9	0.2	75.4
		Feces	43.6	86.0	8.8
		Total	88.5	86.2	84.2
Gestation, 246–265 days	Dry	Urine	53.3	0.6	96.9
		Feces	29.9	79.7	5.1
		Total	83.2	80.3	102.0

In a study by Bear[9] and associates a record was kept of the nutrients consumed by six Holstein cows during two 14-day periods and of the nutrient content of the milk, feces, and urine output of the cows. The weight of the cows varied from 1,237 to 1,415 pounds, with an average of 1,301 pounds. The average daily milk production was 41.76 pounds and varied from 31.1 to 60.1 pounds.

The cows excreted an average of 114.0 pounds of manure, consisting of 86.9 pounds of feces and 27.1 pounds of urine. The daily ration contained 350.4 grams of nitrogen, of which 70 per cent was excreted. There was little difference in the percentage of the nitrogen in the feed that was excreted by different cows, the smallest percentage being 66 and the greatest 76. Fifty per cent of the excreted nitrogen was in the feces and 50 per cent in the urine.

The daily P_2O_5 consumption of the cows averaged 122.6 grams, of which 63 per cent was excreted. Only 1 per cent of the excreted phosphorus was in the urine. There was considerable variation in the percentage of consumed phosphorus excreted, one cow voiding only 46 per cent during one period and one 73 per cent. It is interesting to note that the cow which excreted 46 per cent of the phosphorus she con-

[8] *Ohio Agr. Exp. Sta. Bull.* 363, 1922.
[9] *New Jersey Agr. Exp. Sta. Bull.* 730, 1946.

sumed during one period voided 70 per cent during the other test period. The quantities of milk secreted daily during the two periods were 42.68 pounds and 36.96 pounds, respectively. There was also a variation of from 54 to 69 per cent in the phosphorus excreted by another cow in the two periods. No logical explanation for these variations is apparent.

The average daily intake of K_2O by the cows was 238.6 grams. Of this amount they excreted 205.2 grams or 86 per cent. The urine contained 84 per cent of the excreted potassium. The largest percentage of consumed potassium excreted was 97 and the smallest 74. The cow which excreted the 97 per cent during one test period voided 94 per cent during the other period, and the cow eliminating 74 per cent in one trial period excreted 83 per cent during the other.

The percentages of consumed nitrogen, phosphorus, and potassium found to be excreted in this experiment agree quite well with those determined by Forbes for cows in the 49th to 68th day of gestation and 139th to 158th day of lactation. Bear also found 65 per cent of the calcium in the feed to be excreted by the cows, and 87 per cent of it was in the feces. In summarizing the data from the experiment Bear points out that: (1) the average annual production of manure per cow was 21 tons, of which 5.25 tons or 25 per cent was urine; (2) each ton of clear manure contained 9.5 pounds of nitrogen, 3 pounds P_2O_5 (1.31 lb. P), and 8 pounds K_2O (6.6 lb. K); (3) with added bedding and consequent reduction in moisture content, a ton of the manure would contain approximately 10 pounds of nitrogen and 10 pounds of potash, and 5 pounds of phosphoric acid.

Nutrients Excreted by Steers. A careful study by Grindley [10] and associates showed that 2-year-old steers excreted from 24 to 33 per cent of the organic matter in the feed. When the ration consisted of equal parts of clover hay and ground corn the larger percentage of organic matter was excreted, but as the proportion of corn to hay was increased until the ratio of 5 to 1 was reached the percentage of organic matter excreted decreased regularly. Evidently fattening cattle on a concentrated ration excrete only a small proportion of the organic matter they consume. On the other hand it is to be expected that cattle eating a high-roughage ration will excrete a much higher percentage of the organic matter in their feed.

The same study showed the percentages of the nitrogen in the feed that were excreted to be 82, 87, 87, respectively, as the ratio of corn to clover hay increased. When 1 part of corn was replaced by 1 part of linseed oil meal the excreted nitrogen rose from 90 to 93 per cent. It

[10] *Illinois Agr. Exp. Sta. Bull.* 209, 1918.

is of interest also to note that as the proportion of corn in the ration increased the percentage of excreted nitrogen in urine rose from 31.5 to 44.0. With the substitution of 1 part of oil meal for 1 part of corn the nitrogen in the urine increased to 64 or 65 per cent.

The percentage of phosphorus excreted increased from 93 to 96 when the ratio of corn to hay was raised from 1:1 to 2:1. However, a further increase in the proportion of corn resulted in a decrease of the amount of phosphorus excreted to 85 per cent. The results of the experiment as a whole show that fattening steers excrete a high percentage of the nitrogen and phosphorus they consume.

HANDLING AND CONSERVATION OF MANURE

The excessive and often unnecessary loss of plant nutrients from manure on some farms is a matter of common observation. On the other hand, manure suffers very little deterioration in value on many farms. A short discussion of methods of handling manure is, therefore, included here.

Handling of Manure. Methods of handling manure are frequently a compromise between procedures that will conserve the plant nutrients and those that require a minimum amount of labor. If the number of livestock kept is sufficiently large to produce a load of manure per day, most farmers will draw the excrement to the field and spread it daily. Although losses of nutrients under this system are appreciable, especially on rolling land and during the winter months, there is much from a practical viewpoint to recommend the practice.

On farms having a smaller number of livestock the manure is frequently thrown onto an unprotected pile where considerable loss of nutrients occurs. The use of storage pits or sheds in which the manure may be stored with little loss from leaching is not increasing in many sections of our country. Fortunately there appears to be a growing interest in the use of pen-type stables. In such stables the manure is allowed to accumulate for several months, with the daily addition of sufficient bedding to keep the animals clean. Under such conditions the liquid is absorbed, and the loss of nitrogen by volatilization is much reduced because of compaction of the manure through the tramping of the cattle.

Types of Bedding. With the increased use of combines the quantities of straw available for bedding livestock have decreased. Shavings and sawdust have served largely as a substitute, although in some localities appreciable quantities of peat have been used as bedding.

Peat moss has a very high absorptive capacity for liquids and will also adsorb considerable ammonia, thus making a very desirable bedding material.   The main objections to it are the cost, if purchased, and the difficulty in drying it if obtained from a local bog.

Neither shavings nor sawdust are as efficient in absorbing liquid manure as is straw.   The cutting of straw also increases its absorptive

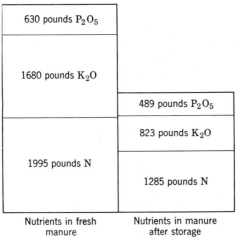

630 pounds P_2O_5

1680 pounds K_2O

489 pounds P_2O_5

823 pounds K_2O

1995 pounds N

1285 pounds N

Nutrients in fresh   Nutrients in manure
     manure   after storage

Fig. 40.   The amounts of nitrogen, potash, and phosphoric acid excreted annually by 10 dairy cows compared to the amounts of the same constituents in the manure after some 3 months' storage in a small exposed pile.   Every livestock farmer should consider carefully how much of the plant nutrients excreted in manure on his farm it is practical for him to return to the soil.   (Amounts of nutrients in manure are based on results of Bear et al. in *New Jersey Agr. Exp. Sta. Bull.* 730, and quantities lost are based on results by Ames and Gaither for steer manure given in *Ohio Agr. Exp. Sta. Bull.* 264.)

capacity.   Cut straw is reported to be capable of absorbing up to 5 times its weight of liquid, whereas before cutting it will take up only 2 to 3 times its weight.   A good grade of peat moss can retain as much as 10 times its weight of water.

It has been suggested that the low nitrogen content of sawdust and shavings would reduce the value of the manure because of the requirement of microorganisms for nitrogen during the decomposition of the bedding material.   Experience with sawdust used as a mulch or mixed with soil lends support to this suggestion.   Odland and Knoblauch [11] compared the crop-producing power of straw-bedding manure with that of manure containing shavings or sawdust for a period of 18 years, using

[11] *Rhode Island Agr. Exp. Sta. Bull.* 251, 1935.

a variety of crops. A summation of the average yields shows 27.36 tons for the soil receiving sawdust or shaving manure and 30.29 tons for the land treated with straw manure. The difference is small, and the experimenters ascribe the superiority of the latter manure to the greater absorptive capacity of the straw and hence the application of slightly more excrement in the straw manure than in the sawdust manure.

The Michigan experiment station also carried on a study of the relative value of dairy-cow manure containing shavings with that containing straw. The manures were applied at the rate of 8 tons per acre for wheat in a rotation of wheat, clover, corn, and oats. The treatments were replicated 3 times, and the plots were randomized, there being 6 treatments in the entire experiment. At the end of 7 years the results were as shown in Table 85.

TABLE 85. COMPARATIVE VALUE OF STRAW MANURE AND
SHAVINGS MANURE *

7-Year Average Yield of

Treatment	Wheat, bu.	Clover, lb.	Corn, bu.	Oats, bu.
Straw manure	34.6	4,305	38.9	45.9
Shavings manure	29.5	3,547	33.9	44.4
No manure	22.3	3,323	35.5	45.0

* Mimeographed release.

These results indicate a somewhat higher value for the straw manure than for that containing shavings for all crops except oats.

The Use of Preservatives in Manure. Many years ago it was proposed that some chemical be added to manure which would decrease the loss of ammonia gas and possibly also supply some element which would increase the fertilizing value of the excrement. Gypsum was one of the first materials suggested, on the assumption that the ammonia would combine with the SO_4 radical, thus making a non-volatile salt. Calcium carbonate or bicarbonate would be the other product of the reaction. Although this reaction undoubtedly takes place to some extent, the increased value of the manure has never proved sufficient to encourage the wide use of gypsum in stables.

Superphosphate has gained some favor as a material to sprinkle in gutters of cattle barns and on the floor under the bedding. The calcium sulfate in the phosphate will react with ammonia in the same way as does gypsum. Some ammonia may also combine with the monocalcium or dicalcium phosphate although the calcium liberated from the calcium sulfate is more likely to unite with the phosphate. Midgley [12] suggests that the reaction proceeds as follows:

$$CaH_4(PO_4)_2 + 2CaSO_4 \cdot 2H_2O + 4NH_3 \rightarrow$$

$$Ca_3(PO_4)_2 + 2(NH_4)_2SO_4 + 4H_2O$$

He studied the loss of nitrogen from cow manure when mixed with superphosphate and stored in crocks at room temperature. The data in Table 86 give some of his results. It is evident from these data that the main

TABLE 86. EFFECT OF 16 PER CENT SUPERPHOSPHATE ON THE LOSS OF NITROGEN FROM COW MANURE

	Loss of Nitrogen in 3 Months, per cent		
Treatment	Feces	Urine	Feces + Urine
Untreated	7.0	89.2	41.9
Superphosphate *	4.9	70.6	33.9
Difference	2.1	18.6	8.0

* Forty pounds per ton.

loss of nitrogen is from the liquid rather than from the solid manure and that the superphosphate reduces this loss appreciably.

Further work by Midgley [13] has shown that hydrated lime when mixed with cow manure reduces the rate of decomposition and of ammonia production for several days during warm weather and for much longer periods when it is cold. However, the lime becomes carbonated rapidly when decomposition of the manure is taking place, and then ammonification proceeds at a normal rate. On the other hand the mixing of hydrated lime with fermented manure results in an increased loss of ammonia. Calcium carbonate has little effect on decomposition of manure or loss of ammonia.

Bryan and Andrews [14] also showed the antiseptic action of superphosphate and hydrated lime by applying these materials at the rate of 2 pounds per cow per day to a concrete stable floor. The number of bacteria surviving after different time intervals was then determined. On a damp floor the number of organisms was reduced in 30 minutes from 1,900,000 per 16 square centimeters to 10 by hydrated lime and from 2,000,000 to 173 by superphosphate. The treatments were somewhat less effective on a dry floor.

[12] *Vermont Agr. Exp. Sta. Bull.* 419, 1937.
[13] *Vermont Agr. Exp. Sta. Bull.* 456, 1940.
[14] *Michigan Agr. Exp. Sta. Quart. Bull.* 16, No. 4, 1934.

The effect of different amounts of hydrated lime and of superphosphate on the loss of nitrogen from poultry manure and cow manure were studied in the laboratory by Carter and Millar.[15]   The manure was mixed with the preservative, placed in 1,000 c.c. Erlenmeyer flasks, and a current of air was drawn over it.   The ammonia given off was determined at intervals for 36 days.   The untreated cow manure lost 19 per cent of its nitrogen in 36 days, while that treated with 5 per cent superphosphate lost 2 per cent and that containing 5 per cent hydrated lime lost 17.3 per cent.   When 2.5 per cent of the chemicals were added, the losses were 9 per cent and 28.5 per cent for the phosphate and lime, respectively.

Under similar conditions poultry manure treated with 10 per cent of the preservatives lost 13.2 per cent and 28.8 per cent, respectively, from the phosphate- and lime-treated samples, compared to 69.6 per cent from the untreated manure.

MANURE AND CROP PRODUCTION

The value of a ton of manure in terms of crop production is a much discussed topic.   Rates and time of application and place in the rotation that manure is applied have much to do with the returns received from it.   A short consideration of some experimental data bearing on these points is justified.

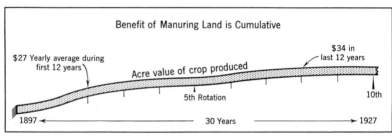

Fig. 41.   The returns from applications of manure to soils low in organic-matter content become additive as the manuring is continued.   The results shown in this figure were obtained with a rotation of corn, wheat, and clover, with an application of 8 tons of manure for the corn.   The values used in making the computation were barely one-half present farm prices of crops.   From *Ohio Ext. Bull.* 262. Courtesy of J. Slipher.   Used with permission.

Increase in Crop Yields.   Virtually all state experiment stations have conducted trials to determine the value of manure as a fertilizer.

[15] *Michigan Agr. Exp. Sta. Quart. Bull.* 16, No. 3, 1934.

The results vary with the composition of the manure, rate, time, and method of application, the crops grown, with climate, and with other factors. In humid climates at ordinary rates of application manure has usually given from moderate to large increases in yield of most commonly grown crops. This has been due in part to the relatively large amounts of plant nutrients applied and their rate of availability. In certain cases some credit must be given to the microelements contained in the manure. It has been suggested also that animal excrements contain growth-promoting substances in addition to the plant nutrient content. Although this contention cannot be definitely disproved there does not appear to be sufficient evidence to support it strongly.

In climates of limited rainfall manure must be used with caution because of the stimulation of plant growth by the readily available nitrogen. Too rank a growth of crops, particularly of those which grow well into or throughout the summer, may result in increased drought damage.

Reinforcement of Manure. A comparison of the compositions of manure and the most widely used commercial fertilizers show the former to be low in phosphorus so far as the needs of the majority of soils are concerned. In other words, full utilization of the nitrogen and potassium in manure is seldom realized because of the relatively small amount of phosphorus it contains. Accordingly heavier applications, designed to supply the needed quantities of phosphorus, result in waste of potassium and often of nitrogen in most soils. To overcome this phosphorus deficiency the addition of superphosphate to manure has been recommended. If the phosphate is sprinkled in the gutters and on the stable floors its conserving effect on the manure is realized in addition to the balancing of the plant nutrient content of the excrement. When the phosphate is thrown on top of a load of manure before spreading, little if any conservation of nutrients will result. Although many experiments have demonstrated the increased crop-producing value of reinforced manure, the data from the Ohio station are among the earliest published. Some results are presented in Table 87. In this experiment the phosphates were mixed with the manure at the rate of 40 pounds per ton. The "yard manure" was exposed to the weather in a flat, compact pile for 3 to 4 months, but the "stall manure" was taken directly from the stable to the field and applied in December or January. Had this manure been stored in a compact pile under cover until time for plowing under for corn the difference in yields resulting from stall and yard manure would probably have been greater. In considering these data it should be remembered that the treatments were not replicated. Every third plot was untreated. The increases in yield resulting from reinforcement are large enough to warrant recommendation of the

TABLE 87. COMPARATIVE YIELDS FROM STALL AND YARD MANURE WITH AND
WITHOUT REINFORCEMENT *

26-Year Average Yields
in Bu. or Lb. and Increase for Reinforcement

Treatment	Corn	Increase	Wheat	Increase	Clover	Increase
None	36.8		14.2		2,937	
8 tons yard manure †	55.9		22.8		3,655	
8 tons stall manure	61.9		23.8		4,151	
8 tons yard manure + superphosphate	64.7	8.8	28.2	5.4	4,466	811
8 tons stall manure + superphosphate	67.7	5.8	28.6	4.8	4,897	746
8 tons yard manure + rock phosphate ‡	65.1	9.2	25.9	3.1	4,388	733
8 tons stall manure + rock phosphate	67.5	5.6	27.3	3.5	4,675	524

* Ohio Agr. Exp. Sta. Bull. 381, 1924.
† Weight based on manure before exposure in piles.
‡ There was twice as much P_2O_5 in the rock phosphate as in the superphosphate.

practice under similar conditions. There is no appreciable difference in the value of superphosphate and rock phosphate as supplements for the manure. It is significant, however, that the rock contained twice as much phosphorus as the superphosphate.

In a somewhat similar experiment covering 28 years (1920–1947) and involving the use of 4 tons of manure in place of 8, the addition of 380 pounds of superphosphate resulted in increases in yield of 2.4 bushels of corn, 3.8 bushels of oats, 7.7 bushels of wheat, and 400 pounds of clover. The test was conducted on the Fry Farm in Ohio.

In recent years the question has been raised whether more benefit will not be derived from a given amount of superphosphate if it is placed near the seed at planting time than if it is applied with the manure. No conservation of nitrogen in the manure would result from this method of application, but otherwise there is evidence to support the contention that the direct is a more profitable method of phosphate application. However, if the phosphate is not to be placed near the seed it will be advisable to mix it with the manure before applying. Workers at both the Massachusetts and Vermont experiment stations have shown that mixing superphosphate with manure increases its effectiveness. (See Fig. 42.)

Place in the Rotation to Apply Manure. On most farms less manure is produced than the farmer would like to apply to his crops, and hence a question arises as to which crops should be manured. The crops grown have a bearing on the answer to this question, for if one crop is of much higher value per acre than the others it should be manured if it is benefited in yield or quality or both by manuring. Sometimes, however, a high value-per-acre crop is increased in yield but lowered in quality by manure and then it may be advisable to apply the excrement for other crops.

Fig. 42. Mixing superphosphate with manure increases its effectiveness. *Left:* Phosphate was mixed with the soil before the manure was added. *Right:* Phosphate and manure were mixed before application. From *Vermont Agr. Exp. Sta. Pamphlet* 24, 1950. Used with permission.

The Ohio experiment station [16] studied the effects of applying 8 tons of manure to different crops in a rotation of corn, oats, wheat, and hay. In all cases an application of 380 pounds of 0-20-0 was divided between corn and wheat. The average results for 28 years showed that the crop to which the manure was applied received the most benefit. Increases in corn yield varied from 18.7 to 24.7 bushels and in yields of wheat from 13.2 to 18.3 bushels depending on the place in the rotation the manure was applied. Variations in oat yields were small, but

[16] *Ohio Agr. Exp. Sta. Book* Series B-1, 1951.

increases in pounds of hay ranged from 1,210 to 2,070. Evidently under Ohio conditions a farmer must decide which crop he wishes to improve most in determining how to use the manure.

Workers at the Indiana station [17] conducted a somewhat similar experiment on both a heavy light-colored soil and a sandy soil. Both soils had been limed and grew a rotation of corn, wheat, and a mixture of clover and alfalfa. On the heavy soil, applying 4 tons of manure for corn and 2 tons on wheat in the winter proved more advisable than applying the entire 6 tons on either crop. In fact, 6 tons of manure on wheat resulted in some smothering of the clover and lodging of the wheat. The hay crop received the most benefit from applying the manure as a topdressing on wheat or on the new seeding after wheat harvest. Manuring the sod after harvesting the first hay crop was not so beneficial as applying the manure to the new seeding. Everything considered, the split application between corn and wheat proved most desirable.

On the sandy soil 5 tons of manure per acre were used. The least efficient practice was to plow under the entire application for corn. Likewise, applying it all to the new seeding after wheat harvest proved undesirable. Wheat was especially benefited by manure. In consequence, using all or one-half of it as a winter topdressing on the wheat was advisable. The unusual practice of applying the manure to corn after planting also proved beneficial to the corn, wheat, and hay.

On the other hand, results of experiments in New York indicate a rather low utilization of the nitrogen in manure by wheat. A common practice is to apply the manure to a sod which is to be plowed for corn. If the supply permits, a second- or third-year hay crop may be manured, as well as pastures.

Connecticut experiments [18] have shown good results in intensive vegetable production from substituting a liberal application of manure for one-half the commercial fertilizer usually used. The manure not only increased yields but also increased the organic-matter content of the soil, which is highly desirable for vegetables.

Poultry manure at rates of 6 tons per acre on fertile soils, and in addition to 400 pounds of 5-10-10 fertilizer, has proved advisable for corn, sorghum, and small grains in North Carolina.[19] Manure is not recommended on legume-grass sods but is beneficial to grass pastures. Also, manure applications are not desirable for burley tobacco, and

[17] *Indiana Agr. Exp. Sta. Bull.* 398, 1935.
[18] *Connecticut Agr. Exp. Sta. Bulls.* 439, 1940, and 560, 1952
[19] Mimeographed release.

when applied to cotton so much growth may be produced that fruiting is reduced.

Because of the comparatively slow availability of much of the nitrogen in manure it is customary to apply it for crops which grow during the warmer part of the year and crops which are not likely to be damaged by a large nitrogen supply. Perhaps corn is manured more frequently than any other crop.

Suggestions Regarding Use of Manure. The many experiments dealing with manure have led to a number of generalizations concerning its handling and use, some of which are listed here.

1. If not applied to the soil shortly after being voided, manure should be stored under cover and compacted to avoid aeration and drying. The pen type of barn offers an excellent method of manure storage.

2. When applied, manure should be incorporated into the soil as quickly as is feasible.

3. Light applications give greater returns per ton of manure than heavier ones but usually not such large increases per acre. Applications should be adjusted to give the most profitable returns over a period of years, taking into consideration the value of the crop per acre, the labor involved, and the quantity of manure available.

4. Although manure exerts considerable residual effect, the crop for which it is applied receives the most benefit. Accordingly, in some rotations more frequent and lighter applications are advisable.

5. Virtually all soil types in humid climates give increased yields of most crops when manured.

6. Because of the comparatively low content of phosphorus in manure, supplementary applications of superphosphate or of fertilizers high in phosphorus content are desirable.

REFERENCES

Ames, J. W., and Gaither, E. W. Barnyard manure: production, composition, conservation, reinforcement, and value. *Ohio Agr. Exp. Sta. Bull.* 246, 1912.

Bear, F. E., King, W. A., and Bender, C. B. The dairy cow as a conserver of soil fertility. *New Jersey Agr. Exp. Sta. Bull.* 730, 1946.

Carter, L. S., and Millar, C. E. The effect of superphosphate, hydrated lime, and straw on the loss of nitrogen from manure during storage. *Mich. Agr. Exp. Sta. Quart. Bull.* 16, No. 3, 1934.

Dunn, L. E., and Wheeting, L. C. Utilization of barnyard manure for Washington soils. *Wash. Agr. Exp. Sta. Bull.* 395, 1941.

Hegnauer, L., and Hill, O. J. Better storage for manure. *Wash. State College Ext. Bull.* 253, 1940.

Handbook of Experiments in Agronomy. Ohio Agr. Exp. Sta. Spec. Cir. 53, 1938, and *Book* Series B-1, 1951.

Midgley, A. R., and Mueller, W. O. Effects of lime on the nitrogen content of cow manure. *Vermont Agr. Exp. Sta. Bull.* 456, 1940.

Midgley, A. R., and Weiser, V. L. Effect of superphosphates in conserving nitrogen in cow manure. *Vermont Agr. Exp. Sta. Bull.* 419, 1937.

Midgley, A. R., and Dunklee, D. E. Fertility runoff losses from manure spread during the winter. *Vermont Agr. Exp. Sta. Bull.* 523, 1945.

Slipher, J. A. Manure: its management in barn and field. *Ohio State Univ. Ext. Bull.* 262.

Smith, G. E. Sanborn Field. Fifty years of field experiments with crop rotations, manure, and fertilizers. *Missouri Agr. Exp. Sta. Bull.* 458, 1942.

Turk, L. M., and Weidemann, A. G. Farm manure. *Mich. State College Ext. Bull.* 300, 1949.

Walberg, F. B., Spielman, A. A., and Miller, V. L. The value of liquid manure for pastures. *Wash. Agr. Exp. Sta. Bull.* 457, 1945.

Wheeler, H. J. *Manures and Fertilizers.* The Macmillan Co., New York, 1921.

17

Contributions of Commercial Fertilizers to Soil Productivity

For well over a century commercial fertilizers have played an increasing part in the production of crops in the United States, and for a somewhat longer period in European countries. In the early years fertilizers contributed little to the total yields of crops both because of limited usage and because much of American soil was undepleted by cropping. Under present conditions, however, the situation is quite different, and various estimates have been made of the percentage of crop production in the United States that may be attributed to fertilizers. Perhaps 25 per cent [1] for the country as a whole is as reliable an estimate as can be made, although this figure is entirely too low for some sections and much too high for others.

In view of the importance of fertilizers to American agriculture it is fitting that a brief summary of their use and contribution to crop production in different parts of the country be presented in this book. The subject will be considered under three headings.

Discussion Topics

Production and use of fertilizers in the United States.
Fertilizer application for different crops.
Returns from application of fertilizer.

PRODUCTION AND USE OF FERTILIZERS IN THE UNITED STATES

Fertilizer manufacture in the United States, which originally relied largely on wastes and by-products as sources of materials, has now become almost entirely a chemical-recovery and manufacturing industry. Many of the processes involve most delicately controlled reactions and

[1] *Fertilizer Rev.*, July–September 1953. National Fertilizer Association, Washington, D. C.

separations, and the industry in many instances represents a high development of chemical technology.

Fertilizer Production.   Mixed fertilizers were first prepared in the United States in Baltimore in 1849,[2] although ground bones, Peruvian guano, and nitrate of soda had been in use to some extent for some 20 to 25 years.   The manufacture of fertilizers increased at a rather rapid rate, and by 1880 production had reached 1,150,000 tons, and in 1900

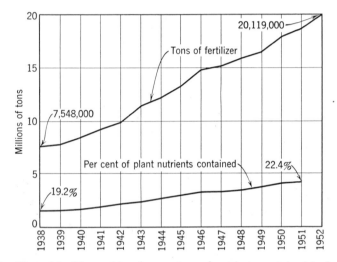

Fig. 43. Tons of fertilizer sold and percentage of nutrients contained in fertilizers 1938–1952.   Prepared from a figure in *Fertilizer Rev.,* April–June 1952.   Used with permission.

it amounted to 2,000,000 tons.[2]   The growth of the industry has continued steadily, except during the depression years, until, in the year 1950–1951, 20,570,920 tons were prepared for use in continental United States and 480,820 tons for the territories.[3]   The most rapid increase in production has taken place since 1940, when only 7,830,963 tons were produced.   The demand for food and fiber crops during and after World War II and the comparatively high prices of crops were largely responsible for this rapid increase in fertilizer manufacture. Figure 43 shows the trend of fertilizer production in the United States since 1938 and also the increase in the plant nutrient content of fertilizers during the period.

[2] *Commercial Fertilizers,* by G. H. Collings (4th edition).   Blakiston Co., Philadelphia, 1947.

[3] *Commercial Fertilizers: Consumption in the United States, 1950–51,* by W. Scholl and H. M. Wallace.   U.S.D.A., Washington, D. C.

Use of Fertilizers. From a small beginning in the Central Atlantic states the use of commercial fertilizers has now spread to every state in the Union. As yet, however, only small quantities are used in some states, and this may always be so because of insufficient rainfall, an inadequate supply of irrigation water, and the nutrient content of the soil. Furthermore, the area of arable land in different states and the response of crops to fertilization vary greatly. It is also noteworthy

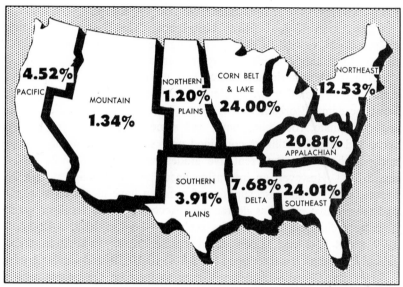

Fig. 44. Percentage of total fertilizer used in different regions in 1950. From *Fertilizer Use at the Half-Century Mark.* National Fertilizer Association. Used with permission.

that the use of fertilizers is affected markedly by the prices of farm products. During periods of high crop prices fertilizer usage increases and when prices drop appreciably the quantity of fertilizer applied also decreases.

The percentages of the total tonnage of fertilizers sold in different groups of states in 1950 are shown in Fig. 44. The high consumption of fertilizer in the South Atlantic states is of much interest and is of long standing. North Carolina is the heaviest user of fertilizer among the states, having applied 1,899,226 tons in the year 1950–1951.[3] California ranked second with 1,448,576 tons, Georgia third with a tonnage of 1,311,954, and Alabama came fourth with 1,305,060 tons. For the calendar year 1950, North Carolina alone used one-tenth of the total fertilizer applied. Although the Eastern and Southeastern states have been large users of fertilizer for many years the extensive application of these materials in the East North Central and West North Central states is a comparatively recent development. For example, the East North Central states used 898,949 tons in 1940, 2,081,813 tons in 1945, and 3,956,916 tons during 1952. During the same periods the West North Central states consumed 142,380 tons, 490,584 tons, and 1,570,818 tons, respectively. The Mountain states have also increased their use of fertilizers from 32,015 tons in 1940 to 280,878 tons in 1950–1951, and the Pacific states from 266,490 tons to 1,659,337 tons.

Changes in Use of Plant Nutrients. The Eastern and Southeastern states, as well as those bordering the Gulf, have long used fertilizers containing considerable quantities of nitrogen and potash, in addition to phosphoric acid which was usually present in higher percentages than the other two nutrients. On the other hand, in the Central West the demand originally was primarily for phosphoric acid. Much superphosphate, rock phosphate, and some bone meal were used as such, and mixed fertilizers contained only small quantities of nitrogen and potash. Some representative grades were 1-8-1, 2-16-2, 3-12-4, and 2-8-2. However, an increasing need for nitrogen and potash has become evident, and also supplies of nitrogen have increased markedly and the relative price has decreased. Accordingly the fertilizer grades have been changed, and analyses such as 4-16-8, 5-10-5, 3-12-12, 3-18-9, and 4-12-8 may be considered representative. In addition, a considerable demand has developed for 8-8-8, 10-10-10, and similar grades.

There has likewise been a tendency to increase the percentages of nutrients and narrow the ratios between the nutrients in fertilizers used in the Eastern and Southern states. The increased supply of available phosphorus in many soils, resulting from long-continued heavy applications of fertilizers containing fairly high percentages of this element, is in part responsible for the narrower nutrient ratios in present-day fertilizers. Some representative grades are 3-9-18, 5-10-5, 3-9-9, 2-12-12, 5-10-10, and 8-8-8.

In the West Central states, however, there appears to be little need for potash except in the states bounded on the east by the Mississippi River. In the areas of somewhat less rainfall phosphoric acid frequently gives profitable increases in yield and nitrogen has proved beneficial to many crops. Some grades used in the Plains states are as follows: 13-26-0, 16-20-0, 15-15-0, 13-39-0. It is noteworthy that the percentage of plant nutrients contained in fertilizers has been increasing steadily. How far this movement can go without decreasing the drilling qualities of the fertilizer and its ability to resist hardening in storage, and also without materially increasing the cost per unit of nutrients, will depend largely on the advances in chemical technology.

FERTILIZER APPLICATION FOR DIFFERENT CROPS

In general fertilizers are applied most frequently and in largest amounts to crops which return the highest value per acre. Also there is a tendency to think of returns from fertilizer in terms of its effect on the crop to which it is applied without too much consideration for residual effects on following crops. This statement is not true, however, in many cases in which fertilizer is applied to a small grain in which a legume or legume-grass mixture is to be seeded and also in the fertilization of a green-manure crop being grown in preparation for the production of special crops such as potatoes or other vegetables.

Crops Receiving the Most Fertilizer. A relatively high percentage of the total fertilizer used is applied to a comparatively few crops. This situation comes about because of the large acreage of some of these crops, because of their high value-per-acre, and because they respond especially well to fertilization. Also, some crops are grown on soils of such low fertility that very small yields are obtained unless fertilizer is used. Table 88 shows the percentage of the total fertilizer produced which is applied to several crops.

TABLE 88. PERCENTAGE OF TOTAL FERTILIZER APPLIED TO SEVERAL CROPS IN 1950 AND AVERAGE RATE OF APPLICATION *

Crop	Per Cent of Total Acreage †	Per Cent of Total Fertilizer	Lb. per Acre	Crop	Per Cent of Total Acreage †	Per Cent of Total Fertilizer	Lb. per Acre
Corn	20.14	26.1	113.3	Hay	18.18	6.8	33.0
Cotton	4.55	10.3	203.4	Pasture	...	5.1	...
Vegetables	0.78	10.4	...	Tobacco	3.74	6.9	1,598.5
Wheat	17.43	8.4	50.0	Oats and			
Potatoes ‡	0.54	6.6	993.8	barley	14.32	6.8	41.4

* Compiled from data in *Fertilizer Rev.* and *Agricultural Statistics*.   † Based on acreage of crop land.   ‡ Both sweet and Irish.

From these figures it will be noted that 55.2 per cent of the total fertilizer used was applied to the first four crops listed. Although a few crops receive such a large share of the fertilizer it does not follow that the entire acreage of these crops is fertilized. For instance, only 50.2 per cent of the land planted to cotton in 1949 received fertilizer.

As would be expected, in different groups of states different crops receive vastly different proportions of the fertilizer used. Thus in the Northern Plains states 48.7 per cent of the fertilizer was applied for wheat and 25.7 per cent for corn, whereas in the Cornbelt and Lake states corn received 35.9 per cent of the fertilizer and wheat 19.9 per cent. The Southeast applied 28.2 per cent of its fertilizer for corn and 22.4 per cent for cotton. In the Northeast 24.0 per cent of the fertilizer was used for potatoes and sweet potatoes, 18.1 per cent for vegetables, and 17.0 per cent on corn. Oats and barley received 24.0 per cent of the fertilizer in the Mountain states and sugar beets 26.7 per cent. In the Pacific area the percentages of the fertilizer applied for vegetables and fruits and nuts were 32.2 and 26.8, respectively.

RETURNS FROM APPLICATION OF FERTILIZER

The rapid increase in the use of fertilizers is based on the fact that large profits are received from the money invested in them. It has been

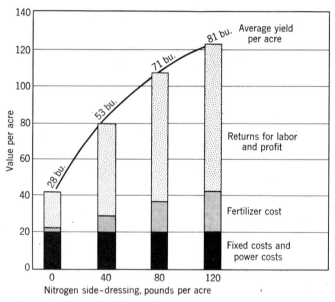

Fig. 45. On soils of low fertility additions of fertilizer frequently lead to large increases in yields and profits unless insufficient moisture or some other factor limits crop production. This figure presents the results of 49 corn experiments in North Carolina conducted during the period 1944–1948. The values used are: corn, $1.50 per bushel; labor, $0.30 per hour; and mule power, $0.22 per hour. From *North Carolina Agr. Exp. Sta. Bull.* 336, 1949. Used with permission.

‑‑ated that for every dollar spent for fertilizer a return of from 2 increased crop yields has been received.[4]

., July–September 1953. National Fertilizer Association, Wash-

Possibilities of Increased Fertilizer Use. Commenting on the percentage of crop production which can be credited to fertilizer use, Clifford R. Hope, Chairman of the Committee on Agriculture, U. S. House of Representatives, has suggested that ultimately the amount might reach 40 per cent.[4] In view of this possibility it is well to consider what experimental results in various states or areas indicate concerning the quantities of fertilizer that may be used profitably on

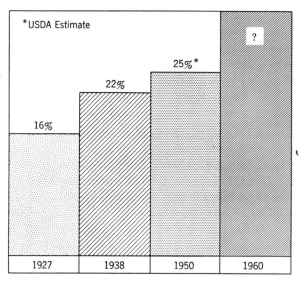

Fig. 46.   Percentage of crop yields in the United States resulting from use of fertilizer. From *Fertilizer Use at the Half-Century Mark*. National Fertilizer Association. Used with permission.

various crops.   In surveys of the use of fertilizer for several major crops in different regions and of the quantities recommended by state experiment stations, the data in Table 89 were compiled.

These figures present an optimistic picture for the future use of fertilizer. The additional tonnage recommended for the four crops considered amounts to 14,298,130. It is also reasonable to suppose that crops occupying smaller acreages might be fertilized more heavily to advantage. Furthermore, the possible increased production of food and fiber that it is estimated would result if the recommended additional fertilizer were applied would supply a much greater population. It is estimated that the population of the United States will reach 189,000,-000 by 1960. The estimated increases in various products that would follow the use of the recommended amounts of fertilizer are: beef,

Soil Fertility

TABLE 89. Pounds of Fertilizer Used and Recommended for Different Crops in Various Regions *

Lb. per Acre of

Region	Grasslands		Corn		Wheat		Cotton	
	Used 1950	Recom-mended	Used	Recom-mended	Used	Recom-mended	Used	Recom-mended
United States	21.5	...	113	...	50	101	203	...
Northeast	29.9	450	254	450	247	300	...	...
Cornbelt and Lakes area	13.9	150	80	175	200	250	94 †	300
Appalachian	63.2	300	285	500	303	400	450 †	600
Southeast	73.1	450	290	500	347	400	594	600
Delta	62.0	275	118	500	...	...	222	475
Southern Plains	7.9	50	38	175	16	70	21	175
Northern Plains	0.4	50	8	50	8	50	...	...
Mountain	1.3	50	11	100	1	70	34 †	100
Pacific	6.1	50	36	75	4	50	50	100

* Prepared from data in *Fertilizer Rev.*, July–September 1951, also October–December 1951. National Fertilizer Assoc., Washington, D. C.

† 14,000 acres in Illinois, Kansas, Kentucky, and Nevada not included.

2,927,924 tons; corn, 688,000,000 bushels; wheat, 133,304,000 bushels; cotton, 2,748,000 bales; and if milk were produced in the humid areas in place of beef the increase would be 18,950,000 tons.

18

Rotations and Farming Systems

The kind of farming followed has much to do with the kind and relative acreage of the crops grown on a given farm. For instance, in livestock farming the main consideration in the selection of crops and the acreage devoted to each is the provision of ample feed of the kinds needed for the type of livestock kept. Other points which determine the cropping system followed are: a fairly uniform distribution of labor through as long a season as is feasible; a source of income from several crops or farm enterprises rather than from one only; the topography of the land and its susceptibility to erosion; the texture, drainage, and productivity of the soil; the climatic conditions, that is, crops should be grown which are adapted to the local climate; the relative value of different crops and the market demand for them; the supply and kind of labor available; the capital available and the immediate need for cash; and the effect of different crops and farming systems on soil productivity.

Some cropping plans followed in different parts of the country and under different systems of farming, the reasons for them, and the general effect upon soil productivity will be considered. Also attention will be called to some factors which limit the benefits that may be derived from a good rotation. The discussion is taken up under the following headings.

Discussion Topics

Cash-crop production in the Central West.
Crop rotations in Northeastern United States and Canada.
Southern cropping systems.
Cropping systems used in dryland farming.
Rotations on irrigated land.
Cash-crop *vs.* livestock farming.
Limitation in rotation benefits.

CASH-CROP PRODUCTION IN THE CENTRAL WEST

The production of grain crops to be sold for cash has always held a prominent place in midwestern agriculture. However, the tendency for many farmers to keep virtually no livestock has been increasing, and dairying and beef and pork production have tended to become concentrated on livestock farms.

The proportion of corn in the rotation increases with increase in available moisture supply, as one travels eastward or northward from the hard winter-wheat belt. Also, with increase in effective moisture oats occupy a larger acreage and clovers come into more common use. Finally, with more and a better distribution of rainfall a considerable number of crops appear in the rotation including corn, oats, wheat, rye, barley, soybeans, clovers, alfalfa, lespedeza, and in certain areas potatoes, sugar beets, field beans, some flax, and small acreages of several other special crops. By arranging the crops mentioned in various ways a large number of rotations or crop sequences have been developed in different localities, only a few of which can be mentioned here. This discussion will be limited to cropping systems of the more humid Central West, as "dryland farming" is considered in a later section.

One- and Two-Year Cropping Systems. Annual growing of a given crop and 2-year cropping systems are seldom practiced in the Central West although a number of the older field experiments included such cropping systems. Numerous tests have shown that several crops, especially wheat and corn, will yield fairly well when grown annually with liberal applications of fertilizer or manure. Nevertheless the superiority of a two-crop system over annual cropping has been amply demonstrated even when neither crop is a legume or sod. The results of some of the long-continued annual cropping and 2-year rotation experiments are presented in Chapter 19.

Three-Year Rotations. The inclusion of 3 crops in a rotation offers the opportunity for many crop sequences. Most of the older rotation experiments include a sod crop with the purpose of providing hay for feeding and hence are not in common use in cash-crop farming. There is a growing conviction, however, that a legume sod with the hay sold may result in sufficiently increased yields of following crops to warrant utilizing an eighth, a sixth, or even a fourth of the crop land for a 1-year hay crop. There is also the possibility that plowing the entire hay crop under may prove profitable when increased yields of other crops and reduced labor costs are considered. This is especially true in the production of high value-per-acre crops such as potatoes and other vegetables. From the viewpoints presented the results of some 3-year rotation experiments, including a year of sod, may be appropriately reviewed.

In the majority of these studies corn followed the sod crop because it uses large amounts of nitrogen, is seldom injured by a liberal supply of this nutrient, is a high value-per-acre crop, and is planted at a time which permits the sod to grow the entire fall and during the early spring. In most trials a leguminous sod has proved more beneficial to corn than a non-leguminous sod, although the Ohio station [1] reports a 20-year average yield of 67.7 bushels of corn following timothy and only 66.3 bushels following clover.[2] In this trial the soil was brought to a pH of 7.0; 6 tons of manure were applied for corn and 200 pounds of 0-16-0 were used for each crop. Possibly the manure supplied sufficient nitrogen so that the quantity of the nutrient in the clover was not needed. In the Ohio tests alfalfa and sweet clover proved superior to clover in increasing corn yields. These results are in harmony with the generally accepted idea of the greater value of "deep-rooted" legumes for soil improvement.

Soybeans are seldom planted after a sod, although there is no reason for thinking they would not benefit by this position in the rotation. When potatoes are grown they usually follow the sod.

The third crop in the rotation is usually a small grain, frequently oats or barley because of the difficulty in seeding wheat on time after corn unless the corn is cut for ensilage.

Among the many rotations studied by the Kentucky station,[3] those given in Table 90 are of special interest because one includes orchard grass, one tobacco, and two have soybeans in place of a sod crop.

It will be noted that corn yielded better after clover than after orchard grass, soybeans, or wheat. Wheat produced especially well after tobacco. In other rotations the Kentucky station [3] compared the effect of different legumes on yields of corn and wheat. The studies included plowing under the entire legume crop compared to plowing under the sod after hay harvest. The results are discussed in Chapter 15.

Three-year rotations consisting entirely of grain crops have received little attention, probably because they have been assumed to be decidedly soil-depleting. Such a rotation has been tested on the Oblong Field in east south central Illinois.[4] The 7-year average yield of corn in a corn,

[1] *Ohio Agr. Exp. Sta. Book* Series B-1, 1951. The Ohio station has studied a large number of 3-year rotations.

[2] In this discussion "clover" refers to red clover unless otherwise stated.

[3] *Kentucky Agr. Exp. Sta. Bull.* 374, 1937.

[4] *Illinois Agr. Exp. Sta. Bull.* 516, 1945.

TABLE 90. EFFECT OF DIFFERENT ROTATIONS ON CROP YIELDS *

Rotations and Yields, bu. or lb.

Kind and Number of Crops Harvested	Corn Wheat Clover	Corn Wheat Orchard Grass	Tobacco Wheat Clover	Corn Wheat Soybeans	Corn Soybeans Wheat
Corn, 15 crops	57.7	54.3	1,192 †	50.9	44.9
Wheat, 15 crops	22.0	19.3	27.2	19.2	20.3
Hay, 16 crops	2,801	1,230	2,633	4,353	4,015

   * *Kentucky Agr. Exp. Sta. Bull.* 374, 1937.
   † Pounds of tobacco.

soybean, soybean rotation was 56.1 bushels compared to 57.7 bushels in a corn, oats, wheat (sweet clover) rotation. Also rotations such

Fig. 47. The rotation followed has a great influence on yields of corn grown on Marshall silt loam. The rotations followed are (from left to right): corn-oats; corn-oats and sweet-clover catch crop; corn–oats-meadow (a mixture of alfalfa, red clover, and bromegrass); corn-oats-2 years of meadow; corn-corn-oats-2 years of meadow; corn-corn-oats-2 years of meadow (yield is for second corn crop). From *Soil Sci. Soc. Amer. Proc.,* 17: No. 3, 247, 1953. Courtesy of G. Stanford.

as the last one, including grain crops with leguminous catch crops, have not been studied sufficiently to determine their value. For example, a corn, wheat (clover), oats (clover) rotation with crop residues returned would supply considerable organic matter and nitrogen to the soil. Sweet clover or other adapted legumes could be substituted for clover if insect pests and other conditions made it advisable. Also, a corn (catch crop), oats, wheat (sweet clover) rotation might prove advantageous. More work could well be done on rotations of this type.

Four-Year and Longer Rotations. Many variations of the old corn, oats, wheat, clover rotation have been tried. The substitution of alfalfa for clover has proved desirable on many soils when sufficient lime is present or has been applied to insure a catch of alfalfa. When climatic conditions permit the wheat and oat crops may be reversed and a leguminous catch crop seeded in the wheat. In regions where the corn yield is frequently reduced materially by drought, especially on medium- and light-textured soils, it may prove desirable to have wheat follow the clover. This is similar to the Norfolk rotation followed widely in Europe. The Michigan station [5] followed such a rotation for 16 years on a sandy loam soil, and it has been in use on a number of experimental fields in Illinois for many years. Average yields from one of the Illinois [4] fields for the period 1910–1942, using a sweet-clover catch crop in the wheat but no other soil treatment, have been 49.9, 51.0, and 23.2 bushels for corn, oats, and wheat, respectively, and 1.44 tons of clover hay.

In some areas of the Corn Belt two crops of corn are grown with a small grain and clover. When two corn crops are grown in succession the yield of the second one is usually considerably lower than that of the first unless some special fertilization is given it. For example, the Ohio station [6] reports 15-year average yields from a rotation of corn, corn, wheat, clover of 66.2 bushels of corn for the first crop and 55.9 bushels for the second. That this result is not always obtained, however, is shown by the yields from seven experimental fields in Illinois for a 9-year period. The average yield for the first corn crop was 58.7 bushels and for the second 56.6 bushels. It has been pointed out by those in charge of the Illinois field experiments [7] that when two crops of corn follow a legume sod or a leguminous green manure the first crop is usually appreciably larger than the second. However, if no sod or green manure precedes the corn, which would then be planted on a small grain stubble, the yield of the second corn crop usually exceeds that of the first. The explanation lies in the utilization of nitrogen by the organisms decomposing the small grain stubble and the resulting shortage of nitrogen for the first corn crop.

[5] *Michigan Agr. Exp. Sta. Bull.* 366, 1951.
[6] *Ohio Agr. Exp. Sta. Book* Series B-1, p. 171, 1951.
[7] Personal correspondence.

In a few states it is a common practice to replace one of the corn
crops with soybeans. It must be recognized that the growing of two
intertilled crops in a 4-year rotation results in the rapid dissipation of
the soil organic matter unless large amounts of organic material are
returned. Possibly with the present system of leaving most of the crop
residues on the land and the increasing use of catch crops and of nitrogen fertilizer this fault may be corrected.

Workers in Illinois have made an interesting comparison of three
4-year rotations which included 1, 2, and 3 years of corn respectively.
The rotations and corn yields for the period 1903–1942 are given in
Table 91.

TABLE 91. CORN YIELDS IN THREE 4-YEAR ROTATIONS *

Soil Treat- ment †	Average Yield of 40 Crops, bu. per acre					
	Rotation I Corn, Oats, Red Clover, Wheat (Red Clover)	Rotation II Corn, Corn, Oats, Red Clover		Rotation III Corn, Corn, Corn, Soybeans		
	Corn	Corn 1st yr.	Corn 2nd yr.	Corn 1st yr.	Corn 2nd yr.	Corn 3rd yr.
R − rP	65.0	62.3	56.0	52.3	45.7	43.8
R	59.6	57.1	50.5	48.0	43.3	40.3
M	65.5	60.5	56.4	54.2	49.0	42.7
M − rP	67.3	63.9	60.6	56.1	50.7	45.6

* *Illinois Agr. Exp. Sta. Bull.* 516, 1945.

† R = crop residues; rP = rock phosphate; M = manure.

These data show that the rotation containing two small grains, a sod
crop, a catch crop, and only one cultivated crop gave the highest corn
yields for all treatments. Also rotation III, containing four intertilled
crops, was definitely inferior to rotation II, including a small grain and
a leguminous sod. Whether the same results would have been obtained
if heavy application of commercial nitrogen fertilizer had been applied
cannot be determined from the data. The lower yields of the second,
and in rotation III the third corn crop, compared to those of the first
crop are well illustrated by the results.

Rotations covering more than 4 years generally include more than 1 year of hay and are better suited for livestock than for cash-crop farming. One type of long rotation including a large number of grain crops compared to sods is in reality a combination of 3- and 4- or 5-year rotations. For example, the Michigan station has used a cropping system consisting of corn, oats, wheat, alfalfa, alfalfa, corn, oats, wheat (sweet clover) for many years. This is merely a combination of a 3- and 5-year rotation.

This idea or general type of a cropping system has been greatly expanded in Illinois and, under the title of a "4-field" or the "Bauer rotation," is finding wide acceptance in the state. Dr. Bauer has pointed out that many crop combinations are possible under this system. For example, if a simple 4-year rotation is desired, some crop combinations might be C-C-O-A,[8] C-B-O-A, C-O-W-A, C-B-W-A, C-C·B-O·W-A. On the other hand, if it is desired to leave alfalfa in for 2 years, the plan could be: C-C-O-A-A-C-C-O Swt. cl., etc. Soybeans could be substituted for corn on one field or a part of a field, and wheat or barley could be substituted for oats whenever desired. Also clover and timothy could be used in place of alfalfa.

CROP ROTATIONS IN NORTHEASTERN UNITED STATES AND CANADA

In the Northeastern states a number of special crops such as potatoes, tobacco, and vegetables occupy a large acreage, and in addition there are many dairy, poultry, and fruit farms. Accordingly, cropping systems including the special crops and the production of feed for livestock may well be considered.

Potato Rotations. Cropping systems designed to increase potato yields have been studied for many years by several stations, and perhaps those in Rhode Island [9] started in 1894 are the oldest. Results for the first 52 years showed the yield of potatoes following a non-leguminous sod to be 36 bushels higher than that obtained when the crop followed a sod containing legumes. Furthermore, potatoes after a mixture of alfalfa and timothy yielded more than potatoes following clover. Similar results showing the superiority of a non-leguminous sod for potato production were obtained by Odland, Smith, and Damon.[10] On the

[8] C = corn; B = soybeans; O = oats; A = alfalfa; Swt. cl. = sweet clover; C·B = field divided between beans and corn, etc.
[9] *Rhode Island Agr. Exp. Sta. Bull.* 303, 1949.
[10] *Rhode Island Agr. Exp. Sta. Bull.* 243, 1934.

other hand, Terman [11] in Maine obtained somewhat larger potato yields following various legumes (average results from 7 legumes) than he did from 5 mixtures of oats and legumes and from 2 non-legumes. The oat-legume mixtures proved somewhat inferior to the legumes but decidedly better than the non-legumes.

In summarizing his results Terman ranks Japanese millet as the most satisfactory non-legume to use as a green-manure crop preceding potatoes. Corn, oats, Sudan grass, rye-grass, and sunflowers were classed as "fairly satisfactory" green manures. The non-legumes should be fertilized with nitrogen or a fertilizer high in nitrogen content unless the soil contains an abundance of this nutrient.

The quantity of organic matter in the soil and that supplied by sods, green manures, or other additions is an influential factor in determining potato yields, according to Chucka and associates.[12] This is one reason why well-fertilized non-legumes are favored as crops to precede potatoes. Tests showed that from 3.5 to 5 tons of dry matter were obtained from Japanese millet, corn, or sunflowers and only 1 to 2 tons from red clover, crimson clover, vetch, and soybeans. Sudan grass, oats, rye-grass, and buckwheat supplied intermediate amounts of dry material. Another reason for holding non-legumes in high favor as crops to precede potatoes is the fact that they can be grown at lower soil pH values than can legumes, and thus scab can be more easily controlled. The Maine station [13] has shown that this disease causes little damage when the pH of the soil is maintained at 5.5 or below. Some other states have not been so successful in controlling scab of potato by maintaining soil pH at a low level.

That the type of organic matter which is decaying in the soil has a bearing on the prevalence of potato scab is suggested by the work of Wheeler.[14] When potatoes were grown continuously or followed sweet clover the percentage of scabby tubers was high and increased rapidly after the first few years. Potatoes following alfalfa were much freer of scab, and the percentage of infection did not increase so rapidly as it did with the sweet-clover rotation or continuous culture. In a rotation of potatoes and corn with a rye green-manuring crop there were yet fewer scabby tubers and a slower rate of increase of the disease. There appears to be some grounds for the belief that decaying rye decreases the activity of the scab organisms, although more work needs to be done on the problem.

[11] *Maine Agr. Exp. Sta. Bull.* 474, 1949.

[12] *Maine Agr. Exp. Sta. Bull.* 414, 1943.

[13] *Maine Agr. Exp. Sta. Bull.* 449, 1947.

[14] *Michigan Agr. Exp. Sta. Quart. Bull.* 28, No. 4, May 1946

There is considerable difference of opinion concerning the most desirable length of rotations for potatoes. The Michigan station recommends a rather long rotation including a legume or a grass-legume mixture but with a non-legume immediately preceding the potato crop. Only enough lime is used on acid soils to permit of establishing the legume. On the other hand, the Maine station,[15] after many years of experimentation with rotations of varying length, recommends growing the crop from 1 to 4 years and following it with a green manure, grain, and hay, or with peas in which clover is seeded. In some cases 2 years of grain and hay are recommended, and on the best land potatoes may be grown annually.[16]

Rotations for Specialized and General Farming. A number of experiments have been conducted to determine the effect of different crops on those that follow. The results may be useful in planning rotations if other considerations do not prove of more significance. Studies by the Rhode Island station were among the earliest and longest continued of this nature. In the early years of the work, marked effects of certain crops on those that followed were observed on unlimed soil. These results could be explained in part by the influence of the preceding crops on soil reaction, and when the soil was limed the depression of following crops was not so great. Crops following themselves frequently gave lower yields than when they followed other crops but not always. Also the nitrogen factor in these and other experiments is frequently important. Crops leaving highly carbonaceous and easily decayable residues often exert a depressing effect on following crops because of insufficient nitrogen in the soil. On the other hand, easily decayable nitrogenous residues may overstimulate the early growth of some following crops, such as potatoes, with a depression of yields, or may prove beneficial as with corn. Frequently no explanation is evident for the effect of a crop on those that follow. In general more attention is given to the sequence of crops in the production of vegetables than in the growing of grains.

Dodd and Pohlman [17] found the yields of oats, wheat, and corn to be significantly larger when grown after soybeans than after oats, but this was not true for buckwheat or potatoes. Corn proved an inferior crop to precede oats or soybeans, but the beans yielded especially well after wheat. Bean yields after oats and potatoes were intermediate. Oats yielded well after wheat and potatoes. Other studies in West

[15] *Maine Agr. Exp. Sta. Bull.* 474, 1949.

[16] Rotations for different classes of land, as designated by the Soil Conservation Service, are given in Bull. 474 of the Maine station.

[17] *West Virginia Agr. Exp. Sta. Bull.* 265, 1935.

Virginia [18] included a large number of cropping systems grown on limed and unlimed soil treated with 200 pounds per acre per year of 0-20-0. Corn yielded well in rotations containing clover plus timothy or catch crops of rye plus vetch. The yield was poor, however, under annual cropping with catch crops and in a 2-year rotation with soybeans including two catch crops of sweet clover. Rye plus vetch proved to be a better green-manure crop in several rotations than sweet clover.

In order to compare the values of 1-, 2-, and 3-year old sods Dr. Lyon [19] studied six 5-year rotations in which alfalfa or timothy occupied the soil for 1, 2, and 3 years respectively. The yields of fodder corn and wheat for two courses of the rotations are shown in Table 92. The

TABLE 92. YIELDS OF FODDER CORN AND WHEAT FOLLOWING 1, 2, AND 3 YEARS OF ALFALFA OR TIMOTHY

Rotation	Dry Matter in Lb. per Acre for 2 Years	
	Fodder Corn	Wheat (Straw + Grain)
Alfalfa 3 years, corn, wheat	18,692	15,424
Alfalfa 2 years, corn, wheat, rye	17,450	16,866
Alfalfa, corn, wheat, rye, oats	19,377	15,390
Timothy 3 years, corn, wheat	10,675	9,706
Timothy 2 years, corn, wheat, rye	11,495	9,567
Timothy, corn, wheat, rye, oats	10,747	10,749

data show clearly the superiority of the alfalfa over the timothy sod. Furthermore there appeared to be no advantage, so far as the yields of following crops were concerned, of maintaining the sod for more than 1 year. Results of more recent experiments in other states substantiate this finding. In the Northeastern states, as in the Corn Belt, it is customary to plant corn after a sod crop and to apply manure not needed for special crops to the sod before plowing. Pastures are also manured when the supply permits. Comparatively heavy applications of commercial fertilizer for grain crops are customary. Special crops are heavily fertilized.

Canadian Studies. Beginning in 1911 intensive studies of rotations were conducted on the experimental farms throughout Canada. On the whole, the cropping systems used were those considered advisable for different types of farming in the respective areas. The results for the Prairie provinces were reported in 1944 by Hopkins and Lea-

[18] *West Virginia Agr. Exp. Sta. Bull.* 306, 1943.
[19] *Cornell Univ. Agr. Exp. Sta. Bull.* 500, 1930.

hey [20] and are reviewed in the section of this chapter dealing with dry-land farming. Ripley [21] has studied the data with a view to determining the effect of different crops on those that followed immediately rather than the comparative value of the entire rotations. The field data from Ottawa were also supplemented by results from greenhouse and laboratory studies.

Summer fallow proved to be especially beneficial in the Western provinces where moisture supply was the limiting factor. The crops ranked in the following decreasing order in regard to their beneficial influence on succeeding crops: corn, potatoes, peas, millet, oats, and wheat. The amount of moisture left in the soil at harvest time determined the comparative effect of a crop on those that followed.

Though beneficial in the West summer fallow was of little benefit to succeeding crops in eastern Canada. Small grains were benefited to a slight extent and sometimes corn, but the practice was detrimental to potatoes. Small grains also gave higher yields following intertilled crops than when they followed other small grains. The work at Ottawa showed that crops which were followed by a high soil nitrate content had a more favorable effect on the succeeding crops than did crops which were followed by a low nitrate content in the soil. Some crops in the first group are: alfalfa, red clover, rye, and timothy. Soil nitrate content and yields of following crops were lower, however, after corn, oats, and potatoes. Ripley points out that, although crops following alfalfa and clover gave increased yields, the increases were not so great as could have been expected had the soil been of lower nitrogen content. Furthermore, on soils relatively rich in nitrogen and deficient in phosphorus and potassium the legumes might have little beneficial influence on succeeding crops because of the high utilization of the mineral elements by the legumes.

SOUTHERN CROPPING SYSTEMS

Studies of cropping systems in the South have centered largely around the growing of cotton, although some attention has been given to tobacco, and more recently soil-management systems for corn production have been studied.

Cropping Systems for Cotton. The longest-continued rotation studies including cotton that have come to the writer's attention are those at the Alabama experiment station. The work, which was started

[20] *Can. Dep. Agr. Pub.* 761, 1944.

[21] *Sci. Agr.,* 21: 522, 1941. The paper contains a good review of the literature dealing with the effect of crops on those that follow.

in 1896, is discussed in Chapter 19. The results show a marked response of cotton to a leguminous catch crop both in annual cropping and in rotation.[22]

Several rotations at the Sand Mountain experiment station in northeastern Alabama [23] also show the need of the cotton crop for nitrogen and demonstrate that this need can be supplied either by a catch crop of vetch or in commercial fertilizer. The 18-year average yield of cotton grown annually with an application of 600 pounds of 8-8-8 was 1,521 pounds. When a catch crop of vetch was grown and the nitrogen was left out of the fertilizer the cotton yield was 1,747 pounds. In this case 200 pounds of 0-8-8 was used for the cotton and 400 pounds for the vetch. Likewise, in a cotton-corn rotation the cotton yield was 559 pounds with 600 pounds of 0-8-8 and 1,531 pounds with 600 pounds of 8-8-8.

Another interesting test compared different legumes planted in alternate rows with corn, the rows being 7 feet apart. In some cases the corn rows were 3½ feet apart and the legume was seeded in the row. The 6-year average yields of cotton and corn in a corn-cotton rotation

TABLE 93.   EFFECT OF A LEGUME IN ALTERNATE ROWS OR IN SAME ROW WITH CORN *

6-Year Average Yields (1933–1938)

Crop Planted in Alternate Rows with Corn †	Cotton,‡ lb.	Corn, bu.	Green Weight of Summer Legume, lb.
Peanuts	1,086	12.1	3,541
Soybeans	911	10.8	3,901
Velvet beans	963	8.3	8,621
Cowpeas	1,005	9.2	4,550
Crotalaria	1,108	13.0	6,433
None	950	15.0	. . .
Soybeans § in same row	987	14.2	2,509
Crotalaria § in same row	1,162	18.1	4,759
None §	916	15.7	. . .

* Unpublished data from mimeographed release.
† Corn rows 7 ft.
‡ Cotton received 600 pounds of 0-10-4 in all cases.
§ Rows 3½ ft.

and the green weights of legume produced are given in Table 93. Under the conditions of this experiment crotalaria proved a superior crop

[22] *Better Crops with Plant Food.* August–September 1949.
[23] Unpublished data from mimeographed release.

to plant in corn preceding cotton. The cotton yields following soybeans and velvet beans were not greatly different from those after corn with no interplanted legume.

The marked response of cotton to the incorporation into the soil of leguminous cover crops has been demonstrated by several experiment stations. In North Carolina, Welch [24] and associates obtained good results by drilling either Austrian peas, vetch, crimson clover, and oats and vetch in the cotton-corn rotation between the cotton rows after the first picking and in the corn and peanut soil following disking after

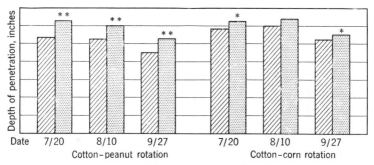

Fig. 48. Effect of a cover crop of vetch in two rotations on the structure of a fine sandy loam, as measured by a penetrometer. Measurements were made in the cotton plots and on the crop ridge or row. Significance at the 0.05 level is indicated by * and at the 0.01 level by **. From *Soil Sci. Soc. Amer. Proc.,* 15: 230, 1950. Courtesy of C. D. Welch et al.

harvest. The rotations were cotton-corn and cotton-peanuts, and a starter fertilizer was placed 2 inches below and 3 inches to each side of the corn and cotton seed. The yields of cotton were some 15 per cent higher in the cotton-corn rotation, and the soil was more compact and more acid under the cotton-peanut system. That the increased cotton yields were due to the nitrogen supplied by the legumes was shown by the obtaining of equally large increases from nitrogen fertilizer. However, the cover crops did improve the soil structure, as is shown in Fig. 48.

Results of experiments at the Pee Dee station in South Carolina,[25] and also those of Coleman [26] in Mississippi, have substantiated the beneficial effects of leguminous cover crops in cotton production. The nitrogen content of the soil has a marked influence on the response of cotton to cover crops, however, as was shown by a very small in-

[24] *Soil Sci. Soc. Amer. Proc.,* 15: 229, 1950.
[25] *South Carolina Agr. Exp. Sta. Bull.* 262, 1929.
[26] *Mississippi Agr. Exp. Sta. Bull.* 336, 1939.

crease in yield on Olivier and Ochlocknee soils in Mississippi following Austrian peas and a large increase on Granada soil. The latter soil is low in nitrogen content and the other two are well supplied with the nutrient.

A study of cropping systems on the "buckshot" soils of the Delta area in Mississippi shows the advantages of growing winter legumes and of following rotations including corn and soybeans. On the other hand, plowing under sorghum decreased cotton yields. A summary of the data is presented in Table 94. Improved physical condition is

TABLE 94. EFFECT OF VARIOUS CROPPING SYSTEMS ON COTTON YIELDS ON "BUCKSHOT" SOIL *

Cropping System	6-Year Average Yield	Cropping System	6-Year Average Yield
Cotton annually with winter legumes	1,611	Cotton annually with winter legumes	1,724
1st year after sorghums †	983	1st year after corn and soybeans	1,616
2nd year after sorghums †	1,553		
1st year after soybeans †	1,816	2nd year after corn and soybeans	1,478
Cotton annually	1,212		

* Mississippi Agr. Exp. Sta. Service Sheet 357, 1943.
† Plowed under.

evidently a major factor in managing this soil, although nitrogen supply is also important, as evidenced by the decreased yield following the plowing under of sorghum.

The increase in supplies of nitrogen fertilizers and the decrease in cost raises a question as to whether leguminous cover crops will prove as advantageous in cotton production in the future as they have in the past. To what extent these crops improve the physical condition of the soil and how significant any such improvement may be in increasing yields has not been thoroughly investigated.

Tobacco Culture.[27] Tobacco is grown in about an equal number of Southern and Northern states. Hence it cannot be considered typically a Southern crop. However, as a matter of convenience, tobacco growing, in general, will be considered at this point.

Tobacco is grown on soils varying in texture from loamy sands to clay loams and in organic content ranging from very low to very high. One characteristic required of all tobacco soils is good drainage, and a soil reaction of pH 5.0 to 6.0 is considered desirable. Sandy soils low in

[27] A comprehensive discussion of tobacco culture is contained in *The Production of Tobacco*, by W. W. Garner. Blakiston Co., Philadelphia, 1946.

nutrients produce a thin leaf, comparatively weak in aroma, light-bodied, and yellow in color and hence are especially desirable for flue-cured tobacco. An increase in nutrients, especially nitrogen, results in a change of color to shades of brown but in little thickening of the leaves. Heavy soils usually produce thick, dark, heavy-bodied leaves which are gummy and have a pronounced aroma. Fertilization varies with soil conditions and the type of tobacco grown.

Fig. 49. Various crops and especially different weeds have a marked influence on the growth of the following tobacco crop. Tobacco following (*A*) lamb's-quarters and (*B*) horseweed. Six-year average yields were 825 pounds and 1,194 pounds, respectively. From *J. Agr. Research,* 59: No. 11, 1939. Courtesy of J. E. McMurtrey, Jr.

Likewise the cropping systems followed in different tobacco-growing areas are quite variable. The crop sequence followed is governed by several factors, among which are the following: the area of first-class tobacco soil available; the effect of the systems on the supply of nitrogen and other nutrients left in the soil; and the effect of preceding crops on the yield and quality of tobacco. Many crops exert a marked influence on the following tobacco plants, which may be sometimes explained by a depletion of nutrient reserves or the harboring of disease organisms, but which frequently is not understood. The beneficial effect of certain weeds as horseweed and ragweed has also not been explained. Only in the growing of the heavier types of tobacco do legumes occupy a prominent place in the cropping system. In the following paragraphs a brief description of the soils and cropping systems used in several tobacco-growing areas will be given.

Flue-cured tobacco is grown preferably on sandy loam soil, although a considerable acreage is produced on loamy sands and silt loams. As a whole, the soils are low in organic matter and nutrient content and are strongly acid. Moderate additions of non-nitrogenous organic material are desirable. Because of the limited acreage of choice land there is a tendency to grow tobacco for a number of years and then to rest the land by allowing it to grow up to weeds for several years or by growing a small grain followed by grass. Horseweed and ragweed have especially desirable effects on the following tobacco. Winter cover crops of small grains or Italian rye-grass are frequently used, and on the poorer soils a legume is sometimes included in the cover crop.

Cigar tobacco is grown on a wide variety of soils because the requirements for wrapper, binder, and filler are quite different. Choice wrapper tobacco [28] is grown under cloth shelters, and, because of this fact and the limited acreage of the most desirable sandy loam soils, tobacco is planted every year. Cover crops of small grains are grown, and in some areas, when disease becomes too prevalent, the soil is planted to corn or vegetables or allowed to grow up to weeds for a short period. The "open-field" wrapper and filler is also produced each year to a large extent with small-grain winter cover crops.

Filler tobacco is grown year after year in some states, but in others a 4-year rotation consisting of tobacco, wheat, clover or alfalfa, and corn is followed. At times the rotation is cut to 3 years by omitting the corn and sometimes it is lengthened to 5 years by having 2 years of sod. The filler type of tobacco in states west of the seaboard is usually grown on silt loams.

Burley tobacco is produced largely on silt loams, and many of them are especially high in organic matter. For many years virgin soils or old bluegrass sods were largely used for the crop. However, it is pointed out [29] that, with the development of disease-resistant varieties, continuous culture is becoming more common. A rotation frequently used consists of tobacco for 2 years, wheat seeded to timothy and red clover, and sod for several years. A cover crop of rye should follow the first tobacco crop. A 2-year rotation of tobacco and wheat is sometimes used, and a volunteer growth of ragweed following the wheat is considered beneficial.

Dark air-cured and flue-cured tobacco is produced on soils varying from sandy loams to clay loams. A commonly used rotation is tobacco followed by wheat with a seeding of timothy and clover. A rather liberal use of legumes in the rotation is permissible because the quality of the leaf is not reduced by a moderate supply of nitrogen.

[28] Anderson discusses in detail the growing of tobacco in the Connecticut area in *Connecticut Agr. Exp. Sta. Bull.* 564, 1953.
[29] *Kentucky Agr. Ext. Service Cir.* 482, 1950.

Maryland tobacco is grown on light soils, and usually a period of annual cropping is followed by a rest period of several years. A volunteer cover of weeds was found beneficial by Brown and McMurtrey.[30] A promising 2-year rotation consists of tobacco followed by hairy vetch which is allowed to mature and is followed by weeds. Annual cropping is increasing in favor and includes a winter cover crop of rye or grass.

General Farm Rotations. In an effort to determine methods of obtaining high corn yields in North Carolina, Krantz [31] studied the value of legumes and of fertilizers, particularly those of high nitrogen content, by means of numerous field experiments. Results showed that winter legumes under soil treatments which permitted a large growth would furnish much of the nitrogen needed by corn. However, nitrogen fertilizers in addition to the legumes proved advantageous usually, and adequate supplies of other plant nutrients and a suitable soil reaction were, of course, necessary. Some of the results from the field trials are contained in Table 95. This soil had not grown a winter legume

TABLE 95. EFFECT OF WINTER LEGUMES AND OF NITROGEN FERTILIZERS ON YIELDS OF CORN ON NORFOLK FINE SANDY LOAM *

Yields of Corn (15.5% moisture), bu. per acre ‡

Soil Treatment †	1944	1945	1946	1947	Average
No N and no cover crop	20.1	10.1	18.0	13.2	15.4
No N and a winter legume	39.7	50.1	88.6	95.8	68.5
Increase for legume	19.6	40.0	70.6	82.6	53.2
No cover crop: 60–90 lb. N §	59.1	46.3	82.7	90.6	69.7
Winter legume: ‖ 60–90 § lb. N	64.8	71.6	109.1	117.1	90.7
Increase for legume	5.8	25.3	26.4	26.5	21.0
No cover crop: 120–180 lb. N	73.1	73.4	106.5	112.4	91.4

* Taken from Table 6, *North Carolina Agr. Exp. Sta. Bull.* 366, 1949.
† One ton of lime was applied when the experiment was started, and an annual application of 80 pounds of P_2O_5 and 80 pounds of K_2O was made.
‡ Results are the average of those from two locations.
§ Sixty pounds of nitrogen used in 1944 and 1945 and 90 pounds in 1946 and 1947.
‖ Top growth of winter legumes was 1,285, 1,809, 3,753, and 3,731 pounds, respectively, for the years 1944–1947.

previously, and it will be noted that the amount of growth materially increased as nodulation improved. Also, the corn yields increased in proportion to the increased growth of legume.

[30] *Maryland Agr. Exp. Sta. Bull.* 363, 1934.
[31] *North Carolina Agr. Exp. Sta. Bull.* 366, 1949.

Moisture supply was a determining factor in the response of corn to nitrogen applications, as was to be expected. Nevertheless, increased yields were obtained in dry years as well as in those with normal precipitation. These results are somewhat at variance with those obtained in the Piedmont [32] where a small increase in crop yields was obtained from green manures but a large increase from heavy fertilization. Apparently a low nutrient content of the soil nullified the benefits of green manures in the latter experiments. The effect of clover and alfalfa in combination with timothy and of clover alone on the yields of corn and wheat in several rotations in southwest Virginia was studied by Perkins and associates. All the crops received 200 pounds annually of 4-12-4 from 1930 to 1936. Beginning in 1937 the fertilizer was changed to a 0-14-6. Some of the data are summarized in Table 96.

TABLE 96.   EFFECT OF LEGUME AND LEGUME-GRASS SODS ON CROP YIELDS *

Yields, 1930–1941, bu. or lb.

Rotation	Corn	Small Grain	Hay
Corn, wheat, clover	60.7	23.1	3,698
Corn, clover-timothy (2 years)	49.8	...	1,687
Corn, wheat, clover-timothy (2 years)	55.3	21.0	2,979
Corn, wheat, wheat, clover-timothy (2 years)	51.3	20.5	3,306
Corn, wheat, clover-timothy (3 years)	53.3	19.6	2,515
Corn, alfalfa-timothy (4 years)	56.9	...	2,837
Corn, corn, alfalfa-timothy (4 years)	56.5	...	3,483

* *Virginia Agr. Exp. Sta. Bull.* 339, 1942.

Of special interest in these results are the high yields of all three crops produced in the corn, wheat, clover rotation. The mixing of timothy with the clover resulted in an appreciable decrease in yields of corn and, strangely, of hay. This result may have been due to the utilization by the timothy of some of the nitrogen fixed by the clover or, possibly, to the use of the nitrogen by the organisms decomposing the timothy residues. The decrease in yield of corn and wheat when the sod was maintained for 3 in place of 2 years lends support to the idea that nitrogen supply was a limiting factor in crop production on this soil. The increased corn yields after the substitution of alfalfa for clover in the hay mixture also indicates a nitrogen shortage and again points to the superiority of alfalfa over clover for soil improvement under many conditions. The high average yield of corn when

[32] *North Carolina Agr. Exp. Sta. Bull.* 341, 1943.

two crops were grown in succession followed by 4 years of alfalfa-timothy is worthy of note.

The need of corn for nitrogen on Southern soils was also shown in Mississippi.[33] A catch crop of Austrian peas greatly increased the yield, but rye decreased it. However, rye plus 30 pounds of nitrogen produced a large increase, and on two soils nitrogen alone was better than rye plus nitrogen. Evidently the organisms decomposing the rye robbed the corn of some of the applied nitrogen. Also drilling crotalaria or soybeans in the row with corn or between the rows at "lay-by" time did not prove advisable.

At the Tennessee experiment station an interesting study was made of the duration of the beneficial effect of sericea on soil productivity as measured by the yield of corn. An area was seeded to the legume which was harvested for hay each year. After 3 years two plots from the area were plowed and planted to corn annually for the next 11 years. Each year, thereafter, two additional plots were plowed and cropped to corn continuously for the duration of the experiment. The results are recorded in Table 97.

TABLE 97. YIELDS OF CORN FOLLOWING SERICEA SOD OF DIFFERENT AGES AND FOR DIFFERENT NUMBER OF YEARS CORN WAS GROWN AFTER PLOWING THE SOD *

Age of Sod, years	Yields per Acre, bu.	Age of Sod, years	Yields per Acre, bu.	Age of Sod, years	Yields per Acre, bu.
3	60.6	7	48.1	11	25.7
4	60.4	8	37.2	12	33.6
5	52.5	9	25.9	13	21.4
6	40.7	10	33.8		

Year after Plowing Sod	Yield per Acre		Year after Plowing Sod	Yield per Acre	
	Actual, bu.	Adjusted, bu.		Actual, bu.	Adjusted, bu.
1st	70.3	69.0	7th	36.1	35.6
2nd	65.6	64.6	8th	34.7	33.8
3rd	59.1	57.5	9th	28.5	29.8
4th	52.8	50.7	10th	28.8	28.1
5th	46.7	43.6	11th	21.4	26.6
6th	41.2	39.4			

* Tennessee Agr. Exp. Sta. Bull. 197, 1945.

Because weather conditions varied considerably from year to year an attempt was made to correct the corn yields for this factor. The

[33] Mississippi Agr. Exp. Sta. Bull. 336, 1939.

actual and corrected yields are both shown in the table. It was felt that a deficiency of potassium might be limiting corn yields, and hence tests were started to determine if this were true. Results showed that potassium applied the second year after plowing up the sod increased yields for the next 2 years but that the effect diminished rapidly.

It will be noted that the beneficial effect of the sod on corn yields decreased quite regularly as time elapsed after plowing, with corn being grown each year. It is of interest to note that corn on nearby plots which had not grown sericea produced an average yield of 17½ bushels for the 11-year period. It would seem, therefore, that the beneficial effect of the sericea sod had not entirely worn off 11 years after it was plowed under.

CROPPING SYSTEMS USED IN DRYLAND FARMING

In areas receiving rather small amounts of total precipitation, and especially in those in which rainfall during the growing season is uncertain and frequently small, the storage of moisture in the soil before planting a crop often becomes a determining factor in crop production. The moisture shortage is also accentuated by high rates of evaporation and transpiration and by the fact that many summer storms are of a torrential nature and hence the soil is able to absorb only a small part of the rainfall. Under these conditions the crops grown and the crop sequence followed has much to do with the success of the farming enterprise. Some studies of cropping systems and soil-management practices under dryland farming conditions are presented in the following pages.

Summer Fallow.[34]   The value of summer fallow as a means of storing soil moisture and increasing crop yields has been studied for many years by most of the experiment stations in the "dryland farming" areas of the United States. Only a few representative data from these studies can be presented here.

There are various methods of preparing and maintaining fallow land. Time of plowing is involved, as well as soil treatment before plowing and tillage after plowing. Also, a lister may be used in place of the plow. That fall or early spring plowing is advantageous is shown by the results reported by Brandon and Mathews.[35] The 16-year average yields of winter wheat on land prepared by the methods described were

[34] An evaluation of summer fallow is presented by O. R. Matthews in *U.S.D.A. Cir.* 886, 1951.
[35] *U.S.D.A. Cir.* 700, 1944.

as follows: fall plowed and worked level, 10.8 bushels; fall plowed and left rough, 12.5 bushels; spring plowed, 12.3 bushels; and summer plowed, 7.3 bushels. Furthermore, some tillage of land to be spring plowed is frequently advisable. This preliminary preparation should be given shortly after harvest in order to kill weeds and should leave crop residues largely on the surface. Tillage during the fallow year should be sufficient to control weeds and should leave the soil rough and preferably cloddy with crop residues on the surface. The importance of preventing vegetative growth on fallow is shown by the fact that in Nebraska [36] fallow land left untilled until June contained 60 per cent less moisture in the fall than did fallow soil kept free of vegetation.

There are many data to show the value of a well-managed fallow on storage of soil moisture. Mathews [37] reports the storage of 5.3 inches of water from an annual precipitation of 19.6 inches as an average for 20 years. The length of the fallow averaged 12.5 months. Also, Zook and Weakley found an average storage of 5.3 inches of water, or 36.3 per cent, during a 24-year period in Nebraska with an annual precipitation varying from 10.2 to 28.1 inches and averaging 20 inches.[37a] The amount of stored water also varied greatly from year to year, the lowest amount being 1.8 inches, or 8.5 per cent, and the highest 9.7 inches, or 41.7 per cent.

All crops usually grown under dryland farming conditions yield better when planted on fallow soil than when following another crop. The 30-year average results from the Akron, Colorado, station [38] are representative. The yields in bushels of the various crops grown on stubble and fallow land, respectively, were: wheat, 7.0 *vs.* 16.3; barley, 15.5 *vs.* 28.1; oats, 16.9 *vs.* 31.1; and corn, 12.6 *vs.* 17.5.

It will be noted that winter wheat yields especially well when grown on fallow. This result is in accord with those from various other stations. For example, the Washington station [39] reported a 15-year average yield of 42.6 bushels on fallow soil compared to 26.2 bushels in a wheat-corn rotation. The North Platte, Nebraska, station [40] obtained a 30-year average yield of 26.4 bushels on fallow and 15.7 bushels on wheat stubble. Likewise at Hays, Kansas,[41] the 28-year average yield

[36] *Nebraska Agr. Exp. Sta. Bull.* 362, 1944.

[37] *U.S.D.A. Cir.* 886, 1951.

[37a] *U.S.D.A. Tech. Bull.* 1007, 1950.

[38] *U.S.D.A. Cir.* 700, 1944.

[39] *Washington Agr. Exp. Sta. Bull.* 344, 1937.

[40] *Nebraska Agr. Exp. Sta. Bull.* 362, 1944.

[41] *Kansas Agr. Exp. Sta. Bull.* 273 and unpublished data. Reported in *Nebraska Bull.* 362.

was 24.4 bushels on fallow, compared to 15.4 bushels under continuous cropping. In view of the marked increase in yield of wheat when grown on fallow and the high value of the crop per acre, it is generally considered advisable to use any fallowed soil on the farm for this crop.[42] It should be remembered, however, that fallow is most effective in years of normal and subnormal precipitation and that in unusually wet years wheat on fallowed ground may lodge badly.

Fig. 50. Winter wheat after summer fallow (*left*) and after rye (*right*). The yield after fallow was 20.2 bushels per acre, but the crop was a failure after rye. The greater growth of the wheat on the left edge of the right-hand plot is due to the moisture obtained from the unplanted soil between the plots. This "border effect" is often seen in field experimental work. From *Nebraska Agr. Exp. Sta. Bull.* 362, 1944. Courtesy of L. L. Zook. Used with permission.

Corn has not especially benefited by being grown on fallowed soil, and at Hays, Kansas,[43] spring wheat has proved to be one of the crops least benefited by fallowing. The 38-year average yield of spring wheat on fallow was 9.5 bushels, compared to 7.1 bushels under annual cropping.

The question of whether it is advisable to use fallow rather than grow a crop every year is pertinent. The problem has been carefully studied by several dryland stations. The 28-year average wheat yield in Nebraska,[40] reduced to an annual basis, was 3.8 bushels greater on fallow than on continuously cropped land plowed late. However, when the plowing was done early, 5.8 bushels more were produced under continuous cropping. The actual yields for the years the land was in wheat were 25.1 bushels for the fallow, 15.2 bushels for the early plowed

[42] *U.S.D.A. Cir.* 700, 1944.
[43] Unpublished data. Used with permission.

stubble, and 10.7 bushels for the late plowing. Likewise at Hays, Kansas,[43] the 38-year average yield of winter wheat on fallowed soil was 22.4 bushels, compared to 16.3 bushels for wheat grown annually. Calculated on an annual basis the wheat yielded 11.2 bushels on fallowed soil, which is 5.1 bushels less than the yield for annual cropping. Studies of this nature have shown that more wheat can be actually produced in a period of years by annual cropping than by growing the crop every other year on fallow. The time of plowing for the fallow and subsequent tillage, as well as the method of seedbed preparation in the annual cropping system, may have much to do with the results obtained. The actual cost per bushel of producing and harvesting the crop under the two systems is a pertinent consideration also. It is noteworthy, however, that a larger and larger acreage of land is being fallowed, and the acreage will doubtless increase in abnormally dry periods.

Rotations Including Fallow. When a crop rotation is followed with wheat planted on fallowed soil the effect of the other crops on yields may be seen. Studies of this nature at the North Platte station [44] produced the following 23-year average yields of wheat in the indicated cropping systems: oats, fallow, wheat, 27.4 bushels; corn, oats, fallow, wheat, 29.1 bushels; corn, oats, sorgo, fallow, wheat, 24.6 bushels; and fallow, wheat, 26.3 bushels. It is evident from these data that a rotation of crops was beneficial to wheat, except when sorgo preceded the fallow. The tendency for sorghums to reduce the soil-moisture content to a low level is well recognized.[45]

Rotations without Fallow. The Kansas experiment station and the United States Department of Agriculture have cooperated in studies of a large number of rotations at Hays, Kansas. The work, which started in 1908, shows that the yields of crops in general have not been affected greatly by the rotation followed unless the cropping system included fallow or some crop that left the soil especially dry. This observation is supported by the data in Table 98, which presents the highest and lowest 38-year average yields for various crops grown in different rotations. Rotations were not considered in which a crop was grown 2 years in succession or in which a fallow preceded the crop under consideration.

Crop yields are not the only factor to consider, however, in evaluating rotations for dry-farming areas. The matter of distribution of labor, maintenance of soil fertility, and control of soil blowing are also pertinent.

[44] *U.S.D.A. Tech. Bull.* 1007, 1950.
[45] *U.S.D.A. Cir.* 700, 1944.

TABLE 98. EFFECT OF DIFFERENT ROTATIONS ON YIELDS OF SEVERAL CROPS
OVER A 38-YEAR PERIOD *

Highest and Lowest Average Yields, bu.

Yield	Corn	Oats	Barley	Winter † Wheat	Spring ‡ Wheat	Kafir §
Highest	10.3	26.3	23.5	17.6	8.5	24.1
Lowest	8.1	23.4	19.0	. . .	5.9	21.7
Differences	2.2	2.9	4.5		2.6	2.4

* Unpublished data. Used with permission.
† 28-year average. First crop of wheat in a corn, barley, wheat, wheat rotation.
‡ 22-year average.   § 23-year average.

In planning a rotation Brandon and Mathews [46] suggest that crops
which reduce available moisture to a low level should be followed by
crops of low moisture requirement or by crops which are planted late
enough to permit moisture accumulation in the soil. If a fallow is to
be used it may well follow a crop which leaves the soil especially dry.
In discussing rotations for northwestern Nebraska, Werner et al.[47] suggest that the amount of moisture in the soil be considered in deciding
on which crop to plant. For example, it is recommended that potatoes
not be planted unless there are 3 feet or more of moist soil. Likewise,
fall wheat should not be seeded after a small grain unless the soil is
moist to a depth of 2 feet, and for a spring-seeded small grain to follow
a small grain successfully there should be 3 feet of moist soil.

In studying a considerable number of cropping systems in the Palouse
country the Washington experiment station [48] found that when spring
wheat followed winter wheat the other crops in the rotation had little
effect on spring wheat yields. Also, winter wheat yielded better after
corn than after sunflowers.

Rotations Including Legumes. Nitrogen supply is a factor which
frequently limits crop production in much of the dry-farming area. In
fact, if adequate moisture were assured nitrogen supply could well become the main limiting element in plant growth. Results obtained with
various cropping systems in the Palouse country [49] by the Washington

[46] *U.S.D.A. Cir.* 700, 1944.
[47] *Nebraska Agr. Exp. Sta. Bull.* 363, 1944.
[48] *Washington Agr. Exp. Sta. Bull.* 344, 1937.
[49] Soil-improving rotations for gently sloping soils and for more rolling lands
of the area were suggested by Soan, Jacklin, and Kaiser in *J. Amer. Soc. Agron.,*
31: 300, 1939.

experiment station illustrate the need for nitrogen in soils of the area and the value of legumes in the rotation (Table 99).

TABLE 99. YIELDS OF CROPS IN SEVERAL ROTATIONS IN THE
PALOUSE COUNTRY

Yields, Bu. (1920–1934)

Rotation	Winter Wheat	Spring Wheat	Field Peas
Wheat,* peas	31.6		18.5
Wheat, corn	26.2		
Wheat, spring wheat, peas	32.0	21.2	19.6
Wheat, spring wheat, corn	26.8	18.1	
Wheat, peas, spring wheat, corn	29.9	32.4	21.2
Wheat, clover 2 years, spring wheat, corn	31.0	29.0	
Spring wheat annually		19.1	
Spring wheat annually, manure each 3rd year		21.3	
Spring wheat, peas		31.0	20.1
Peas annually			20.2

* Winter wheat unless otherwise specified.

There is danger, however, in including a legume in the rotation in many seasons because of the stimulation of plant growth during the early part of the growing season, with a consequently increased moisture requirement and possible drought damage later. For example, Wheeting and Vandecaveye [50] tested the value of straw plowed under after alfalfa, as a means of reducing the supply of available nitrogen and the damage to the wheat resulting from an excess of this nutrient. They found that 1 ton of straw increased wheat yields by about 3 bushels and 2 tons produced a 5-bushel increase.

The moisture used by the green-manure crop is also a factor in its effect on the succeeding crop. Studies at Akron, Colorado,[51] including rye, peas, and sweet clover as green manures, showed the yields of following crops to be higher after rye than after the legumes. In this instance the results were ascribed to the earlier plowing of the rye and hence the removal of less moisture from the soil by the green manure. The sweet clover was more detrimental to the following crops than were the peas because it left the soil drier.

On the other hand, Duley and Russell [52] have shown that on eroded land the growing of a legume greatly improves soil productivity.

[50] *Washington Agr. Exp. Sta. Bull.* 344, 1937.

[51] *U.S.D.A. Cir.* 700, 1944.

[52] *Nebraska Agr. Exp. Sta. Ann. Rep.,* p. 7, 1948.

Seedbed Preparation. The method of seedbed preparation has considerable influence on crop yields under dry-farming conditions, primarily because of the differences in the amounts of moisture stored in the soil before planting and also the variation in the proportion of rainfall absorbed by the soil during the growing period. The data in Table 100 from the Hays, Kansas, station show the highest and lowest

TABLE 100. VARIATIONS IN CROP YIELDS DUE TO DIFFERENCE IN METHODS OF SEEDBED PREPARATION *

Average Yields, bu. per acre

Yields	Barley, 38 years	Kafir, 35 years	Milo, 32 years	Oats, 38 years	Spring Wheat, 38 years	Winter Wheat, 38 years
Highest	18.4	19.1	17.4	24.4	7.1	16.3
Lowest	14.5	13.6	11.6	18.7	5.4	8.9
Difference	3.9	5.5	5.8	5.7	1.7	7.4

* Unpublished data. Used with permission.

average yields of several crops grown annually with different methods of soil tillage. Early fall plowing or listing or early fall disking, followed by plowing or listing, proved preferable to late fall or spring plowing or listing. Subsoiling, in addition to plowing, was not of sufficient benefit to warrant the expense, except for milo.

Studies have been conducted involving use of more modern methods of soil tillage than were available in the early years of the work. The results from some of these practices, applied for wheat grown annually, are of interest. The 8-year average yields in bushels from four replications for the indicated tillage methods are: one-way, 19.6; chisel, 18.4; plow, 18.6; and subsurface, 19.3.[53] The yields indicate little difference in the effectiveness of the cultural methods studied under the conditions prevailing at the Hays station.

Rotation Studies in Western Canada.[54] Rotation experiments under dryland farming conditions have been conducted on some eight Dominion experimental farms in three western Canadian provinces. Some of these studies have been in operation since 1911. A summation of results has been presented by Hopkins and Leahey.[55] In most loca-

[53] From a mimeographed release. Used with permission.

[54] Although results of experiments under dry-farming conditions in Canada are similar in many respects to those obtained in the United States, it seems well to consider the Canadian work briefly because of the difference in latitude.

[55] *Can. Dep. Agr. Pub.* 761, 1944.

tions the experiments have involved a comparison between a 3-year or 4-year grain-farming rotation and one or more mixed-farming cropping systems. The rotation for grain production consisted of summer fallow, wheat, wheat, and sometimes oats. The mixed-farming rotations usually included a summer fallow followed by wheat, 2 or more years of hay, corn, and oats. Sometimes potatoes, barley, an annual hay crop, and a second year of summer fallow and of wheat were included. The sequence of crops was not always the same in the different experiments, and 1 or more applications of manure were made. At times green-manuring crops were also included.

In general a summer fallow was highly beneficial to the succeeding wheat crop, although in some locations receiving more than average precipitation the benefit was not great. For example, at Morden in Manitoba, with a precipitation of 19.5 inches, the 20-year average yield of wheat after fallow was 27.5 bushels and that of the second wheat crop (wheat after wheat) was 23.7 bushels. For a 10-year period wheat after corn yielded 26.5 bushels and after summer fallow 28.3 bushels. On the average, the second year of wheat after a summer fallow yielded very much less than the first crop, as is shown by an average yield in 12 comparisons of 23.2 bushels for the first crop and 15.8 bushels for the second crop.

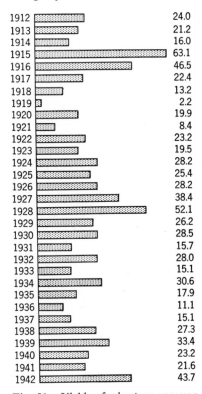

Year	Yield
1912	24.0
1913	21.2
1914	16.0
1915	63.1
1916	46.5
1917	22.4
1918	13.2
1919	2.2
1920	19.9
1921	8.4
1922	23.2
1923	19.5
1924	28.2
1925	25.4
1926	28.2
1927	38.4
1928	52.1
1929	26.2
1930	28.5
1931	15.7
1932	28.0
1933	15.1
1934	30.6
1935	17.9
1936	11.1
1937	15.1
1938	27.3
1939	33.4
1940	23.2
1941	21.6
1942	43.7

Fig. 51. Yields of wheat on summer fallow at the Dominion experiment station at Lethbridge, Alberta. Thirty-one-year average yield was 25.5 bushels. The great effect exerted by climatic conditions on crop yields even when good cultural practices are used is shown by this figure. Droughts are more frequent in dry-farming areas than in more humid climates, and often several dry years come in a row or close together. For example, a wheat farmer would have had a difficult time between 1918 and 1921 unless well financed, whereas from 1926 to 1930 he would have fared well. The average precipitation at Lethbridge is 15.76 inches. From *Can. Dep. Agr. Pub.* 761, 1948.

Sometimes the summer fallow resulted in a damaging infestation of weeds in the succeeding wheat crop. This situation pertained particularly in the grain rotations. An application of ammonium phosphate proved very helpful in controlling annual weeds in wheat in a number of cases.

In the black soil and gray wooded soil areas, which receive more rainfall than the brown and dark brown soils, the mixed-farming rotations proved superior in total crop production to the grain-crop rotations. However, this result did not hold true in the drier soil areas. The results from a series of rotations of different length at Lethbridge, Alberta, where the annual precipitation is 15.76 inches, are of interest in showing the value of a summer fallow in different cropping systems. It will also be noticed that wheat yields in the grain rotations are higher, with one exception, than in the mixed-farming systems. The data are presented in Table 101.

TABLE 101. YIELDS OF WHEAT AFTER SUMMER FALLOW IN DIFFERENT ROTATIONS AND UNDER CONTINUOUS CROPPING *

	Yields of Wheat, bu. per acre	
Type of Cropping	31-Year Average	Average for Last 10 Years
Continuous	12.3	10.0
2-year S.F.†—W.	27.4	27.7
3-year S.F.—W.—W.	25.5	23.9
6-year S.F.‡—W.—W.—O.—H.—H.	21.8 ‖	17.8
6-year S.F.—W.§—O.—S.F.‡—H.—O.	29.5	32.0
5-year S.F.‡—W.—W.—Sw. cl.—Sw. cl.	22.8 ¶	17.5

* Compiled from data in Table 12, *Can. Dep. Agr. Pub.* 761, 1944.
† S.F. = summer fallow; W. = wheat; O. = oats; H. = hay; Sw. cl. = sweet clover.
‡ Manured.   ‖ For first crop when wheat is grown more than 1 year.
§ Winter wheat.   ¶ 21-year average.

Green manuring has not proved a valuable practice in western Canada, and the crop increases from applications of animal manure have been somewhat uncertain. Table 102 gives the results of trials with green and animal manure at four experiment stations. At the Lethbridge station, plowing under an entire sweet-clover crop produced only a slightly larger yield of wheat than plowing under the stubble after harvesting sweet-clover hay. The 15-year average yield for the first practice was 16.3 bushels and for the second 14.1 bushels.

TABLE 102. EFFECT OF GREEN MANURE AND ANIMAL MANURE ON YIELDS
OF WHEAT *

Average Yields of Wheat, bu. per acre

Treatment in Fallow Year	Brandon, 15 years	Indian Head, 9 years	Scott, 13 years	Lacombe, 9 years
Summer fallow	35.0	36.1	21.9	37.6
Peas plowed under in early fall	33.8	33.5	21.6	36.3
Peas plowed under in blossom	32.5	32.6	21.2	36.5
Summer fallow, 12 tons manure	36.4	40.2	26.4	40.9

* Can. Dep. Agr. Pub. 761, 1944.

ROTATIONS ON IRRIGATED LAND

Although the acreage of land in humid climates where supplemental irrigation is practiced has increased rapidly since 1946 and now constitutes a considerable total, the present discussion will be limited to cropping systems which have been studied on irrigated areas in the arid or semiarid regions of the West. Crops included in the rotations will of course vary with the location of the project, and all the studies made of cropping systems under irrigation cannot be reviewed.

Rotations in Montana. Among the studies of longest duration are those started by the Montana station in 1912. These include continuous cropping and 2-, 3-, 4-, and 6-year rotations. Some of the data collected are presented in Table 103. No manure or fertilizer was

TABLE 103. YIELDS OF SEVERAL CROPS GROWN CONTINUOUSLY AND IN
ROTATIONS OF DIFFERENT LENGTHS *

Average Yields, 1912–1941 †

Cropping System	Bu. per Acre of					Tons of Beets
	Flax	Wheat	Oats	Corn	Potatoes	
Continuous	6.8	15.7	33.0	23.0	119.2	7.79
2-year rotations ‡	...	31.6	71.3	40.2	165.9	8.07
3-year rotations ‡	...	...	61.1	37.2	175.6	7.70
4-year rotations	...	...	90.5	...	219.2	7.72

* Montana Agr. Exp. Sta. Bull. 414, 1943.
† In a few cases data for 24 years in place of 30 years have been included.
‡ Results from one to three rotations.

applied, and only the 4-year rotations contained legumes. The data show the great advantage, in terms of increased yields, of growing crops in rotations, with the exception of beets, even when no soil-improving crop is included. Results for the 4-year rotations illustrate the benefits of having legumes in the cropping system for oats and potatoes but not for beets.

Applications of manure proved highly beneficial to potatoes and beets in the 2-year rotations and to beets in the 3-year rotations. Increases in oats were around 8 to 9 bushels.

A study of crop yields by 6-year periods shows that neither the 2- nor the 3-year rotations maintained yields throughout the experimental period. Furthermore, the applications of manure failed to maintain soil productivity as measured by crop yields at the beginning and close of the tests. On the contrary, in 4-year rotations, including 2 years of alfalfa, the yields of oats increased during the experimental period and the yields of potatoes were maintained for 24 years. Some decrease in potato production occurred during the last 6-year period. Beet yields, however, were only maintained for 18 years and then decreased markedly during the last two 6-year periods. The investigators ascribe this decrease to the reduction in supplies of available nutrients, especially phosphorus, and to an unbalanced nutrient supply which increased susceptibility of the young plants to disease.

Yields of crops grown continuously for a long period of time without addition of manure or plant nutrients, aside from the quantities that may have been contained in the irrigation water, decreased markedly. For example, the yields of several crops for the first and last 6-year periods, respectively, were as follows: oats, 40.9 bushels *vs.* 29.0 bushels; wheat, 25.4 bushels *vs.* 14.9 bushels; potatoes, 173.6 bushels *vs.* 72.7 bushels; and alfalfa, 4.3 tons *vs.* 2.9 tons.

Washington Rotations. A large number of rotations were tested at the irrigation branch experiment station in Washington, and some of the results for the period 1938–1945 are contained in Table 104. The data illustrate the advantage of growing the four crops considered in rotations rather than annually. Corn followed sugar beets more advantageously than it did wheat or potatoes. On the other hand, wheat did equally well after corn or potatoes, but potatoes yielded much more when planted after wheat than after corn or sugar beets. The introduction of a legume into the rotation increased the yields of all other crops, and as was to be expected pasturing sweet clover was more beneficial to following crops than was mowing it for hay. Why potatoes yielded less when planted on sweet-clover sod than when following a corn crop grown on the sod is difficult to explain.

TABLE 104.   YIELDS OF SEVERAL CROPS GROWN IN DIFFERENT ROTATIONS
UNDER IRRIGATION *

Average Yields, bu. or tons

Rotation	Corn	Wheat	Potatoes	Sugar Beets
Corn annually	18.4			
Corn, potatoes	23.6		0.70	
Corn, wheat	24.5	30.4		
Corn, sugar beets	34.5			5.7
Wheat annually		22.7		
Wheat, potatoes		30.9	1.29	
Potatoes annually			0.37	
Sugar beets annually				4.9
Potatoes, sugar beets			0.44	5.4
Wheat, sweet-clover hay 2 years, potatoes, sugar beets		40.4	2.63	7.0
Wheat, sweet-clover pasture 2 years, potatoes, sugar beets		32.0	3.69	7.6
Wheat, sweet-clover hay 2 years, potatoes, corn	42.6	31.1	2.14	
Wheat, sweet-clover hay 2 years, corn, potatoes	45.2	47.9	2.88	
Wheat, alfalfa 3 years, potatoes, sugar beets, corn	57.1	40.8	5.75	12.2

* *Washington Agr. Exp. Sta. Bull.* 481, 1946.

A series of rotations similar to the last one in Table 104, but in which the sequence of the crops following alfalfa varied, was studied at the Washington station.   Generally the crop growing immediately after alfalfa was benefited most and those planted 3 years after plowing the sod were benefited least.   For example, sugar beets averaged 14.5 tons the first year after alfalfa and only 7.8 tons when grown the third year after the legume.

CASH-CROP vs. LIVESTOCK FARMING

The interpretation of the terms livestock and grain farming varies somewhat in different regions and to some extent with time.   Early concepts of a livestock farm included the feeding of all crops grown on the farm and the purchase of little if any feed, although some grain was bought, especially in poor crop years.   In more recent years, the purchase of concentrated feeds has become a common practice in many localities, and even hay is bought rather extensively in states where a large number of livestock are kept on a limited acreage.   This situation applies more generally to dairy farms in the densely populated East.

On the other hand, many men who consider themselves livestock farmers produce from one to several cash crops, thus diversifying their farming enterprises. This type of farm organization is sometimes designated
as "mixed farming."

Also, ideas of what constitutes a cash-crop farm have changed to a
certain extent. In earlier years, a farmer who sold most of his crops
but kept several cows, a few hogs, and a flock of poultry was considered a cash-crop operator, even though he produced his own meat, eggs,
and milk and might obtain some income from the sale of such products.
At present many farm operators buy their milk and meat and possibly
their eggs. Many grain farmers, however, still keep a cow, a few chick-
ens, and a sow or two.

In livestock farming the above-ground parts of crops are harvested
and manure is returned for soil improvement. The grain farmer primarily harvests just the grain or marketable portion of his crops and
leaves the remainder on the land for soil betterment.

Rotations on Grain and Livestock Farms. Cropping systems on
farms devoted to livestock enterprises are planned primarily to supply
the feed required by the animals. The production of adequate hay is
the first requirement. Generally, also, greater attention is being given
to more and better pastures than in years past. Pasture-improvement
practices are being stressed in all parts of the country. Grain crops are
selected from the standpoint of the production of the greatest amount of
digestible nutrients per acre and also with the view of being able to
substitute one crop for another in the event of a poor yield of one feed
crop. Cropping systems are usually longer in livestock than in grain
farming and may contain several years of hay. Accordingly, not so
much attention is given to the use of catch crops because of the supply
of manure and the sods available for plowing.

Effect on Soil Productivity of Cash and Livestock Farming. In
planning the cropping systems on many of their experimental fields
which cover the state, workers at the Illinois station have included both
cash and livestock programs. In the livestock system of soil management manure, including litter, in proportion to the crop yields during
the previous rotation, is applied to corn for the following rotation.[56] On
some plots manure alone is applied, on others limestone, manure, and
rock phosphate.

[56] In recent years the amount of manure has been calculated on the basis of
the sale of one-third of the crops and the feeding of two-thirds of them. On
this basis 1 ton of manure can be used for every ton of crops produced. The
amounts applied have varied from less than 1 ton per acre to almost 4 tons,
depending on the productivity of the soil.

In the grain or residues system, corn stover, straw from small grains or soybeans, catch crops, and the second growth of clover or other legume hay are plowed under. These residues are used alone, with limestone, limestone and rock phosphate, and with limestone, rock phosphate, and potassium. The comparative yields of crops grown under both systems are of interest. The average value [57] of the increased yield per acre resulting from manure applications has been $3.92 on 21 fields.[58] The range in value has been from −$1.51 to $7.14. In contrast, the average value per acre per year of the increases from crop residues on 23 fields has been $1.24, with a range from −$1.51 to $4.48. Although the actual returns will vary with crop values the relative returns will be about the same. The superiority of livestock farming over cash-crop farming is evident when no soil treatment in addition to manure or residues is used. If the treatment which gave the greatest increase on each field is considered, a value of $11.02 is obtained as an average for 21 fields under the livestock system. With the grain-farming system, however, the "best treatment" gave an increase valued at $8.28 for 24 fields. It is evident that, when lime, rock phosphate, or potassium or a combination of them is used as soil needs require, in addition to manure or crop residues, the superiority of the livestock system is much reduced.

The long-time average yields of several crops from ten fields receiving manure, lime, and rock phosphate in one case and residues, lime, and rock phosphate in the other, respectively, were as follows: corn, 62.7 bushels *vs.* 57.0 bushels; oats, 55.4 bushels *vs.* 52.3 bushels; and wheat, 32.2 bushels *vs.* 30.4 bushels. It will be noted that there is not a great difference in the yields of the crops sighted under the two farming systems. Although the data are not given, it is noteworthy that when potassium was included in the treatment under the residues system the yields were yet closer together. It can be concluded, therefore, that, under Illinois conditions, when suitable fertilizers are used in conjunction with crop residues crop production can be maintained at a level not much lower than that obtained with a livestock system including the use of phosphate and lime. Possibly with the use of appreciable quantities of commercial nitrogen the difference between the two systems can be further reduced.

The Ohio station has also made a direct comparison between cash-crop and livestock farming. The rotation consisted of corn, soybeans

[57] *Illinois Agr. Exp. Sta. Bull.* 516, 1945.

[58] In making the calculations the following prices for crops were used: wheat and soybeans, $1.00 per bushel; corn, $0.50 per bushel; oats, $0.30 per bushel; and hay $10.00 per ton.

for seed, wheat, and mixed hay.   Three hundred and twenty pounds
of 0-20-0 fertilizer was applied for corn and 240 pounds for wheat.   In
the livestock system 15.5 tons of manure were also applied for corn.
Wheat grain was sold and the rest of the crops fed to cattle confined to
a covered shed, the straw being used for bedding in livestock farming.
The manure accumulated in this way was of superior quality, containing
16 pounds of nitrogen, 1.8 pounds of phosphorus, and 10 pounds of
potassium per ton.   The grain-farming plan called for the sale of corn,
soybeans, and wheat seed and the return of all residues to the soil, including plowing under of the clover crop.   During the last 10 of the 30
years for which results are reported (in Table 105), sweet clover was

TABLE 105.   COMPARISON OF LIVESTOCK AND GRAIN FARMING *

Farming	30-Year Average Yields, bu. or tons			
System	Corn	Soybeans	Wheat	Clover
Livestock	75.8	24.9	34.0	2.34
Grain	68.8	22.4	29.3	...
Difference	7.0	2.5	4.7	...

* *Ohio Agr. Exp. Sta. Book* Series B-1, 1951, p. 158.

substituted for the mixed clovers previously grown in the grain system
and the seed was harvested, leaving the straw on the land.   These data
show livestock farming to be superior to grain farming in maintaining
yields under the conditions of the experiment.   Furthermore, at the end
of 40 years the soil which received manure contained 2,550 pounds of
nitrogen per acre and that receiving crop residues 2,240 pounds per
acre.   In considering these data it should be remembered that the manure was handled in such a way as to avoid mechanical losses and those
due to leaching and volatilization.   It was applied to the land only a
short time before plowing.

The West Virginia station compared livestock with grain-farming
methods using three rotations.   The crops were harvested, fed, and the
manure returned to the soil devoted to livestock farming.   As representative of cash-crop farming, the grains were sold and the straw and
stover and the second crop of hay were left on the land.

Invariably 200 pounds of 0-20-0 per acre per year were applied.   The
results for the period 1925–1936 for crops appearing in both systems of
farming are presented in Table 106.   In this comparison the livestock
system of soil management proved slightly superior to the cash-crop
system so far as yields of all crops are concerned.   The rather marked
difference in the yield of wheat was due in part to the lateness of seeding

TABLE 106. COMPARISON OF CROP YIELDS UNDER LIVESTOCK AND GRAIN-
FARMING SYSTEMS *

Yields, bu. or tons per acre (1925–1936)

Rotation	Farming System	Corn	Wheat	Oats	Hay
Corn, soybeans,	Livestock	72.8	22.7		1.41
wheat, hay †	Grain	69.1	17.7		1.22
Corn, oats,	Livestock	69.7	...	22.7	1.12
clover	Grain	68.1	...	22.0	1.01
Corn, soybeans	Livestock	65.8	...	...	...
	Grain	60.2	...	...	...

* *West Virginia Agr. Exp. Sta. Bull.* 306, 1943.

† Clover and timothy harvested for hay in livestock system and for seed in grain system.

after the harvest of soybeans for seed in the grain system. Also, the 3- and 4-year rotations that contained a sod crop produced more corn than the corn-soybean rotation.

A comparison of the value of manure and crop residues was made by the Indiana experiment station using a 3-year rotation. In the grain-farming system, the corn stover, straw, and second cutting of clover were left on the land. In livestock farming all crops were removed, and 1 ton of manure for each ton of crop harvested, except wheat grain, was applied. The yields under the two farming systems, with addition of lime and lime plus fertilizer, are shown in Table 107. The fertilizer

TABLE 107. COMPARISON OF THE EFFECTS OF CROP RESIDUES AND MANURE
ON CROP YIELDS

Average Yields, bu. and lb. per acre

Soil Treatment	Corn		Wheat		Hay	
	1942–1947	1948–1950	1942–1947	1948–1950	1942–1947	1948–1950
Lime, manure	62	62	16	13	2,200	2,300
Lime, residues	38	47	9	9	1,300	700
Difference	24	15	7	4	900	1,600
Lime, manure, 2-12-20 *	90	76	28	22	5,300	5,100
Lime, residues, 2-12-20 *	79	74	23	20	4,800	3,200
Difference	11	2	5	2	500	1,900
Lime, manure, 0-12-0	79	71	25	20	4,200	3,500
Lime, residues, 0-12-0	51	52	18	14	3,400	1,900
Difference	28	19	7	6	800	1,600

* Twelve per cent potash was used after 1947.

was used at the rate of 300 pounds per acre for wheat and 100 pounds drilled in corn rows. The superiority of the livestock system on this soil is very apparent. The data indicate an insufficient supply of both available phosphorus and potassium under both systems of soil management. The superiority of livestock farming appears to be due largely to a greater supply of available potassium.

LIMITATION IN ROTATION BENEFITS

In studying the value of rotations, consideration should be given to the fact that crops other than legumes add no nutrients to the soil. Consequently, crop residues or manure made from crops grown on the soil to which the manure is applied simply return to the soil part of the nutrients extracted from it by the plants (with the exception of nitrogen in the case of inoculated legumes). With this thought in mind it is evident that the full benefit of a rotation cannot be realized if the deficiency of one or more nutrients limits plant growth, although it is, of course, true that certain crops may extract from the soil more of a given nutrient or nutrients than another crop and return it as residue in a more available form. The inability of a rotation to produce high yields in a soil with marked deficiencies is illustrated by the results of a test in Kentucky shown in Table 108. The rotation consisted of corn, wheat, and legumes plus grass. Similar results were obtained on a Cecil clay loam in North Carolina.[59]

TABLE 108. A GOOD ROTATION DOES NOT INSURE HIGH CROP YIELDS *

Average Yields, bu. or lb.

Soil Treatment	Corn 16 Crops	Wheat 14 Crops	Hay 14 Crops
Lime and phosphate	57.2	13.2	3,720
No lime or phosphate	30.0	4.8	1,568
Difference	27.2	8.4	2,152

* *Kentucky Agr. Exp. Sta. Bull.* 374, 1937.

Many of the rotations started years ago were inadequately fertilized and frequently the fertilizer used was not properly balanced to meet soil deficiencies and crop requirements. Other factors which greatly influence the results obtained in rotation studies are adequate liming, suitable tillage practices, and drainage. Too often, even in recently planned experiments, one or more of these factors has not been given sufficient

[59] *North Carolina Agr. Exp. Sta. Bull.* 331, 1942.

consideration. Replication is another precaution for the procuring of dependable results which is frequently slighted.

REFERENCES

Anderson, P. J. Growing tobacco in Connecticut. *Connecticut Agr. Exp. Sta. Bull.* 564, 1953.

Batchell, M. S., Salter, R. M., and Wachter, H. L. Tobacco culture and fertility tests. *Ohio Agr. Exp. Sta. Bull.* 590, 1938.

Brandon, J. F., and Mathews, O. R. Dry land rotation and tillage experiments at the Akron (Colorado) field station. *U.S.D.A. Cir.* 700, 1944.

Chucka, J. A., Hawkins, A., and Brown, B. E. Potato fertilizer—rotation studies on Aroostook farm, 1927–1941. *Maine Agr. Exp. Sta. Bull.* 414, 1943.

Daniel, H. A., and Finnell, H. H. Climatic conditions and suggested cropping systems for northwestern Oklahoma. *Oklahoma Agr. Exp. Sta. Cir.* 83, 1939.

Hansen, D., and Post, A. H. Irrigated crop rotations. *Montana Agr. Exp. Sta. Bull.* 414, 1943.

Hartwell, B. L., and Damon, S. C. A twenty-year comparison of different rotations of corn, potatoes, rye, and grass. *Rhode Island Agr. Exp. Sta. Bull.* 167, 1916.

Hopkins, E. S. Long-time crop and culture rotations. *Soil Sci. Soc. Amer. Proc.,* 10: 295, 1945.

Hopkins, E. S., and Leahey, A. Crop rotations in the prairie provinces. *Can. Dep. Agr. Pub.* 761, 1944.

Matthews, E. M., and Hutcheson, T. B. Experiments on flue-cured tobacco. *Virginia Agr. Exp. Sta. Bull.* 329, 1941.

Nelson, C. E., and Larson, C. A. Crop rotations under irrigation at the irrigation branch experiment station near Prosser, Washington. *Washington Agr. Exp. Sta. Bull.* 481, 1946.

Odland, T. E., Smith, J. B., and Damon, S. C. The influence of crop plants on those which follow: IV. *Rhode Island Agr. Exp. Sta. Bull.* 243, 1934.

Puhr, L. F., and Worzella, W. W. Fertility maintenance and management of South Dakota soils. *South Dakota Agr. Exp. Sta. Cir.* 92, 1952.

Roberts, G. Legumes in cropping systems. *Kentucky Agr. Exp. Sta. Bull.* 374, 1937.

Roberts, G. E., Kinney, J., and Freeman, J. F. Soil management and fertilization for tobacco. *Kentucky Agr. Exp. Sta. Bull.* 379, 1938.

Schafer, E. G., Wheeting, L. C., and Vandecaveye, S. C. Crop rotations—effect of crop rotations on succeeding crops—effect of crop rotations on productivity of the soil. *Washington Agr. Exp. Sta. Bull.* 344, 1937.

Sears, O. H. Soybeans—their effect on soil productivity. *Illinois Agr. Exp. Sta. Bull.* 456, 1939.

Shaw, B. T. Long-time crop and fertilizer rotations. *Soil Sci. Soc. Amer. Proc.,* 10: 300, 1945.

Stinson, F. A., and Murwin, H. F. Flue-cured tobacco growing in Ontario. Canadian Dept. of Agr., *Farmer's Bull.* 101, 1941.

Terman, G. L. Green-manure crops and rotations for Maine potato soils. *Maine Agr. Exp. Sta. Bull.* 474, 1949.

Thorne, D. W., and Peterson, H. B. *Irrigated Soils,* second edition. Blakiston Co., Philadelphia, 1954.

Weidemann, A. G., and Millar, C. E. Results from long-time field experiments in Hillsdale soil. *Mich. Agr. Exp. Sta. Bull.* 366, 1951.

Werner, H. O., Kiesselbach, T. A., and Goss, R. W. Dry-land rotation experiments with potatoes in northwestern Nebraska. *Nebraska Agr. Exp. Sta. Bull.* 363, 1944.

Williams, C. B., Jackson, S. K., and Meacham, F. T. Influence of crop rotation and soil treatments upon the yield of crops in rotations on Cecil clay loam. *North Carolina Agr. Exp. Sta. Bull.* 256, 1928.

Zook, L. L., and Weakley, H. E. Crop rotation and tillage experiments at the North Platte (Neb.) substation. *U.S.D.A. Tech. Bull.* 1007, 1950.

19

A Summary of Old Field Experiments

Of the several procedures used to determine plant response to the application of various materials to a soil and the soil deficiencies that are limiting plant growth, the field-plot method is accepted as the most dependable. Other systems of measuring soil deficiencies are usually calibrated by comparing the results with those obtained from field experiments. Although field trials have some very distinct advantages over other methods of studying soil deficiencies, they also possess some definite limitations.

It will be recalled that Boussingault is credited with conducting the first field tests on his farm at Bechelbronn, Alsace, in 1834. His "balance sheet" records show the weights of dry matter, carbon, hydrogen, oxygen, nitrogen, and mineral matter removed in the crops of a rotation, the quantities applied in the soil treatments, and the differences which must have been taken from the soil, water, and air. Some five rotations were studied in this way, and data were collected on the composition of crops at different stages of growth. Furthermore, he did not overlook problems in animal nutrition.

Much time and large sums of money have been expended in carrying on the field experiments established in the United States between 1876 and 1915. Although the plans of these experiments were not in accord with present-day ideas of the requirements of a scientific investigation, the results obtained were the basis of many modern field studies and have also contributed valuable information which has aided in bringing about the high level of crop production experienced in many areas today. Accordingly, a brief review of the plans and results obtained from some of these older studies should not be out of order. The review will be approached under the following headings.

Discussion Topics

The Rothamsted experiment station.
Field studies in Illinois.
Fertilizer experiments in Pennsylvania.

395

The Ohio experimental farms.
Missouri's Sanborn Field.
The Rhode Island rotation tests.
Alabama's old rotation.
Cylinder studies in New Jersey.
Washington's wheat cultural experiments.

THE ROTHAMSTED EXPERIMENT STATION

The oldest agricultural experiment station now in operation is located near the village of Harpenden, about 24 miles from London. The soil on the farm is of heavy texture, being described as "rather a heavy loam resting upon chalk, capable of producing good wheat when well manured; not sufficiently heavy for beans, but too heavy for good turnips or barley." [1] The uniformity of the soil fits it admirably for field experimental work. Although the climate of this part of England is considered quite humid, the 60-year average rainfall at Rothamsted is 28.34 inches. Fortunately, the precipitation is well distributed, February, March, April, and May being the driest months and October and November receiving the heaviest rainfall.

Early History of the Farm. The land in the area has a long agricultural history, as relics have been found at Rothamsted of colonists who had come by the first century B.C. These early Celtic farmers used a large ox-drawn plow with iron colter and share and a moldboard. Two of their practices, the applying of chalk to the land and growing of small grains, are still followed. The area was dominated by the Romans until the fifth century, and they were replaced by the Saxons in the sixth century. The Celtic farmers remained during the changes in domination. At this time the farm was given the name of "Rochamstede."

In 1623 the estate was sold to Daine Armi, the daughter of a Flemish refugee, and became the property of her son, John Whittewronge. In 1763, the manor passed into the hands of the Bennet family through the marriage of Elizabeth Whittewronge to Thomas Bennet. The marriage of May Bennet to Thomas Lawes transferred the property to the Lawes family. The son, John Bennet Lawes, inherited the estate in 1783, and his son, bearing the same name, became the owner of the 250 acres in 1834 and founded the experiment station. The station now comprises about 527 acres. Sir John Lawes was greatly interested in chemistry. In 1842 he obtained a patent for making superphosphate by treating mineral phosphates with sulfuric acid, a process devised by Liebig

---

[1] *The Book of the Rothamsted Experiments,* by A. D. Hall. E. P. Dutton & Co., New York, 1905. Used with permission.

(making use of bones) but not commercialized by him. Lawes later operated two large superphosphate factories.

By 1835 Lawes was carrying on pot experiments. These were expanded into field trials and rapidly increased in number. Finding himself in need of assistance he employed a German chemist named John Gilbert in 1843, which is the accepted date of the founding of the experiment station. Gilbert was more systematic and painstaking in his work than Lawes but was not so imaginative and original in his thinking. The two men worked together for nearly 60 years, Lawes dying in 1900 and Gilbert in 1901.

Organization of the Experiment Station. There are four main divisions of the station, namely, chemical, physical, biological, and statistical. Each of the fourteen departments is under the supervision of a head, who in turn is under a director who has charge of the entire station. A. D. Hall was the first director after Sir John Lawes and served from 1902 to 1912. He was followed by E. J. Russell, who in turn was replaced by W. G. Ogg in 1943.

Plan of the Field Experiments. The farm was divided into various fields for experimentation with different cropping systems. Some of the older fields most frequently referred to, the cropping systems followed, and the date and size of establishment are as follows:

1. Agdell; 4-year rotation: swedes, barley, clover or beans, wheat; 1848; 3 acres.

2. Barn; root crops continuously; 1843; 8 acres.

3. Park Grass Plots; sod continuously; 1856; 7 acres.

4. Broadbalk; wheat continuously; 1843; 11 acres.

5. Hoos; barley continuously; 1852; 5½ acres.

It is not feasible to go into detail concerning the soil treatments used in these experiments or the results obtained. It should be borne in mind, however, that Lawes was greatly concerned with Liebig's theory that plants obtain their nitrogen from the air in the form of ammonia. His early experiments did not support this theory. As a result the treatments of many of his field experiments were influenced by this controversy, and we find him using different nitrogen sources in varying amounts, with different combinations of minerals, and for comparison the mineral mixtures alone. Perhaps a somewhat detailed presentation of the treatments on the Broadbalk field are in order, especially since the results of this experiment are frequently referred to.

The field is divided into ½-acre plots, 351 yards long by 7 yards wide, with the exception of plot 20, which is ⅙ of an acre, and plots 2A and 2B, which are each about 3/10 of an acre. The plots are separated by an unplanted strip of soil. A tile drain runs down the center of each

TABLE 109. TREATMENT AND YIELDS OF BROADBALK FIELD ROTHAMSTED EXPERIMENT STATION, PERMANENT WHEAT, 1843–1949

Average Yields of Dressed Grain, bu. per acre

Plot No.	Annual Treatment	1844–1851	1852–1861	1862–1871	1872–1881	1882–1891	1892–1901	1902–1911	1912–1921	1922–1931	1932–1941	1942–1949*	98-Year Average
2A	Manure, 14 tons	...	...	...	...	...	...	32.3	23.5	20.4	28.0	30.2	...
2B	Manure, 14 tons	28.0	34.2	37.5	28.8	38.2	39.2	35.1	26.4	23.7	30.1	39.2	31.9
3–4	Not fertilized	17.2	16.0	14.4	10.3	12.5	12.3	10.9	7.9	9.0	15.3	18.4	12.6
5	Minerals †	...	18.4	15.5	12.1	13.8	14.9	13.5	9.0	11.5	16.5	20.2	14.4
6	Minerals, 206 lb. sulfate of ammonia ‡	...	27.2	25.7	19.1	24.6	23.1	21.4	15.0	16.3	22.5	25.6	22.0
7	Minerals, 412 lb. sulfate of ammonia	...	34.7	35.9	26.9	35.0	31.8	31.0	22.4	23.4	29.0	34.0	30.3
8	Minerals, 618 lb. sulfate of ammonia	...	36.1	40.5	31.2	38.2	38.5	37.2	25.4	23.4	31.9	38.4	34.0
9	Minerals, 275 lb. nitrate of soda §	...	...	...	...	...	28.2‖	28.3	19.8	20.2	25.7	28.1	...
10	412 lb. sulfate of ammonia	25.1	23.2	25.2	17.3	19.4	18.3	18.4	13.4	16.9	25.5	27.8	20.4
11	412 lb. sulfate of ammonia, 350 lb. super-phosphate	...	28.3	27.8	21.8	22.8	19.5	19.2	13.4	17.8	24.1	27.0	22.1
12	412 lb. sulfate of ammonia, 350 lb. super-phosphate, 366 lb. sodium sulfate	...	33.4	34.3	25.0	30.1	26.7	27.4	18.6	19.6	27.5	31.5	27.3
13	412 lb. sulfate of ammonia, 350 lb. super-phosphate, 200 lb. potassium sulfate	...	32.9	34.8	26.8	32.2	29.1	32.1	21.6	22.0	27.5	32.6	29.1
14	412 lb. sulfate of ammonia, 350 lb. super-phosphate, 280 lb. magnesium sulfate	...	33.5	34.3	26.5	31.2	25.0	25.0	17.4	20.2	27.6	32.2	...
15	Minerals, 412 lb. sulfate of ammonia	...	32.8	34.1	26.6	31.8	27.0	29.8	18.4	19.4	26.2	31.1	27.2
16	Minerals, 550 lb. nitrate of soda	...	...	...	...	37.8¶	32.3	32.5	23.3	23.2	31.5	37.6	27.7
17**	Minerals, 1 year and 412 lb., sulfate of ammonia next year	...	...	...	...	...	27.5	30.6	19.7	19.0	28.4	32.7	...
18††	Minerals, 1 year and 412 lb., sulfate of ammonia next year	...	31.7	31.5	25.8	32.9	16.8	14.3	9.3	11.4	15.6	19.3	27.9
19	1,889 lb. rape cake	...	18.6	16.8	11.7	13.9	27.4‡‡	25.5	14.6	17.7	26.4	31.7	14.7
20	Minerals without superphosphate, 412 lb. sulfate of ammonia	...	...	...	...	...	...	22.3§§	15.5‖	16.1‖	25.6	26.9	...

* Eight-year averages in this column.

† Minerals contain 350 lb. superphosphate, 200 lb. potassium sulfate, 100 lb. sodium sulfate, 100 lb. magnesium sulfate.

‡ $(NH_4)_2SO_4$ applied ⅓ in fall and ⅔ in spring, except on plot 15 where all is applied in the fall.

§ $NaNO_3$ is all applied in the spring. Plot 16 receives 2 applications a month apart.

‖ Eight-year average. §§ Six-year average.

** Yields for years nitrogen is applied.

†† Yields for years minerals are applied. ‡‡ Nine-year average.

¶ Seven-year average.

plot at a depth of 2 to 2½ feet and empties into a brick trench so that the drainage from each plot may be collected separately. The treatments varied during the first 8 years, so that only 3 of the plots have received uniform treatment since 1843. On the rest of the plots the treatments now in use were started in 1852. The field has grown wheat continuously since 1843 with the following modifications. Because of the severe infestation of weeds, especially wild oats and "black bent" grass (*Alopecurus agrestis*), all the plots were divided into five sections beginning at the western end of the field, and a system of fallowing was

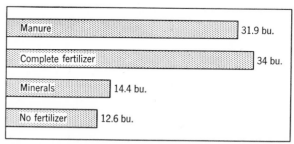

Fig. 52. Ninety-eight-year average wheat yields resulting from annual applications of manure, 14 tons, complete fertilizer, mineral nutrients without nitrogen, and no fertilizer at the Rothamsted experiment station.

instituted. During the 2-year period 1925–1927 the first three sections were fallowed. During the next 2-year period sections 4 and 5 were fallowed. In 1929–1930 the entire plots were cropped. Beginning in 1930–1931 one section of each plot has been fallowed each year.

The fertilization of the plots and the yields of grain are given in Table 109.

It should be remembered that, when these treatments were arranged, Lawes and Gilbert had in mind Liebig's contention that if plants were supplied with the minerals contained in their ash they would draw their nitrogen, carbon, and oxygen from the air. The "minerals" used were based on the composition of the ash of wheat and were supplemented with various sources of nitrogen. Also the "minerals" were used without nitrogen and nitrogen without minerals.

Perhaps the first criticisms that could be made of the plan of the experiment in the light of modern field-test techniques is the lack of replication and the fact that only one plot remained unfertilized. The length of time the experiment has run, however, entitles the data to careful consideration. Some observations which may be made in view of the data are as follows:

1. Wheat could be grown continuously on this land for a great many years and a relatively high yield maintained if it were not for the difficulty in controlling weeds.

2. Without fertilization the yield drops to a low level and remains virtually constant except for fluctuations due to seasonal differences. On a percentage basis variations in yield due to seasonal conditions are surprisingly large.

3. Yields from fertilizer treatment which do not include nitrogen are little higher than those from unfertilized soil.

4. When minerals are supplied the yields increase with increasing additions of nitrogen until the maximum of 618 pounds of $(NH_4)_2SO_4$ is reached. Whether further increases would result from additional nitrogen is not known.

5. Application of minerals plus liberal quantities of nitrogen result in yields equal to those from annual applications of 14 tons of animal manure.

6. With minerals, nitrate of soda appears to be somewhat more efficient in increasing yields than an equivalent quantity of sulfate of ammonia. Difference in time of application, however, makes this conclusion questionable.

7. Mineral nutrients are needed in addition to nitrogen for highest yields.

Other observations might be made on the basis of the effect of different treatments on soil characteristics, composition and weight of the grain, and baking quality of the flour made from the wheat. The comparative effect of the application of manure on the organic-matter content of the soil is cited in Chapter 6.

Space does not permit further discussion of these oldest field experiments. The student is urged, however, to spend at least a little time in reading some of the publications regarding them. It should be pointed out that the work at Rothamsted now includes innumerable studies in the field, laboratory, and greenhouse, concerning many of the most fundamental problems involved in soil management and crop production, and making use of the most modern techniques. The work of the station has also been expanded to include experiments at numerous places in England, including the Woburn station, established in 1876.

FIELD STUDIES IN ILLINOIS

Field-plot experiments were started in Illinois by George E. Morrow in 1876, and the plots still bear his name. These are the oldest experimental plots in this country. Originally there were 10 plots, 3 of which now remain. The original cropping systems were: plot 3, corn annually; plot 4, corn, oats; and plot 5, corn, corn, oats, clover + timothy, timothy, timothy. In 1901 the last rotation was changed to corn, oats, clover. According to the plans the soil was to receive no addition of manure or fertilizer. In 1904, however, each plot was divided into equal parts and the following system of treatments started. The two north quarters of each plot remained without additions. The southwest quarters received manure approximately in proportion to the quantity of crops removed, limestone, and rock phosphate. To the southeast quarters are applied manure as above described, limestone, and bone phosphate. Up to 1948 the quantity of limestone applied has totaled 8.85 tons per acre, of rock phosphate 6.6 tons, and of bone phosphate 1.65 tons. The manure used has totaled from 129 to 144 tons. The last application of limestone was for the 1943 crop, and no phosphate has been applied since 1925. In the corn-oats rotation on the southwest and southeast quarters of plot 4, a legume, usually sweet clover, has been seeded in the oats and turned under as a green manure since 1904. All the grain, straw, stover, and hay have been removed from all plots. Crop-yield data are available from 1888 until the present time, results for the years previous to 1888 having been lost.

Because corn is the crop appearing in all the cropping systems the yields of this crop offer the opportunity of comparing the effect of the three systems on soil productivity. The average yields for the 11 years in which corn was grown on the untreated plot in all three rotations are as follows: corn annually, 26.5 bushels; corn, oats, 34.4 bushels; and corn, oats, clover, 51.7 bushels. The benefit from the growing of corn and oats alternately is rather surprising, and the great advantage of including clover in the rotation is amazing. The value of rotating crops and of including clover in the cropping system is further emphasized by an average corn yield of 51.1 bushels for the years the plot growing the 3-year rotation was in corn without treatment and only 46.0 bushels for corresponding years from the continuous corn plot receiving lime, manure, and phosphates. Furthermore the corn-oats rotation plot without treatment grew only 33.5 bushels of corn, compared to 48.3 bushels from the corn continuous plot with manure, lime, and phosphate for corresponding years.

Another interesting study can be made of corn yields under each cropping system and from the plots treated with manure, lime, and phosphate. The data are for the years in which all the plots grew corn, hence the effects of varying climatic conditions are eliminated. The results show a yield of 50.4 bushels with annual cropping, 68.0 bushels under the corn-oats rotation, and 77.7 bushels for the rotation including corn, oats, and clover. It is also of interest to note that, for the same period of years, corn on untreated soil in the 3-year rotation produced an average yield of 55.9 bushels compared to 50.4 bushels on the treated soil under the continuous cropping system. The value of crop rotation and especially of a legume in the rotation is also shown by Fig. 53.

Applying the results from these plots to field conditions it is seen that should one wish to raise the same quantity of corn, let us say 2,000

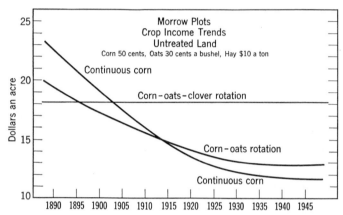

Fig. 53. The dollar value of crop rotation and of a legume in the rotation as shown by the results from the Morrow plots. It will be noted that the high acre value of corn, which made the return high for corn grown continuously in the early years, was soon overcome by the increased yields resulting from crop rotation, particularly when clover was included in the cropping system. Courtesy of F. C. Bauer.

bushels, it would take 83.4 acres if corn were grown annually without soil treatment and only 39.1 acres if the 3-year rotation were followed. Also, if the 3-year cropping system were used and the soil treated with lime, manure, and phosphate the acreage required to produce the 2,000 bushels of corn would be only 26.9.

A study of the effect on soil productivity of the cropping systems and of the soil treatments may be made by comparing the yields during the early years of the experiment with those obtained later. Accordingly, the yields of corn and of oats for the periods 1904–1928 and 1929–1951 are presented in Table 110. The yields of clover are not included because in several years the seeding failed and was replaced by soybeans. The footnotes designate the number of yields averaged in each case, and it will be noted that the numbers are not large for the 2- and 3-year rotations because only one plot was available for each treatment.

TABLE 110.   CORN AND OAT YIELDS FROM THE MORROW PLOTS

Cropping System	Corn Annually		Corn and Oats		Corn, Oats, Clover	
Soil Treatment	None	M.L.P.	None	M.L.P.	None	M.L.P.
			Corn			
1904–1928	25.0 *	39.7 *	35.1 †	60.6 †	49.3 ‡	67.8 ‡
1929–1951	22.9 §	53.9 §	32.0 †	77.5 †	53.5 ‖	82.8 ‖
			Oats			
1904–1928	...	...	34.0 ¶	59.2 ¶	45.1 **	62.7 **
1929–1951	...	...	34.3 ††	63.5 ††	52.8 **	71.2 **

* 25 crops.	‡ 9 crops.	‖ 7 crops.	** 8 crops.
† 12 crops.	§ 23 crops.	¶ 13 crops.	†† 11 crops.

The results show the beneficial effect both of crop rotation and of the soil treatment. It is noteworthy that the yields of corn and of oats during the second period with soil treatment and under all three cropping systems were appreciably higher than during the first period. This fact indicates a cumulative effect from the treatment. Also the increased yield of corn and oats on untreated soil in the 3-year rotation during the second period suggests an improvement in soil productivity due to the clover. It must be remembered, however, that averages of yields for a few years are greatly influenced by climatic conditions.

Some general idea of the change in the productivity of the soil that has taken place under the different cropping systems during the last 64 years can be obtained by comparing the average yield for the first 10 corn crops with that for the last 10 crops. The averages for the untreated soil in different cropping systems are: corn continuously, 40.9 bushels and 20.7 bushels; corn-oats, 41.9 bushels and 32.6 bushels; and for corn-oats-clover, 50.0 bushels and 51.0 bushels. Here again an increase rather than a decrease in the fertility of the soil in the 3-year rotation is indicated. This phenomenon is undoubtedly due to climatic conditions because during the first period there were 4 poor corn years and during the last period there was only 1 year in which the yield fell below 42 bushels per acre.

Further evidence of the effect of the cropping systems on the soil may be gained from a study of the organic-matter content of the soil from the different plots. Soil samples were collected in 1904, 1913, 1923, 1933, and 1943, and the data obtained from analyzing them are contained in Table 111. The samples were taken from corn plots unless otherwise designated.

TABLE 111. NITROGEN CONTENT IN SOIL FROM THE MORROW PLOTS, LB. PER ACRE

Cropping System	Corn Annually		Corn, Oats		Corn, Oats, Clover	
Soil Treatment	None	M.L.P.	None	M.L.P.	None	M.L.P.
1904	4,165	3,960	4,050 *	4,065 *	4,595	4,895
1913	3,510	3,910	3,900	4,260	4,340	4,750
1923	3,090	3,670	3,500	4,220	4,130 *	4,690 *
1933	2,890	3,450	3,220	4,040	3,810 †	4,450 †
1943	2,640	3,180	3,190	3,920	3,700	4,625

* Samples taken from oat plots.   † Samples drawn from clover plots.

It will be recalled that the plots received no manure, lime, or fertilizer previous to 1904, and in consequence any differences in nitrogen content at that time must have been due to the effect of the cropping system or to initial differences in the soil or to both. It will be noted that there was a gradual decrease in the nitrogen content of the soil from all plots and that the greatest loss was from the soil growing corn annually without treatment. Invariably applications of manure, lime, and phosphate resulted in a higher soil nitrogen content. Also rotation, particularly the 3-year rotation, helped to maintain the nitrogen supply.

Beginning in 1901 the Illinois agricultural experiment station started the establishment of experimental fields in various parts of the state for the study of soil problems. Often the land for the experimental work was donated by the community through the influence of Dr. C. G. Hopkins. During the period 1910–1915 some 17 such fields were established and at present there are 20, which have been in operation for 38 years or more.

The soil treatments were designed to represent livestock and cash-crop systems of farming. Treatments under the first system included: (1) manure in proportion to the amount of crops harvested, (2) manure plus lime, (3) manure plus lime and rock phosphate, and (4) nothing. Under the cash-crop system the soil treatments were: (1) crop residues, (2) residues and lime, (3) residues, lime, and rock phosphate, (4) residues, lime, rock phosphate, and potassium, and (5) nothing. The basic treatments have been maintained, and, in more recent years, additional treatments have been added to answer questions arising from developments in the fertilizer industry and in soil-management practices. The data from these fields affords much valuable information, and they should be studied by all advanced students in the field of soil productivity. Unfortunately space does not permit their inclusion in this book.

FERTILIZER EXPERIMENTS IN PENNSYLVANIA

The field experiments at Rothamsted had a marked influence on the early field studies in America. W. H. Jordan studied at Rothamsted before starting the Jordan Soil Fertility Plots at Pennsylvania State College in 1881. These are the oldest field experiments involving the use of commercial fertilizer in this country. The rotation consisted of corn, oats, wheat, and hay (clover-timothy). By having four series of plots, each crop in the rotation could be grown every year. This avoided the problem of the effect of seasonal conditions on yields which comes up when all crops are not grown each year. The fertilizers were applied to corn and wheat. Plots 22 and 23 received 2 tons per acre of fresh burnt lime once in 4 years for the first 40 years. Plot 34 received 2 tons of limestone per acre every 2 years for the same period. In 1922–1923 all plots except two on series II and IV, which had not been limed, were treated with limestone. The only source of organic matter has been the roots and stubble of crops except on plots 16, 18, 20, and 22, which were manured for corn and wheat.

The soil is of the Hagerstown series and is similar to that comprising about 4 per cent of the total area of the state. The soil over most of the field is classed as a silt loam. Unfortunately, the field slopes decidedly and it is doubtful whether any of the plow-soil, which was on the upper end of the field when the experiment started, is now in place.

The objects of the experiment were primarily as follows:

1. To determine the response of crops to nitrogen, phosphorus, and potassium fertilizers applied separately, in combinations of two, and all three.

2. To compare the efficiency of different nitrogen carriers and the value of different amounts of nitrogen.

3. To determine the relative values of superphosphate and ground bone.

4. To study the efficiency of different rates of manuring and compare the results from manure with those from commercial fertilizer.

5. To investigate the effect of land plaster, the need for lime, and the comparative effects of burnt lime and limestone.

It will be noted that many of the early experiments in other states followed much the same pattern. A uniform amount of superphosphate was applied, and of muriate of potash. The ground bone contained the same quantity of P_2O_5 as the superphosphate. Each of the three nitrogen carriers was used in quantities to supply 24, 48, and 72 pounds of N in conjunction with superphosphate and muriate of potash, thus giving a good comparison of their relative efficiency and effect on the soil. In addition blood was used alone, with superphosphate, and with muriate of potash. Manure was applied at the rates of 6, 8, and 10 tons per acre. The data for the period 1881–1931 are reported in *Bulletin* 264 of the Pennsylvania agriculture experiment station. Unfortunately, the results collected since 1931 are not available; hence a complete report of the yields is not given here. However, the average yields for the 40-year period 1882–1921 from the plots receiving each of the three major plant food elements and from the nearest unfertilized plot are of interest (Table 112). They are given in pounds of total plant material

TABLE 112. COMPARISON OF EFFECT OF INDIVIDUAL NUTRIENTS ON CROP
YIELDS

Total Yield of All Crops in a Rotation, lb. per acre

Period	Untreated Plot 1	Nitrogen Plot 2	Phosphorus Plot 3	Potas- sium Plot 4
1882–1889	13,158	14,427	14,832	14,587
1890–1897	10,793	11,856	15,199	12,707
1898–1905	7,862	8,382	11,999	8,918
1906–1913	6,906	8,584	11,528	8,172
1914–1921	6,557	7,733	11,534	7,146
1882–1921	9,055	10,196	13,018	10,306
1922–1930				
Unlimed	4,905	5,849	10,244	6,163
Limed	7,171	8,042	12,052	7,936

harvested and are as follows: for nitrogen, 10,196; for phosphorus, 13,018; for potassium, 10,306; and for no fertilization, 9,055. Evidently the greatest need of this soil was for phosphorus, and it is of interest that the yield from the phosphorus-treated plot for the final 8-year period was virtually the same as for the unfertilized plot during the first 8-year period, that is, 13,018 pounds compared to 13,158 pounds. That the soil was in need of lime is shown by the fact that during the period 1922–1930 the increase in pounds of crops due to liming was 2,193, 2,208, and 1,773 for the nitrogen, phosphorus, and potassium plots, respectively.

The results obtained when the nutrients were applied in pairs, and all three together, present an interesting study. The largest yield was obtained from the plot receiving the complete treatment and averaged 17,536 pounds for the 1882–1921 period. The phosphorus-potassium treatment gave the second highest yield, 15,871 pounds, and the lowest yields, 11,495 pounds, came from the plot receiving nitrogen and potassium. On the other hand, the plot treated with nitrogen and phosphorus yielded only 1,041 pounds less than the one receiving phosphorus and potassium. Again it is seen that this soil was in greater need of phosphorus than of nitrogen or potassium, but when phosphorus was supplied both of the other nutrients increased yields. The two unfertilized plots nearest those receiving the treatments just mentioned averaged 10,990 pounds of crops.

Some of the conclusions which have been drawn from the results obtained on the Jordan plots may be stated as follows:

1. The need of this soil for phosphorus exceeded the need for any other nutrient.

2. Neither nitrogen nor potassium alone, or together, have greatly increased yields. When used with phosphorus, however, each of these nutrients has proved beneficial.

3. Complete fertilizer has given as good results as manure on limed soil.

4. Lime has been of little benefit unless accompanied by additions of plant nutrients, and likewise plant nutrients have been of limited value on unlimed soil.

5. The importance of lime in maintaining productivity is illustrated by a yield of a corn hybrid in 1948 of 21.5 bushels, with an application of complete fertilizer but no lime. However, on the limed plot with the same fertilizer the yield was 92.6 bushels. The pH of the soil on the two areas was 4.05 and 6.5, respectively.

6. Manure applied at the rate of 6 tons per acre in alternate years gave greater returns per ton than when applied at rates of 8 or 10 tons.

THE OHIO EXPERIMENTAL FARMS

The Ohio experiment station was organized in 1882, and very shortly some field experiments in soil management were started on the University farm at Columbus. In 1893, however, the experiment station was moved to Wooster and was made a separate organization, with a governing board entirely apart from that of the University. Dr. C. E. Thorne was retained as director, and he immediately organized field experiments to determine the effect of fertilizers and manure on crop yields. Corn, oats, and wheat were grown continuously and in a rotation including clover and timothy. On two of the continuous culture plots phosphoric acid, potash, and nitrogen were applied in arbitrary quantities, and on two plots they were applied in the same ratio to each other in which they are found in the crop to be grown. Manure was applied at rates of 2½ and 5 tons. The remaining four of the ten plots were unfertilized. Each treated plot lay next to an unfertilized one. The results from the unfertilized plots, from those receiving 5 tons of manure, and from those receiving the heaviest fertilizer application are given in Table 113.

TABLE 113. YIELDS * OF CORN, OATS, AND WHEAT GROWN ANNUALLY FOR 30 YEARS †

Soil Treatment	Corn		Oats		Wheat	
	1894–1908	1909–1923	1894–1908	1909–1923	1894–1908	1909–1923
None	17.8	8.9	33.2	17.5	8.2	6.3
N-P-K ‡	47.2	40.6	48.5	43.5	22.3	22.5
Manure §	39.3	28.4	38.6	33.0	17.3	20.6

* Bushels per acre.
† Ohio Agr. Exp. Sta. Bull. 381, 1924.
‡ 320 lb. $NaNO_3$, 160 lb. 0-16-0, 100 lb. KCl for corn and oats, and 280 lb. $NaNO_3$, 50 lb. dried blood, 160 lb. 0-16-0, 100 lb. KCl for wheat.
§ 5 tons.

The yields of corn decreased rapidly during the first 15 years without treatment and then remained approximately constant. On the other hand, oat yields changed little after the first 5 years, and wheat yields without additions to the soil were continuously low. It is interesting to observe that yields of all three crops were higher for each period on soil receiving fertilizer than on that treated with manure. Also, yields of wheat were maintained by the applications of both fertilizer and manure, although corn yields decreased decidedly, especially under the manure treatment. Oat yields dropped about 5 bushels in the second period. The decrease in productivity of the untreated soil was very marked.

In 1916 the Ohio station started additional continuous culture trials with corn, soybeans, oats, and wheat. Sweet clover was seeded as a catch crop in the oats and wheat. Lime was applied to bring the soil to a pH of 7.0, and 2 tons of manure and 200 pounds of 0-16-0 per acre were applied annually. The 20-year average yields were: corn, 29.2 bushels; soybeans, 13.1 bushels; oats, 49.2 bushels; and wheat, 36.0 bushels. It is of interest to note that at the end of the period the tons of organic matter in the soil growing the different crops were as follows: corn, 15.3; soybeans, 18.0; oats, 27.5; and wheat, 24.2.

The 5-year rotation experiment, started in 1893, attracted wide attention for many years. There were five series, each containing thirty 0.1-acre plots, separated by narrow strips or borders. The first plot,

TABLE 114. SOIL TREATMENTS AND CROP YIELDS FROM THE 5-YEAR ROTATION AT WOOSTER, OHIO

Yields,* bu. of grain and lb. of hay per acre

Plot	Treatment for corn, lb. or tons per acre	Corn 50-Year Avg.	Corn Last 10 Years	Oats 44-Year Avg.	Oats Last 4 Years	Wheat 44-Year Avg.	Wheat Last 4 Years	Clover 44-Year Avg.	Clover Last 2 Years	Timothy 45-Year Avg.	Timothy Last 5 Years
	Average unfertilized plots	32.4	46.4	34.4	42.1	13.8	19.5	1,845	2,121	2,709	2,269
2	Phosphate 80 †	36.0	40.6	42.3	46.0	22.7	24.4	2,510	3,300	3,323	3,409
3	Potash 80 ‡	40.6	47.3	38.0	41.3	15.0	18.7	1,989	2,140	3,002	2,743
5	Nitrate 160 §	36.0	41.0	38.8	47.4	15.4	19.2	2,147	2,220	2,964	2,454
6	Phosphate 80, nitrate 160	41.7	43.8	48.1	55.9	27.2	30.7	3,026	3,650	3,516	3,218
8	Phosphate 80, potash 80	49.6	54.7	47.5	52.4	24.7	27.4	3,072	3,760	3,509	3,562
9	Potash 80, nitrate 160	43.6	51.2	41.5	49.9	17.0	22.4	2,234	2,700	3,041	2,752
11	Phosphate 80, potash 80, nitrate 160	53.3	57.7	51.1	54.7	31.0	36.6	3,284	3,700	3,657	3,663
12	Phosphate 80, potash 80, nitrate 240	55.8	63.5	51.7	56.0	32.6	42.3	3,657	4,520	3,793	4,312
14	Phosphate 80, potash 80, nitrate 160, no fertilizer on oats	49.5	60.7	43.4	54.2	28.4	34.4	2,803	3,410	3,235	3,281
15	No fertilizer on corn or oats	37.2	41.7	37.4	50.7	27.2	30.8	3,405	2,920	2,958	2,694
17	Phosphate 160, potash 80, nitrate 80	54.0	53.1	51.9	56.6	27.9	32.7	3,405	4,060	3,797	3,756
18	Manure 8 tons on corn and wheat	58.4	59.8	45.0	45.6	28.8	35.5	4,176	4,730	4,615	4,503
20	Manure 4 tons on corn and wheat	48.3	52.0	42.2	48.4	23.8	31.1	3,126	3,620	3,779	3,712
21	Phosphate 160, potash 80, oilmeal	53.2	53.7	52.0	59.8	28.6	35.3	3,260	3,990	3,629	4,001
23	Phosphate 160, potash 80, dried blood	52.3	55.0	51.9	61.8	28.9	35.7	3,157	3,900	3,602	3,854
24	Phosphate 160, potash 80, sulfate of ammonia	53.5	55.1	51.5	58.5	27.8	35.5	3,167	3,460	3,653	3,734
26	Same as 11, except P from bone meal	49.8	52.9	47.2	50.5	24.6	31.9	3,243	3,780	3,734	3,432
27	Same as 17, except N from nitrate of lime	52.0	55.1	50.6	58.0	29.2	37.6	3,201	3,800	3,838	3,805
29	Same as 11, except P from basic slag	50.5	51.2	49.3	59.4	28.3	37.3	3,258	3,640	3,832	3,809

* Beginning with the period 1904–1908 yields are from the limed half of the plots.
† Superphosphate.   ‡ Muriate of potash.   § Nitrate of soda.

Oats received the same fertilization as corn, except that none was applied to plot 14, and plots 18 and 20 received no manure.   Fertilization of wheat was the same as for corn with the following changes: Phosphate and potash applications were increased to 160 and 100 pounds, respectively.   Nitrate additions were reduced to 120 pounds plus 50 pounds of dried blood.   Complete fertilizer was applied to plot 15 and plot 17, and the nitrate and blood were reduced to 60 and 25 pounds, respectively.   Beginning in 1924 some of the series were discontinued, so that every crop did not appear every year.   This was especially true from 1938 to 1948.

and every third plot thereafter, was unfertilized, thus placing each treated plot next to an untreated one.   Nitrogen, phosphorus, and potassium fertilizers were applied singly, in pairs, and all together.   Nitrate of soda, oilmeal, dried blood, nitrate of lime, tankage, and sulfate of ammonia were used as nitrogen carriers, and superphosphate, bone meal, and basic slag were compared as carriers of phosphorus.

After a few years clover seedings began to fail, and beginning in 1900 a liming program was inaugurated.   Average yields of the various crops for a long period of years and for a short period at the close of the experiment are presented in Table 114.

It is interesting to note that the long-time average yields of all crops, except timothy, on the unfertilized soil were lower than for the last period of the experiment.   This result may be due in part to climatic conditions, but undoubtedly the use of improved varieties of the grain crops contributed to the higher yields in recent years.   That the soil was deficient in nutrients is shown by the higher average yield of all crops on all plots receiving treatment than on the unfertilized plots.   Of the three elements, nitrogen, phosphorus, and potassium, the latter was most effective in increasing corn yields, but the other crops gave the greatest response to phosphorus.   Likewise, when combinations of two elements were used, corn responded most to the phosphate-potash mixture, and oats and wheat to the phosphate-nitrogen combination.   Clover and timothy responded about equally to combinations of phosphorus with nitrogen or potassium but to a lesser extent to potassium plus nitrogen.   Eight tons of manure produced the largest yield of corn, with complete fertilizer containing 240 pounds of nitrate ranking second. Complete fertilizer was the most effective for oats, with the source of nitrogen making little difference.   On the other hand, wheat gave the highest yields with complete fertilizer containing liberal quantities of nitrate nitrogen.   Eight tons of manure proved to be the best fertilizer for clover and timothy.

Another experiment, which is frequently referred to, was started in 1897 and compared the results from applications of fresh and yard manure, both alone and reinforced with superphosphate, rock phosphate, kainite, gypsum, and fertilizer containing nitrogen, phosphorus, and potassium.   The yields from stall and yard manure both alone and reinforced with superphosphate are shown in Table 115.   That portion of the experiment in which rock phosphate and superphosphate were compared as supplements for manure was continued until 1948.   The average yields of corn for the period 1897–1948 were 71.5 bushels with superphosphate and manure and 67.4 bushels when 320 pounds of rock phosphate were used in place of the 256 pounds of superphosphate.

TABLE 115. CROP YIELDS RESULTING FROM APPLICATIONS OF STALL AND
YARD MANURE ALONE AND WITH SUPERPHOSPHATE *

Yields and Yield Increases 1897–1937

Soil Treatment †	Corn		Wheat		Clover	
	Yield	Increase	Yield	Increase	Yield	Increase
None	38.3	. . .	14.8	. . .	3,001	. . .
Stall manure	62.9	24.6	24.5	9.7	4,277	1,276
Yard manure	59.9	21.6	24.0	9.2	3,924	923
Stall manure, phosphate	72.3	34.0	30.5	15.7	5,120	2,119
Yard manure, phosphate	69.0	30.7	30.2	15.4	4,738	1,737

* *Ohio Agr. Exp. Sta. Spec. Cir. 53*, 1938.

† Eight tons manure used and equivalent of 256 pounds of 20 per cent super-phosphate.

Under the same treatments wheat yields were 30.7 bushels and 27.3 bushels, respectively.

As the Wooster station developed it became widely known for the diversity and practical nature of the field experiments. Experiments were planned to answer the majority of the questions commonly asked by farmers concerning soil-management problems. Some idea of the scope and practical nature of the experiments conducted may be obtained by looking over the Table of Contents in *Special Circular* 53, published by the Ohio agricultural experiment station in 1938. Unfortunately the lack of replication of soil treatments makes an accurate interpretation of the data difficult.

MISSOURI'S SANBORN FIELD

The original plot experiments of the Missouri experiment station were planned by J. W. Sanborn, and the field still bears his name. In 1888 the plans were put into operation by H. J. Waters, who later became president of Kansas State College, and some of the original soil treatments have been continued until the present time. The primary purpose of the experiments was to determine the value of farm manure when applied for several crops grown annually and in rotations of different lengths and to compare the yields of crops grown annually and in rotations both with and without soil treatments.

Corn, oats, wheat, clover, and timothy were grown continuously both without soil treatment and with annual applications of 6 tons of manure.

TABLE 116. SOIL TREATMENTS, CROPPING SYSTEMS, AND YIELDS OF THE PLOTS OPERATED WITHOUT CHANGE FOR 50 YEARS

Plot	Cropping System	Soil Treatment	50-Year Average Yields, bu. or lb.				
			Corn	Oats	Wheat	Clover	Timothy
17	Continuous corn	None.	18.5				
18	Continuous corn	6 tons manure annually.	33.1				
16	Continuous oats	None.		20.1			
15	Continuous oats	6 tons manure annually.		33.0			
9	Continuous wheat	No treatment.			10.31		
10	Continuous wheat	6 tons manure annually.			18.80		
2	Continuous wheat	Nitrogen, phosphorus, potash applied annually in amounts equivalent to those removed by a 40-bu. crop.			20.33		
23	Continuous timothy	No treatment.					2,530
22	Continuous timothy	6 tons manure annually.					5,097
27	3-year rotation: corn, wheat, red clover	No treatment.	31.7		12.7	1,472	
25	3-year rotation: corn, wheat, red clover	6 tons manure annually.	44.4		25.1	4,446	
39	4-year rotation: corn, oats, wheat, red clover *	No treatment. (This plot is near a busy street and has been somewhat contaminated by lime blowing from passing gravel trucks.)	41.0	28.2	23.3	2,216	
34	4-year rotation: corn, oats, wheat, red clover *	6 tons manure annually.	46.7	37.6	22.9	3,999	
13	6-year rotation: corn, oats, wheat, red clover, timothy	No treatment.	37.0	30.9	15.2	2,059	2,631
20	6-year rotation: corn, oats, wheat, red clover, timothy	6 tons manure annually.	49.0	37.3	27.2	4,464	5,054
3	6-year rotation: corn, oats, wheat, red clover, timothy	Nitrogen, phosphorus, potash applied in amounts equivalent to those removed by 80 bu. corn, 60 bu. oats, 40 bu. wheat, and 3 tons clover and timothy.	43.1	42.3	30.8	3,485	5,665
4	6-year rotation: corn, oats, wheat, red clover, timothy	Manure 3 tons annually. One-half amount nitrogen, phosphorus, and potash applied to plot 3.	40.1	50.3	31.1	3,878	5,346

* Rotation changed to corn, oats, clover, wheat in 1914.

In one case wheat was also fertilized with nitrate of soda, superphosphate, and muriate of potash in quantities to supply the amounts of N, P, and K removed in a 40-bushel crop. In the rotations the manure application was also 6 tons annually, except in one case, and the quantities of fertilizer were based on the composition of the crops. In many of the cropping systems the 6-tons-of-manure treatment was replicated several times, and this fact made possible the introduction of a number of new treatments, as was done in 1914, on plots which had been treated similarly for 25 years. Unfortunately, only one plot was used for each rotation, so that each crop appeared once in 2, 3, 4, or 6 years according to the length of the rotation. Also, occasionally a plot was unplanted for a year in all the cropping systems. All crops were removed except the second growth of clover and timothy in the rotations.

The yields of crops from plots which had received the same treatment for 50 years are reported in Table 116. These data show the beneficial effect of the 6-ton annual application of manure on crops grown continuously and in rotation. It is also interesting to observe that the heavy application of commercial fertilizer produced larger yields of oats, wheat, and timothy than 6 tons of manure in the 6-year rotation. Also the replacement of one-half the commercial fertilizer with a one-half application of manure resulted in a considerablly increased yield of oats but not greatly different yields of the other crops. The relatively large yields of the crops grown in rotation, compared to those of the same crops grown continuously, attest to the potency of rotations for maintaining yields.

It is noteworthy, however, that yields of crops grown in rotation without soil treatment decreased rather rapidly during the last 12 to 15 years. Yields of corn and oats grown annually with manure were not greatly different from yields of these crops grown in rotation without manure or fertilizer. A study of the annual yields of wheat shows that when grown continuously, without soil treatment, a satisfactory crop was obtained recently in alternate years only. On the other hand, the manured plot produced a fair crop every year. The low yields of the crops grown continuously, without applications of manure, indicate that the productivity of the soil had been reduced to a low level. Figure 54 shows the corn yields with and without manure from 1889 to 1934.

Workers at the Missouri experiment station have stated that they consider changes in the soil to be a more correct indication of the effect of soil treatments than are crop yields. Accordingly, the nitrogen contents of the soil from the different plots at the close of the 50-year period are given in Table 117. These data show the effectiveness of manure in contributing to the organic content of the soil and that fertilizers are

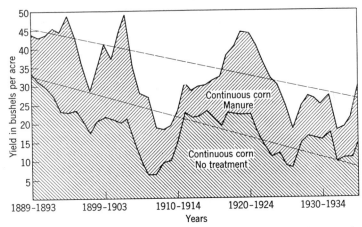

Fig. 54.   Yields of corn as advancing 5-year averages. The decrease in soil
fertility both with and without manure is evident and also the value of manure
for increasing yields.   The great fluctuation in yield from year to year is of
interest. From *Missouri Agr. Exp. Sta. Bull.* 458, 1942.

TABLE 117.   NITROGEN CONTENT OF SOIL RECEIVING DIFFERENT TREATMENTS
AND UNDER DIFFERENT CROPPING SYSTEMS FOR 50 YEARS

Plot	Cropping System	Soil Treatment *	Lb. of Nitrogen in Surface 7 In. of Soil †	Plot	Cropping System	Soil Treatment *	Lb. of Nitrogen in Surface 7 In. of Soil †
17	Corn annually	None	1,500	25	3-year rotation	6 tons manure	3,010
18	Corn annually	6 tons manure	2,480	27	4-year rotation	None	1,970
16	Oats annually	None	2,380	39	4-year rotation	None	2,190
15	Oats annually	6 tons manure	3,370	34	4-year rotation	6 tons manure	3,060
9	Wheat annually	None	2,000	13	6-year rotation	None	2,220
10	Wheat annually	6 tons manure	2,990	20	6-year rotation	6 tons manure	3,330
2	Wheat annually	Fertilizer	1,990	3	6-year rotation	Fertilizer	2,530
23	Timothy annually	None	2,700	4	6-year rotation	½ manure, ½ fertilizer	2,780
22	Timothy annually	6 tons manure	3,910				

* All manure applications are made annually.
† On the basis of analyses of soil from roadways and adjacent uncultivated land the virgin soil contained 3,400 pounds of nitrogen.

little if any more effective than no treatment in maintaining the supply of organic matter in the soil. Had crop residues been returned the application of fertilizers might have proved more advantageous in maintaining the organic content.

The annual growth of a cultivated crop greatly depleted the soil organic matter. The following of a rotation was little if any more effective than the continuous growing of small grains in the maintenance of soil organic content when no soil treatments were made. The continuous growth of manured timothy maintained a high level of organic-matter content.

In 1914 the treatments of a number of plots, which had received an annual application of 6 tons of manure for 25 years, were changed. The objectives of the changes were: (1) With the plots growing wheat continuously, to measure the residual effect of manure, the comparative value of 3 and 6 tons of manure, and the effect on yields of different nitrogen carriers, of complete fertilizer, and of superphosphate. (2) In the 4-year rotation, to measure the residual effect of manure and to determine the effect of complete fertilizer with and without lime on crop yields. (3) For the 6-year rotations, to measure the comparative value of 3- and 6-ton applications of manure and to compare the efficiency of rock phosphate, bone meal, and superphosphate.

Some interesting conclusions may be drawn from the second 25-year period of the experiment. That climate has a great influence on crop yields in this area is shown by the fact that in the 4-year rotation of corn, oats, wheat, and clover, the yields of the grain crops were somewhat higher during the last 25-year period without soil treatment than during the first 25 years with annual applications of 6 tons of manure. In the same rotation, light applications of complete fertilizer during the last period produced higher yields of oats and wheat than did manure during the first period. The reverse was true, however, for corn and clover.

With the 6-year rotation of corn, oats, wheat, clover, and 2 years of timothy, the annual application of 6 tons of manure, plus rock phosphate, produced larger yields of oats, wheat, and timothy than had been obtained with 6 tons of manure without phosphate during the first 25-year period. Wheat grown annually and treated with 3 tons of manure, plus 200 pounds of 0-16-0, yielded more during the second period than it did during the first period with annual applications of 6 tons of manure.

In response to a request for comments on the lessons to be learned from the Sanborn Field experiments, Dean Emeritus M. F. Miller submitted the following statements, which are to be valued because of his long association with the experiments and with soil-fertility research in general.

Some Interesting Findings on Sanborn Field

1. During a 50-year period the yield of continuous wheat, receiving liberal applications of a high-analysis complete fertilizer, was maintained at the same level as that of continuous wheat receiving heavy applications of farm manure.

2. During a 50-year period the crop yields in a 6-year rotation of corn, oats, wheat, clover, timothy, timothy, receiving liberal application of a high-analysis complete fertilizer, were maintained at as high levels as those in the same rotation receiving heavy applications of farm manure.

Generally speaking, heavy applications of high-analysis fertilizer, either with continuous wheat or with a good rotation, had no injurious effect on the crops grown.

3. During a 50-year period the average yields of grain crops in a 6-year rotation of corn, oats, wheat, clover, timothy, timothy, without treatment, were maintained at as high levels as the same grain crops grown continuously and receiving heavy applications of farm manure.

Generally speaking, rotation was as good as manure in maintaining grain yields.

4. Continuous timothy, heavily manured, was the only system which maintained the nitrogen in the surface soil at a level approximating that of the virgin soil during a 50-year period. The lowest amount of surface soil nitrogen, at the end of 50 years, was under continuous corn, without soil treatment, and the highest was under continuous timothy, heavily manured.

5. The surface soil nitrogen, where liberal applications of high-analysis fertilizer were used, was substantially less at the end of 50 years than under similar cropping systems receiving heavy applications of farm manure; and this in spite of the fact that the crop yields under the two systems were approximately the same.

6. Some of the cropping systems and soil treatments on this field were modified at the beginning of the second 25-year period to bring them more nearly into line with modern methods, but the remainder carried through for 63 years unchanged. During the last 13 years of these old systems, signs have developed that the yields under rotations,

without treatment, have been declining more than those under continuous crops without treatment.   It is substantiated by soil tests that the supplies of available minerals in the rotated plots are reaching a lower level than those under continuous cropping, undoubtedly because of the higher yields under crop rotation.

7. Following the adoption of certain newer systems of soil management, at the beginning of the second 25-year period, some remarkable results were secured, particularly under systems that have been most completely modernized during recent years: An interesting contrast in corn yields is shown in the following data, from three widely differing systems, for the year 1951: Continuous corn 63 years, no treatment, 8.6 bushels; continuous corn 63 years, heavily manured, 40.0 bushels; a modern system of rotation and management with complete soil treatments, 134.2 bushels.

This is a most outstanding illustration of the manner in which different systems affect corn yields.

8. In general, these long-time investigations have shown the great significance of maintaining the proper amounts of available plant nutrients in the soil, along with a provision for a liberal turnover of organic matter throughout each cropping system.

9. One of the most valuable things that has come out of these investigations is the opportunity now offered for carrying out chemical, physical, and biological studies of the soil as influenced by widely different cropping systems and soil treatments during a very long period of years.

THE RHODE ISLAND ROTATION TESTS

A 6-year rotation was planned by H. J. Wheeler and G. E. Adams in 1889.   As a preliminary to starting the experimental treatments, the area was uniformly cropped for 4 years to determine the productivity of the different plots.   The soil was acid and the productivity low, as was shown by yields of around $\frac{1}{4}$ ton of hay and $\frac{1}{2}$ ton of corn stover.   The experimental work was gotten under way in 1894 and included some five rotations.

The main purpose of the experiment was to determine whether crop yields could be maintained by use of chemical fertilizers without applications of manure.   It was thought that without manure the cropping system should include much grass if the organic matter of the soil was to be maintained.   Accordingly, the number of years of grass varied from 1 to 4 in the different rotations.   Wood ashes were also considered by

farmers to have some special or "magic" property in the maintenance of
soil productivity, and so 1 manured plot and 1 plot receiving chemical
fertilizer in the 6-year rotation (B) received an application of these
ashes. To check their value corresponding plots received lime and
potash fertilizer. When the results for several years showed the lime-
potash treatment to be as beneficial as the wood ashes, the latter treatment was discontinued.

The results of the experiment are inconclusive concerning the superiority of a rotation containing 4 years of grass over one containing
1 or 2 years of grass for the production of potatoes.[2] However, in 1939,
the soil growing the longer rotation contained 74.5 [3] tons of organic
matter per acre-foot, compared to 64.1 tons in the soil growing grass
for 2 years. It should be noted, however, that in the long rotation red
and alsike clover were grown for 1 year during the early years, and later
the mixture was changed to alfalfa and timothy. The value of manure
for building up the organic content of soil is shown by the fact that soil
growing the long rotation and receiving 10 tons of manure every 6 years
contained 79.2 tons of organic matter.

The study of the comparative value of manure and commercial fertilizer for crop production showed manure to be the better for potatoes,
the long-time (1894–1935) average yields being 276 bushels for manure and 220 bushels for the fertilizer. On the other hand, the fertilizer
produced more corn stover and slightly more hay and corn grain.

ALABAMA'S OLD ROTATION

Alabama possesses the oldest rotation studies including cotton in this
country. Started in 1896 by J. F. Duggar, the experiment has been continued with only minor changes and is yet yielding interesting results.
The cropping systems included the growing of cotton and corn annually,
three 2-year rotations, and one 3-year rotation. Fertilizer applications
consisted of superphosphate and kainite. The quantities of superphosphate used were increased from time to time, and in 1932 the kainite
was replaced by 50 per cent muriate of potash. Nitrate of soda was
applied for oats in the 3-year rotation. Average yields of corn and cotton for long periods in several of the cropping systems are shown in
Table 118.

The beneficial effect of a leguminous catch crop on the yield of corn
grown annually is very striking. Evidently this soil was very deficient

[2] *Rhode Island Agr. Exp. Sta. Bull.* 167, 1916.
[3] *Rhode Island Agr. Exp. Sta. Bull.* 303, 1949.

TABLE 118. AVERAGE YIELDS OF CORN AND COTTON ON THE OLD ROTATION FIELD *

	Corn Yields, bu. per acre		Yields of Seed Cotton, lb. per acre
Cropping System	31 Years	47 Years	47 Years
Corn and legumes continuously	19.0		
Corn alone continuously	12.1		
Corn and legumes ⎫ Cotton and vetch ⎭		22.9	1,048
Cotton and vetch ⎫ Corn and peas ⎬ Oats and peas ⎭		23.1	935
Cotton and vetch continuously			938
Cotton and vetch ⎫ Peas and vetch ⎭			1,067
Cotton continuously No legumes			537

* *Better Crops with Plant Food*, 33, No. 7, 1949. Amer. Potash Institute, Washington, D. C.

in nitrogen, and the low yields of corn both when grown annually and in rotation indicate that the catch crops did not supply enough nitrogen, or that insufficient amounts of other nutrients were supplied, or both. It is of interest that the 31-year average yield of corn with the catch crop was virtually the same as the average yield for the first 10 years of the experiment. On the other hand, without the catch crop the yield dropped from 17.1 bushels during the first 10 years to 10 bushels for the last 7 years of the experiment. A catch crop of vetch also proved highly advantageous in the growing of cotton annually. In addition, cotton yields were increased by the use of 2-year cropping systems, including two catch crops of vetch. The use of a 3-year rotation in which peas accompanied the corn and oats, and vetch was used as a catch crop with cotton, was no more effective in growing cotton than was the annual cropping system using a catch crop.

CYLINDER STUDIES IN NEW JERSEY

In 1898 Voorhees established a series of experiments in 60 metal cylinders, 4 feet long, 23.5 inches in diameter, and without bottoms. The cylinders were buried to within 2 inches of their tops and contained 8 inches of surface soil over well-mixed subsoil. All but 3 of the cultures received annual applications of 640 pounds of superphosphate and 320 pounds of muriate of potash. In addition, lime was added to 20 cylinders and lime and green manure to 20 others. Each set of 20 cylinders also received applications of nitrogenous materials, as follows: (1) fresh solid cow manure, both leached and unleached; (2) fresh solid and liquid cow manure, leached and unleached; (3) each of the above treatments, with the addition of nitrate of soda at rates of 160 and 320 pounds per acre; (4) nitrate of soda 160 pounds and 320 pounds; (5) sulfate of ammonia equivalent to 320 pounds of nitrate of soda; (6) dried blood equivalent to the nitrate; (7) solid cow manure leached, plus the nitrate equivalent of sulfate, and dried blood. The treatments remained unchanged until 1923.[4]

The crop rotation followed consisted of corn, oats, oats, wheat or other small grain, and timothy. After each oat crop, corn was grown to take up unused available nitrogen. This crop was harvested and removed. In the 20 cylinders receiving green manure, two catch crops of vetch were grown during each rotation. Yields for the period 1898–1907 are given in Bulletin 221 of the New Jersey Agricultural Experiment Station and for a period of 40 years in Volume 52 of Soil Science.

In summarizing the results of the study Prince [4] and associates called attention to the following observations. Treatments including manure, fertilizers, lime, and green manure gave the highest yield of crops. Giving the average yields obtained by these treatments a rating of 100, those from cylinders receiving lime but no green manure would rate 91, and yields from cylinders receiving neither would be rated 68. Yield increases resulting from additions of nitrogen correlated closely with the quantities applied.

When nitrogen was applied as $NaNO_3$, $(NH_4)_2SO_4$, or dried blood to limed soil, more nitrogen was removed in crops than was applied. On the other hand, manure applications without addition of other nitrogen sources contained more of the element than was recovered in crops.

The nitrogen content of crops varied from 0.75 to 1.37 per cent. Crops grown on soil receiving phosphate and potash, but no nitrogen, contained the lower percentages of the element, and those grown on soil receiving no phosphate, potash, or nitrogen contained the higher percentages of nitrogen.

At the end of the 40-year period the soil in 56 of the cylinders contained less nitrogen than it did at the beginning of the experiment. The

[4] Soil Sci., 52: 247, 1941.

soils showing no nitrogen loss received annual applications of 16 tons of manure and, in three cases, lime and green manure in addition. Nitrogen contents of the soils, expressed in percentages of those present at the beginning, were as follows for the different treatments: lime + green manure 87; lime 75; and neither lime nor green manure 65.

Manure treatments resulted in the soils having cation-exchange capacities of 500 to 600 pounds per acre, in terms of calcium, higher than unmanured soils 16 years after applications of manure were discontinued. This residual effect of manure is significant from a productivity viewpoint.

WASHINGTON'S WHEAT CULTURAL EXPERIMENTS [5]

Dr. W. J. Spillman planned and put in operation in 1899 a series of experiments at Pullman, Washington, dealing with wheat culture. There were 28 plots located on Palouse silt loam, and the studies dealt primarily with manure applications, use of fallow, tillage methods, and rotations.

Unfortunately, various troubles such as disease and unfavorable climatic conditions resulted in the collection of too few data to make some of the studies, particularly the rotations, of value. However, the following observations are worthy of mention.

The plowing under of 10 tons of manure each fall for winter wheat grown annually resulted in a 12-year average yield of 32.9 bushels, compared to a yield of 18.7 bushels without manure. The result for spring wheat was not so advantageous, the 12-year average yield resulting from the plowing under of manure in the spring being 24.7 bushels, in contrast to 22.5 bushels without manure.

Manure gave about equally good results when applied as topdressing to wheat, in the summer on fallow, or plowed under in the spring of the fallow year. The cropping system was wheat-fallow and the yields approximated 39.5 bushels.

Early spring plowing followed by proper tillage of the fallow resulted in an average yield of 46.6 bushels for six crops of wheat, compared to 34.8 bushels when the plowing was done late with similar soil treatment in other respects.

The spring wheat tests gave a 14-year average yield of 27.8 bushels on spring-plowed soil, compared to 24.9 bushels on fall-plowed plots.

Depth of spring plowing for spring wheat had little influence on the yields. Following are the average yields for 20 crops using the desig-

[5] *Washington Agr. Exp. Sta. Bull.* **160,** 1921.

nated plowing depth: 4 inch, 28.8 bushels; 6 inch, 29.1 bushels; 7 inch, 27.8 bushels; 8 inch, 28.7 bushels; 5 inch one year and 8 inch the next, 28.1 bushels.

REFERENCES

Bauer, F. C., and Griffin, J. H. Comparative effects of soils, fertilizers, and systems of soil treatments on crop yields; 1880–1950 summary. Illinois Agr. Exp. Sta., Dep. Agron. Mimeograph, 1951.

Bauer, F. C., Lang, A. L., Badger, C. J., Miller, L. B., Farnham, C. H., Johnson, P. E., Marriott, L. F., and Nelson, M. H. Effects of soil treatment on soil productivity. A summary of long-time field experiments. *Illinois Agr. Exp. Sta. Bull.* 516, 1945.

Bauer, F. C., Lang, A. L., Farnham, C. H. Urbana soil experiment field studies 1888–1948. Illinois Agr. Exp. Sta. Mimeograph, 1949.

Bell, R. S., Odland, T. E. and Owens, A. L. A half century of crop rotation experiments. *Rhode Island Agr. Exp. Sta. Bull.* 303, 1949.

Davis, F. L. The old rotation at Auburn, Alabama. *Better Crops with Plant Food.* American Potash Institute, Washington, D. C., August, 1949.

Fiftieth anniversary of the general fertilizer tests, 1881–1931. *Pennsylvania Agr. Exp. Sta. Bull.* 264, 931.

Fream, W., and Cox, H. *The Rothamsted Experiments on the Growth of Wheat, Barley, and the Mixed Herbage of Grass Land.* "The Field Office," London, 1888.

Gilbert, J. H. *History and Present Position of the Rothamsted Investigation.* Harrison & Sons, London, 1891.

Hall, A. D. *The Book of the Rothamsted Experiments.* E. P. Dutton & Co., New York, 1905.

Handbook of experiments in agronomy. *Ohio Agr. Exp. Sta. Spec. Cir.* 53, 1938; also *Book* Series B-1, 1951.

Hartwell, B. L., and Damon, S. C. A twenty-year comparison of different rotations of corn, potatoes, rye, and grass. *Rhode Island Agr. Exp. Sta. Bull.* 167, 1916.

Hopkins, C. G. *Soil Fertility and Permanent Agriculture.* Ginn and Co., Boston, 1910.

Prince, A. L., Toth, S. J., Blair, A. W., and Bear, F. E. Forty-year studies of nitrogen fertilizers. *Soil Sci.,* 52: 247, 1941.

Rothamsted Experiment Station, Abridged Report for 1921–1922.

Rothamsted Experiment Station. Plans and Data of the Experimental Field Plots, 1923.

Rothamsted Experiment Station, Report for 1937.

Russell, E. J., and Watson, D. J. *Imp. Bur. Soil Sci. Tech. Com.* 40, 1940.

Schafer, E. G., Gaines, E. F., and Barbee, O. E. Cultural experiments with wheat. *Washington Agr. Exp. Sta, Bull.* 160, 1921.

Smith, G. E. Sanborn Field, fifty years of field experiments with crop rotations, manure, and fertilizers. *Missouri Agr. Exp. Sta. Bull.* 458, 1942.

The maintenance of soil fertility. Thirty years' work with manure and fertilizers. *Ohio Agr. Exp. Sta. Bull.* 381, 1924.

Voorhees, E. B., and Lipman, J. G. Investigations relative to the use of nitrogenous materials. *New Jersey Agr. Exp. Sta. Bull.* 221, 1909.

Index